Table of Contents

Table of Contents

Fetal Alcohol Syndrome Among Aboriginal People in Canada: Review and Analysis of the Intergenerational Links to Residential Schools

Prepared for

the Aboriginal Healing Foundation

By

Caroline L. Tait
Aboriginal Mental Health Research Team
National Network of Aboriginal Mental Health Research
Cultural and Mental Health Research Unit
Sir Mortimer B. Davis-Jewish General Hospital
Montreal, Quebec

2003

Table of Contents

Table of Contents

Acknowledgements

I would like to thank my research assistants, Cori Simpson, Hani Tamel and Amanda Neudorf for their reviews of the research literature and for their input and insights into the writing of the report.

I would also like to thank members of the Aboriginal Mental Health Research Team for their support, particularly Laurence Kirmayer. Gail Valaskakis and Jackie Brennan from the Aboriginal Healing Foundation deserve special thanks for their patience and support over the past few months.

I would also like to thank Patrick McDonnaugh for his assistance in editing the report.

Most importantly, I would like to thank my husband, Adil Ben Boubaker and my son, Skender, who gave their support and encouragement during the writing of the report.

Caroline L. Tait

Definitions

This glossary of terms has been provided as a way of ensuring clarity throughout the document. Please read through these definitions and refer to them as needed.

Aarskog syndrome - this inherited condition is characterized by multiple birth defects, including wide spaced eyes (ocular hypertelorism), front-facing (anteverted) nostrils, a broad upper lip, a malformed ("saddle-bag") scrotum and laxity of the ligaments resulting in bending back of the knees (genurecurvatum), flat feet and overly extensible fingers.

Aboriginal people or Aboriginal - includes Métis, Inuit and First Nations, regardless of where they live in Canada and regardless of whether they are "registered" under the *Indian Act of Canada*.

AIDS - Acquired Immune Deficiency Syndrome - is an illness which occurs after HIV infection that sufficiently compromises a person's immune system.

ACOA - adult children of alcoholics.

Aetiology (etiology) - the study of causes, as in the causes of diseases.

Alcohol dehydrogenase (ADH) - one of the main enzymes involved in alcohol's metabolism to acetaldehyde.

ARBD - alcohol-related birth defects.

ARBEs - alcohol-related birth effects.

Aldehyde hydrogenase (ALDH) - the enzyme that converts acetaldehyde to acetate.

Amelioration - improvement in a patient's condition.

Analgesia - the inability to feel pain.

Atrial septal defect - a hole in the wall (septum) between the upper chambers of the heart (atria). Abbreviated ASD. ASD is a major class of heart malformations.

Biomedical - refers generally to Western forms of medicine that involve biological, medical and physical sciences.

Biomedicine - healing and medical knowledge and techniques based on the application of the principles of the Western science.

BAL - blood alcohol level.

BTC - Breaking the Cycle.

Definitions

CAGE - a screening instrument, it's a simple 4-item yes/no alcohol screen that focuses on the consequences of drinking, rather than the quantity of frequency of alcohol consumption.

Congenital anomalies/malformations - birth defects.

CPA - child physical abuse.

CSA - childhood sexual abuse.

Co-morbidity - when two or more illnesses occur together in one patient.

Delirium tremens - a central nervous system symptom of alcohol withdrawal that is seen in patients with chronic alcoholism.

DTES - referring to a particular neighbourhood in Vancouver called the Downtown Eastside.

DSM - *Diagnostic and Statistical Manual of Mental Disorders*, the official source on definitions related to mental illness. There are four editions of the manual.

Dysmorphology - a term coined by Dr. David W. Smith in the 1960s to describe the study of human congenital malformations (birth defects), particularly those affecting the morphology (the anatomy) of the individual. Dysmorphology literally means, "the study of abnormal form."

Encephalopathy - stroke-like episodes syndrome; brain dysfunction. A disease of the brain, especially one involving alterations of brain structure.

Epicanthic folds - a fold of skin that comes down across the inner angle of the eye.

Epidemiology - a branch of medical science that deals with the incidence, distribution and control of disease in a population.

Esotropia - a condition in which a person is cross-eyed.

FAE - fetal alcohol effects - referring to the presence of some of the criteria for fetal alcohol syndrome (FAS) and a history of alcohol exposure before birth, but where the patient does not meet all of the necessary criteria for the full-blown syndrome.

FAS - fetal alcohol syndrome - a birth defect syndrome caused from prenatal alcohol damage. FAS always involves brain damage, impaired growth and head and face anomalies.

FASD - fetal alcohol spectrum disorders - a term used to describe the range of birth effects caused by prenatal alcohol damage.

Fetal hydantoin syndrome - a rare disorder that is caused by exposure of a fetus to phenytoin (Dilantin), which is an anti-convulsant drug prescribed for epilepsy.

Definitions

Fragile-X syndrome - an inherited disorder that is characterized by moderate to severe mental retardation, by large ears, chin and forehead, by enlarged testes in males, and that often has limited or no effect in heterozygous females — called also *fragile X,* the most common heritable form of mental retardation.

FRAMES - an intervention program that is designed to motivate pregnant women to decrease or stop their use of substances.

Gastroenteritis - inflammation of the stomach and the intestines.

Gonorrhea - a bacterial infection that is transmitted by sexual contact.

Hallucinosis - a pathological mental state characterized by hallucinations.

Hepatitis A and B - inflammation of the liver caused by the hepatitis A and B viruses (HAV, HBV).

Human immunodeficiency virus (HIV) - a type of virus called a retrovirus, which infects humans when it comes in contact with tissues such as those that line the vagina, anal area, mouth or eyes, or a break in the skin.

Hydronephrosis - Distention of the kidney with urine. Due to obstruction of urine outflow (for example, by a stone blocking the ureter, the tube going from the kidney to the bladder).

Hypochondriasis - A disorder characterized by a preoccupation with body functions and the interpretation of normal body sensations (such as sweating) or minor abnormalities (such as minor aches and pains) as indicating problems needing medical attention.

Hypoplastic kidney - a form of congenital kidney disease; under-developed kidney.

Hypoxemia -an abnormally low level of oxygen in the blood.

Hysteria - behaviour displaying overwhelming or unmanageable fear or emotional excess.

In-utero - in the uterus, before birth.

Intergenerational impacts - the effects of sexual and physical abuses that were passed on to the children, grandchildren and great-grandchildren of Aboriginal people who attended the residential school system.

IOM - American Institute of Medicine.

Mandibular hypolasis - under-development of the lower jaw bone.

Mania - excitement displayed by mental and physical hyperactivity.

Maxillar hypoplasis - under-development of the upper jaw bone.

Definitions

Meningitis - inflammation of the meninges, the three membranes that envelope the brain and the spinal cord. Meningitis can be caused by infection by bacteria, viruses and protozoa.

Myocardial infarction - a heart attack.

Narcosis - unconsciousness produced by the influence of narcotics.

Noonan syndrome - a congenital malformation syndrome that is characterized by mildly short stature, a congenital heart defect, a broad or webbed neck, an unusual chest shape, low set nipples and a characteristic facial appearance.

Nystagmus - rapid, rhythmic, repetitious and involuntary eye movements.

Otitis media - inflammation of the middle ear.

Organic brain syndrome - psychiatric or neurological symptoms that arise from damage to the brain.

Pancreatitis - inflammation of the pancreas.

pFAS - partial FAS - a diagnostic category that is often used interchangeably with FAE.

Psychasthenia - a neurotic state of mind, especially by phobias, obsessions or compulsions that one knows is irrational.

Psychotropic - acting upon the mind.

Renal agenesis - a kidney that failed to develop.

Residential Schools - the Residential School System in Canada, attended by Aboriginal students. It may include industrial schools, boarding schools, homes for students, hostels, billets, residential schools, residential schools with a majority of day students, or a combination of any of the above.

Rhinorrhea - a runny nose.

Schizophrenia - brain disease, in which symptoms may include loss of personality, agitation, confusion, unusual behaviour and social withdrawal. The illness usually begins in early adulthood and the cause is unknown, but there appear to be both genetic and environmental components to the disease. Treatment involves neuroleptic medications and supportive inter-personal therapy.

Scoliosis - lateral (sideways) curving of the spine.

SES - socio-economic status. Generally refers to income levels and employment status.

Somatic - relating to or affecting the body either physically or psychologically.

Definitions

Strabismus - a condition in which the visual axis of each eye is not parallel and the eyes appear to be looking in different directions.

Symptomatology - referring to the symptoms that make up an illness, disorder or syndrome: a branch of medical science concerned with symptoms of diseases.

T-ACE - a screening tool used to screen patients for alcohol dependency.

Teratogenic - substances that can cause birth defects.

Tuberculosis - a highly transmittable disease caused by the bacterium mycobacterium tuberculosis and affects the lungs.

TWEAK - a screening tool used to screen patients for alcohol dependency.

Urogenital anomalies - a birth defect that is related to both the urinary system and the genital system (interior and exterior genitalia).

Executive Summary

Scope of the Problem

In the past three decades, fetal alcohol syndrome (FAS), and alcohol-related birth effects (ARBEs) more generally, have emerged as health concerns for Aboriginal people in Canada. At the heart of this concern are two issues: first, the devastating effects that substance addiction has had on Aboriginal people and their communities; and second, the difficulties faced by those individuals, families and communities effected by FAS and ARBEs. Within the research literature concerning FAS/ARBEs and Aboriginal people, intergenerational impacts of the residential school experience as a contributing factor to rates of FAS/ARBEs are examined. However, Aboriginal authors, such as Fournier and Crey (1997), argue that intergenerational links between residential schools, particularly with regard to sexual and physical abuse experienced by children who attended the schools, mass adoption of Aboriginal children in the 1960s and 1970s, and the introduction of alcohol by Europeans into Aboriginal communities, has collectively contributed to high rates of FAS and other related illnesses among Aboriginal people.

This report examines FAS/ARBEs in light of current discussions that identify intergenerational effects that are linked to, or are a result of, the residential school system. The necessary contributing factor in this discussion is alcohol use by pregnant women, as FAS and ARBEs are found only in offspring where *in-utero* alcohol exposure has occurred. However, while *in-utero* alcohol exposure is a necessary factor, debate exists as to whether it is a sufficient variable to produce FAS/ARBEs or that other mitigating factors need to be present for effects to occur (Abel, 1998a). For example, the role of other contributing variables, such as the pregnant woman's overall physical and mental health status, her nutritional intake during pregnancy and other social and historical factors, are presently unknown. Strong evidence exists that these secondary factors can play a significant role in birth outcomes where alcohol exposure in-utero has occurred (Abel, 1998a).

Widespread substance abuse, particularly alcohol abuse, among those who attended residential schools has been identified as both an outcome of the residential school experience and a contributing factor to other negative health and social problems among this group and among subsequent generations of Aboriginal people (Royal Commission on Aboriginal Peoples, 1996b). Although no research studies exist that specifically examine the ways in which residential school experiences contributed to current rates of FAS/ARBEs among Aboriginal people, this report concludes that the residential school system contributed to high rates of alcohol abuse among those who previously attended the schools and among significant numbers of parents and community members who had their children removed from their care because of the school system.

This report also concludes that the residential school system further contributed to alcohol abuse among subsequent generations of Aboriginal people, including women of child-bearing ages. Despite the negative impacts of the residential school system and other forms of colonization, it should be pointed out that not every former student responded in the same way to their experience and, for various reasons, some individuals and communities did better than others. Because of this, alcohol abuse among Aboriginal people in Canada varies and it should be understood as a problem of certain individuals and sub-populations, rather than a problem of *all* Aboriginal people. In relation to FAS/ARBEs, this suggests that programming and services should target those particular populations who are at risk, rather than targeting all groups regardless of their alcohol use levels.

Executive Summary

The colonialist experience of Aboriginal people in Canada suggests that mainstream interpretations and analysis of health and social issues concerning Aboriginal people, specifically one as sensitive as pregnancy and substance abuse, be read from a critical perspective, questioning what is taken for granted as the current state of affairs (Tait, 2003). In doing so, this report complements and critiques a developing body of research and reviews literature aimed at the prevention of substance abuse during pregnancy and the management and care of negative birth outcomes caused by alcohol exposure in-utero. Such a review provides a knowledge base that can then be used to discuss intergenerational links, which connect residential school experiences and present day occurrences of substance abuse by pregnant women and FAS/ARBEs, more generally, among Aboriginal people. It also provides possible directions for Aboriginal communities to take in relation to prevention, identification and interventions for pregnant women with substance abuse problems and for alcohol affected individuals across the life-span.

Objectives

This report reviews and analyzes research literature on FAS and ARBEs among Aboriginal people in Canada. Specific attention is paid to intergenerational variables that are linked to, or are a result of, the residential school experience. Four basic questions are answered:

(1) What is known about the prevalence of FAS and other ARBEs?

(2) What are the individual, biological, psychological, social and economic correlates of FAS and other ARBEs in relation to (i) pregnant women at risk of giving birth to an affected child and (ii) individuals who suffer from FAS/ARBEs?

(3) What evidence is there for a relation of FAS and other ARBEs to the intergenerational effects of residential schools and especially to physical and sexual abuse?

(4) What are the current best practices regarding prevention of FAS and ARBEs and intervention for affected individuals? What are the best practices for communities with high rates of FAS and ARBEs?

'Best Practices'

This report examines the 'best practices' for FAS/ARBE prevention, identification and intervention recently proposed by Health Canada (Roberts and Nanson, 2000) and attempts to situate them within the larger socio-cultural and historical context that impacts upon the daily lives of Aboriginal people in Canada, specifically with regard to local geographical, cultural, health and socio-economic realities. Barriers and gaps in services that prevent the implementation of 'best practices' are identified and, where possible, alternative solutions are given.

The question of what 'best practices' means for Aboriginal people, specifically in relation to traditional indigenous knowledge, is an area which deserves special attention. This is particularly true when dealing with an issue as sensitive as pregnancy and substance abuse, and FAS/ARBEs more generally. However, because this review was limited mainly to scientific literature, the role of traditional indigenous knowledge has been only briefly touched upon. This report suggests that a next step in the identification of 'best practices' would be a re-examination of the information presented in this and similar reports in relation

Executive Summary

to traditional indigenous knowledge and local understandings of health, wellness, illness and distress. This would greatly support culturally sensitive and meaningful FAS/ARBE prevention, identification and intervention strategies for Aboriginal people.

What is Fetal Alcohol Syndrome?

Fetal alcohol syndrome is marked by pre and or post-natal growth deficiency (e.g., low birth weight and height); central nervous system (CNS) dysfunction; and characteristic cranio-facial malformations (e.g., short palpebral fissures [short eye slits], flat upper lip, flattened philtrum [the groove between the nose and upper lip], and flat midface) (Jones and Smith, 1973). The severity of the illness can vary greatly between individuals and specific markers of the illness, such as the facial features, can change over time or manifest themselves differently in the same individual (Stratton, Howe et al., 1996).

Since the first description of FAS in the medical literature, on-going progress has been made in developing specific criteria for delineating this syndrome. However, controversy remains in key areas, including the relative boundaries of the diagnosis, as well as the markers that should be used to define those boundaries (Stratton, Howe et al., 1996). Within the medical literature, diagnostic criteria vary from study to study and, along with other methodological factors, such as the method of case ascertainment and the population surveyed, has meant that estimates on the prevalence of FAS and ARBEs vary widely (Roberts and Nanson, 2000).

Controversy exists with regard to related classifications, such as fetal alcohol effects (FAE) and alcohol-related birth effects (ARBEs), more generally. For example, FAE was originally used to refer to behavioural and cognitive problems occurring in offspring exposed to alcohol in-utero without typical FAS diagnostic features. FAE was understood to be generally less severe than the full-blown syndrome; however, some authors have stressed that FAE involves CNS dysfunction as severe as that occurring in FAS (Abel, 1998a; Streissguth, LaDue and Randels, 1987). Others suggest that the precision of the term FAE, which has never been very exact, has been gradually reduced because of the difficulties found in measuring exposure to alcohol, coupled with the difficulties inherent in quantifying or demarcating behavioural and cognitive problems (Stratton, Howe et al., 1996).

Currently, medical researchers are attempting to standardize diagnostic tools used by clinicians in making a diagnosis of FAS and other related ARBEs. Due to a lack of standardized diagnostic tools, and to many physicians in Canada not being trained in FAS/ARBE referral and assessment, it is difficult for a patient to receive a medical assessment for FAS/ARBEs in most regions of Canada. Confounding factors, such as specific phenotypes (e.g., typical facial features, height, head size) among certain Aboriginal groups that are similar to those found in persons with FAS/ARBEs, have meant that the potential for mis-diagnosis or over-diagnosis of FAS/ARBEs in some Aboriginal communities exists.

Standardized psychological testing for CNS dysfunction may also be inappropriate for Aboriginal children who do not speak English or French as their first language or who live in remote communities. Cultural characteristics of the specific community, as well as consideration of other local factors (e.g., community integration or dysfunction), must be considered in the development of appropriate assessment tools. Research into the testing-retesting of the reliability and validity of FAS/ARBE diagnostic classifications and assessment tools should be undertaken in order to determine how consistent FAS/ARBE diagnostic

Executive Summary

classifications are in identifying Aboriginal individuals with alcohol-related birth effects over the life span. Testing-retesting could involve independent reassessment (the clinician is blind to previous diagnosis) of patients at different intervals over the life span to see if these patients still warrant the diagnostic label.

Alcohol Use

This report examines alcohol abuse among Aboriginal people in relation to residential schools and current rates of FAS/ARBEs. Evident in this discussion are the complexities involved in accounting for why some individuals or groups abuse alcohol, while others do not. Important reoccurring themes in accounting for substance abuse among Aboriginal groups in Canada are the devastating effects of colonization, including residential school experiences and the on-going economic and social marginalization experienced by these groups over a number of generations. In relation to literature written on alcohol abuse and pregnancy, a clear distinction in the two bodies of literature exists, with the body of literature on alcohol abuse and pregnancy taking a much narrower view of abuse than general alcohol research. FAS-specific literature has tended to identify a limited range of variables, focus on information that is mostly medical in nature and collect data primarily in prenatal or obstetric clinical settings (May, 1998). Although the focus in pregnancy and alcohol abuse studies is widening, intergenerational and collective trauma, which have proved to be of great significance in understanding alcohol abuse generally among Aboriginal groups, has received very limited attention.

Residential Schools

The first-hand accounts by former students about their experiences at residential schools are, on the one hand, heart-wrenching because they are accounts about children being subjected to severe acts of violence against their Aboriginal identity and against their physical, psychological, emotional and spiritual well-being. On the other hand, they are accounts that bring forth both disbelief and disgust, as they tell of such a severe degree of systemic violence meted against children, their families and communities by government authorities, and the churches they commissioned, to care and keep safe the children who attended the schools. A review of the historical literature clearly indicates that Aboriginal people suffered greatly because of the residential school system. Widespread abuse at the schools, in its various forms, took an individual and collective toll on the health and well-being of large numbers of Aboriginal people. The resilience of former students and their communities, despite the toll, has been quite remarkable.

In relationship to intergenerational links to substance abuse and pregnancy, and FAS/ARBEs, it is clear that the residential school system contributed to the central risk factor involved, substance abuse, but also to factors shown to be linked to alcohol abuse, such as child and adult physical, emotional and sexual abuse, mental health problems and family dysfunction. The impact of residential schools can also be linked to risk factors for poor pregnancy outcomes among women who abuse alcohol, such as poor overall health, low levels of education and chronic poverty.

Executive Summary

Child Abuse

Child abuse is an important factor when considering intergenerational links between the residential school system and current rates of substance abuse during pregnancy among Aboriginal women. Research shows that child abuse is linked to a number of mental health problems, including adult alcohol abuse. Severity and multiple-episodes of abuse increase risk for these problems. Child sexual abuse in some Aboriginal communities in Canada and the United States is believed to be significantly higher than national averages. Some research suggests that Aboriginal women may experience higher levels of certain symptomatology following childhood or adult sexual abuse, such as somatic symptoms, alcohol abuse, mental health problems, sleep disturbances and sexual difficulties.

Aboriginal victims of abuse and their families may face numerous barriers that prevent them from reporting the abuse. Furthermore, they may have limited support if they do report abuse and it is likely that their perpetrators will not be prosecuted or, if convicted, will not receive appropriate sentencing. Studies involving pregnancy and substance abuse have failed to fully address the question of violence, even though women at high risk of producing alcohol affected children report high rates of child and adult abuse. Some studies report that violence may increase in some instances during pregnancy and that violence has been linked to poor pregnancy outcomes, such as low-birth weight babies.

Institutional child abuse occurs within an institutional setting where children are placed in the care of a group of people who control almost every aspect of the children's lives. Within this setting, children are made particularly vulnerable to acts of violence, including sexual abuse, because they are cut off from family supports and there are generally few or no avenues for them to report abuse. The residential school system was identified by the Law Commission of Canada (2000) as causing the most amount of damage to a group of children than any other institution in Canada. The residential school system was unlike other institutions as it was intended to undermine a culture; because of this, Aboriginal children suffered in a way distinct from children placed in other types of institutions.

Contemporary Health and Social Issues

A review of the literature suggests that Aboriginal people face a barrage of health and social issues that impact negatively upon their communities, including substance abuse by women of child-bearing ages. However, a growing body of literature argues that the severity of problems, such as physical and mental health problems, family dysfunction, violence, poor academic achievement and crime are directly linked to historical and socio-political factors. These studies have found that community control and autonomy (Chandler and Lalonde, 1998), high level of social integration (May, 1991), community development, local control of health care systems, the settlement of land claims and moves toward self-government (Kirmayer, Brass and Tait, 2000) may be important protective factors in preventing ill health and negative social outcomes among Aboriginal groups, including substance abuse and FAS/ARBEs more generally.

Executive Summary

Fetal Alcohol Syndrome: Epidemiology Studies

Epidemiology studies reviewed in this report suggest that rates of FAS/ARBEs, especially among Aboriginal people in North America, may be increasing. However, this claim, along with suggestions that FAS/ARBEs are more prevalent among Aboriginal groups than non-Aboriginal groups, is questionable based on the available research data. For example, researchers selected some of the Aboriginal communities surveyed because alcohol abuse was endemic and FAS/ARBEs were thought to be a major public health problem. Furthermore, while there are few epidemiological studies on FAS/ARBEs among Aboriginal people in Canada, there is even less research on the prevalence of FAS/ARBEs in non-Aboriginal populations. This makes it difficult, if not impossible, to make a valid comparison of the prevalence rates for Aboriginal and non-Aboriginal people in Canada.

Before it can be concluded that Aboriginal children are at an increased risk of being born with FAS/ARBEs, important questions should be addressed. Research examining how demographic, socio-economic and socio-cultural factors may be related to an increased risk of FAS/ARBEs for some Aboriginal groups needs to be conducted (Bray and Anderson, 1989). Furthermore, obtaining an accurate measurement of the prevalence of FAS/ARBEs in a given region involves the study of every family and child or, at least, selecting a representative sample from the region on which to carry out screening. Abel (1998a) argues that studies, which rely on referral only for their sample population, may not account for environmental and cultural factors, especially where minorities are concerned. These studies may also end up with, an over-representation of affected individuals and, thus, higher prevalence rates because of the use of referral as a way to identify study participants, rather than the use of representative sampling. While FAS/ARBEs are a serious health problem, Aboriginal people should be critical of claims that suggest they are at greater risk and should be cautious in applying prevalence rates found in specific high risk communities to other Aboriginal groups.

Alcohol Abuse By Pregnant Women

Alcohol and pregnancy studies have, in many instances, focused on Aboriginal women as a sub-group in North America who are particularly at risk for producing alcohol affected children. In a review of the literature, however, it becomes clear that methodological problems exist in many of the studies arguing that Aboriginal heritage is a risk factor for FAS/ARBEs. Rather, chronic poverty and social marginalization appear to be variables that are more important in identifying women at risk than ethnic identity. Because Aboriginal women are the poorest and most marginalized group in Canada, these factors, rather than their Aboriginal culture or heritage, situate them among women at risk. However, in the delivery of FAS/ARBE prevention and intervention services, Aboriginal women may present certain challenges for service delivery.

The colonial legacy of subordination of Aboriginal people has resulted in a multiple jeopardy for Aboriginal women who face individual and institutional discrimination and disadvantages on the basis of race, gender and class (Browne and Fiske, 2001; Dion-Stout, 1996). Aboriginal women are strongly affected by the pervasive negative attitudes of society towards women who abuse substances; an attitude that has been brought to bear specifically on Aboriginal women with substance use problems (Poole, 2000). Although the research literature is limited, services targeting high risk Aboriginal women, provided by Aboriginal organizations or have a strong Aboriginal component and involvement of Aboriginal

Executive Summary

service providers, are seen to be most effective in meeting the needs of Aboriginal women. Increasingly, the involvement of traditional practitioners and Elders is seen as a positive and often necessary inclusion in 'best practice' programs.

The prevention of substance abuse by pregnant women has typically focused on preventing damage to the developing fetus and, therefore, the emphasis has been on the pregnancy, rather than on the health and well-being of the woman. Research illustrates that women at risk for giving birth to a child with FAS generally have poor overall health and many will die shortly after giving birth to an affected child if their substance abuse problems are not addressed. This suggests that all efforts should be made to address substance abuse by women at risk, rather than maintaining a narrow focus on these women only when they are pregnant.

Aboriginal women experience numerous barriers and gaps in service that prevent them from accessing prenatal and addiction treatment services. Barriers range from long waiting lists at treatment centres to a woman being afraid to lose custody of her baby when it is born if she admits to needing help when pregnant. The geographical location of a community, the range of services available and the level of community integration of services all contribute to whether or not women access prenatal and addiction treatment services. Some Aboriginal communities have begun to integrate traditional practices related to pregnancy and parenting into prevention strategies, with the involvement of traditional practitioners, such as mid-wives.

The 'best practices' identified in this report overwhelmingly support the involvement of local communities and coordination of services in order to improve upon the continuum of care for Aboriginal women struggling with substance abuse problems. FAS/ARBEs is an intergenerational wellness issue, which involves more than preventing pregnant women from consuming alcohol, but rather involves whole communities to gain control over their lives through the development of community-based institutions in areas of culture, education, health, economies and justice.

Person Affected By Fetal Alcohol Syndrome and other Alcohol-Related Birth Effects

This report reviewed the research literature and 'best practices' concerning alcohol affected persons and found that there is a great deal of information lacking about the life trajectory of affected individuals, the role of environmental influences and how best to address the needs of alcohol affected persons at the various stages of their lives. This review found that alcohol affected persons who are Aboriginal may be at risk of multiple environmental insults, which could further exaggerate their illness, such as multiple foster placements, poverty, family dysfunction and long-term separation from family members. Aboriginal communities may also lack the range of services needed to address the needs of alcohol-affected children, which may result in the children being removed from the community, despite there being care givers who could provide a stable and loving home environment.

There is limited written information about the response of Aboriginal communities in dealing with alcohol-affected persons. Hart (1999) suggests that recognition of the diversity of cultures and histories found among and between First Nations, Métis and Inuit communities is important in understanding how communities respond to FAS/ARBEs. Hornby (2000) found that Native American communities he worked with showed more acceptance of persons who were alcohol affected than that found in mainstream society. Aboriginal people, as they have done with treatment for alcohol, are at the forefront of designing culturally appropriate services for their people. In this process, they work with non-Aboriginal health and social service professionals in implementing 'best practices' that are locally determined and based on scientific research and professional biomedical opinions modified to local context, to meet the needs of alcohol-affected persons.

As Aboriginal communities address substance abuse by pregnant women and FAS/ARBEs, the *Guide for Health Professional Working with Aboriginal Peoples* (Smylie, 2000) provides important direction and guidance for Aboriginal communities and health and social service providers who work in these communities. The guidelines, which received input from a number of Aboriginal contributors and supporting organizations, give the following recommendations and are supported by this report:

1. health professionals should have a basic understanding of the appropriate names with which to refer to the various groups of Aboriginal people in Canada;

2. health professionals should have a basic understanding of the current socio-demographics of Aboriginal people in Canada;

3. health professionals should familiarize themselves with the traditional geographic territories and language groups of Aboriginal people;

4. health professionals should have a basic understanding of the disruptive impact of colonization on the health and well-being of Aboriginal people;

5. health professionals should recognize that the current socio-demographic challenges facing many Aboriginal individuals and communities have a significant impact on health status;

6. health professionals should recognize the need to provide health services for Aboriginal people as close to home as possible;

7. health professionals should have a basic understanding of governmental obligations and policies regarding the health of Aboriginal people in Canada; and

8. health professionals should recognize the need to support Aboriginal individuals and communities in the process of self-determination (Smylie, 2000).

The guidelines put forth by Smylie can be extended to other service providers, such as social workers, educators and outreach workers, and can serve as a basis for the identification and implementation of 'best practices' for Aboriginal people in Canada.

Aboriginal communities face different challenges, depending on whether they are rural or urban-based, the degree of substance abuse in the community and the range of other issues confronting them. These include those related to substance abuse during pregnancy and FAS/ARBEs. Aboriginal communities, with the involvement of national Aboriginal political and professional organizations, are better equipped than government ministries to identify the priorities to be addressed within their communities.

Executive Summary

The example of substance abuse and pregnancy, and FAS/ARBEs more generally, illustrate how federal and provincial governments continue to set priorities in Aboriginal health (Tait, 2003). While substance abuse during pregnancy and FAS/ARBEs are health concerns for Aboriginal people, this report has illustrated the need for a cautious approach, including critiquing the scientific and policy literature, and the importance of taking a broad-based perspective that situates the issue within a larger historical and social context.

Chapter 1

Defining the Scope of the Project

Introduction

In the past three decades, fetal alcohol syndrome (FAS) and alcohol-related birth effects (ARBEs) more generally, have emerged as health concerns for Aboriginal[1] people in Canada. At the heart of this concern are two issues: first, the devastating effects that substance addiction has had on Aboriginal people and their communities and; second, the difficulties faced by those individuals, families and communities who face the challenges brought on by FAS and ARBEs. Within the research literature concerning FAS/ARBEs and Aboriginal people, intergenerational impacts of the residential school experience as a contributing factor to rates of FAS/ARBEs are examined. However, Aboriginal authors, such as Fournier and Crey (1997), argue that intergenerational links between residential schools, particularly with regard to sexual and physical abuse experienced by children who attended the schools, mass adoption of Aboriginal children in the 1960s and 1970s and the introduction of alcohol by Europeans into Aboriginal communities, has collectively contributed to high rates of FAS and other related illnesses among Aboriginal people.

The aim of this report is to examine FAS/ARBEs in light of current discussions that identify intergenerational health and social problems that are linked to, or are a result of, the residential school system. The necessary contributing factor in this discussion is alcohol use by pregnant women, as FAS and ARBEs are found only in offspring where in-utero alcohol exposure has occurred. However, while in-utero alcohol exposure is a necessary factor, debate exists as to whether it is a sufficient variable to produce FAS/ARBEs or that other mitigating factors need to be present for effects to occur (Abel, 1998a). For example, the role of other contributing variables such as the pregnant woman's overall physical and mental health status, her nutritional intake during pregnancy and other social and historical factors are at present unknown. Strong evidence exists that these secondary factors can play a significant role in birth outcomes where alcohol exposure in-utero has occurred (Abel, 1998a). Controversy also exists concerning safe and unsafe levels of alcohol exposure and, at present, these levels have yet to be determined. Some research suggests that the threshold level at which alcohol becomes dangerous for the fetus may vary because it is influenced by secondary factors, such as nutrition, genetics and the age of the woman (Abel, 1998a; Astley and Clarren, 2000).

Widespread substance abuse, particularly alcohol abuse, among those who attended residential schools has been identified as both an outcome of the residential school experience and a contributing factor to other negative health and social problems among this group and among subsequent generations of Aboriginal people (Royal Commission on Aboriginal Peoples, 1996b). Although no research studies exist that specifically examine the ways in which residential school experiences contributed to current rates of FAS/ARBEs among Aboriginal people, this report concludes that the residential school system contributed to high rates of alcohol abuse among those who previously attended the schools and among

---

[1] The term 'Aboriginal' is used throughout this document to collectively refer to First Nations, Inuit and Métis people of Canada. The term 'indigenous' is used in the discussion of early contact between indigenous people and Europeans and in discussions concerning cross-country comparisons (i.e., with Australia). When other terms such as 'Indian' or 'Native' are used, this is in keeping with the term used by the author whose work is being discussed. First Nation, Inuit or Métis are used when referring to these groups specifically.

significant numbers of parents and community members who had their children removed from their care because of the school system. This report also concludes that the residential school system further contributed to alcohol abuse among subsequent generations of Aboriginal people, including women of child-bearing age. Despite the negative impacts of the residential school system and other forms of colonization, it should be pointed out that not every former student responded in the same way to their experience and, for various reasons, some individuals and communities did better than others. Because of this, alcohol abuse among Aboriginal people in Canada varies and should be understood as a problem of certain individuals and sub-populations, rather than a problem of *all* Aboriginal people. In relation to FAS/ARBEs, this suggests that programming and services should target those particular populations who are at risk rather than targeting all groups regardless of their alcohol use levels.

The colonialist experience of Aboriginal people in Canada suggests that mainstream interpretations and analysis of health and social issues concerning Aboriginal people, specifically one as sensitive as pregnancy and substance abuse, be read from a critical perspective, questioning what is taken for granted as the current state of affairs (Tait, 2003). In doing so, this report will complement and critique a developing body of research and review literature aimed at the prevention of substance abuse during pregnancy and the management and care of negative birth outcomes caused by alcohol exposure in-utero. Such a review will provide a knowledge base, which can then be used to discuss intergenerational links that connect residential school experiences and present day occurrences of substance abuse by pregnant women and FAS/ARBEs among Aboriginal people. It will also provide possible directions for Aboriginal communities to take in relation to prevention, identification and interventions for pregnant women with substance abuse problems and for alcohol-affected individuals across the life-span.

Objectives

This report reviews and analyzes research literature on FAS and ARBEs among Aboriginal people in Canada. Specific attention is paid to intergenerational variables that are linked to, or are a result of, the residential school experience. Four basic questions are answered:

(1) What is known about the prevalence of FAS and other ARBEs?

(2) What are the individual, biological, psychological, social and economic correlates of FAS and other ARBEs in relation to:

    (i) pregnant women at risk of giving birth to an affected child, and

    (ii) individuals who suffer from FAS/ARBEs?

(3) What evidence is there for a relation of FAS and other ARBEs to the intergenerational effects of residential schools and especially to physical and sexual abuse?

(4) What are the current best practices regarding prevention of FAS and ARBEs and intervention for affected individuals? What are the best practices for communities with high rates of FAS and ARBEs?

Chapter 1

Methodology

For this project, current scientific literature on FAS and ARBEs were reviewed. Wherever possible, unpublished reports and 'gray' literature were included. In the collection of data for this report, priority was given to data available on Aboriginal people living in Canada, including status and non-status Indians, Inuit and Métis, both in rural and urban settings. Available information on FAS/ARBEs in the general Canadian, American and other populations was incorporated wherever it shed light on the issues affecting Aboriginal people in Canada. Other related literature on physical and sexual abuse, alcohol and drug addiction, residential schools and related stressors were also reviewed, even where substance addiction and pregnancy and/or FAS/ARBEs were not explicitly mentioned, to identify potential links. The project examined correlates of substance addiction and pregnancy to identify potential risk and protective factors. Gaps in the research literature and in data collection were identified to serve as guidelines for future research and policy development in official data collection by Aboriginal organizations.

A comprehensive review of evidence for models of prevention, identification and intervention–'best practices'–that have proved to be effective for Aboriginal people was undertaken. Government reports, particularly those that identify 'best practices,' were examined and a critique of the most recent publication by Health Canada, *Best Practices: Fetal Alcohol Syndrome/Fetal Alcohol Effects and the Effects of Other Substance Use During Pregnancy* (Roberts and Nanson, 2000), is given in the final chapters of the report. This adds to the general synthesis of research, clinical and public health literature reviewed in the report and attempts to sensitize the proposed 'best practices' identified by Health Canada to the historical, socio-cultural and environmental context of Aboriginal people in Canada.

In June 2001, literature searches were conducted for this report, which covered several topic areas including the FAS/ARBE specific literature, pregnancy and substance addiction literature and that on illicit drug use, residential schools, sexual and physical abuse, addiction and Aboriginal health. Literature that was FAS/ARBE specific covered the period 1973 through 2001 and included a thorough review of this body of literature. The review of other topic areas was less intensive; however, key texts were examined, as well as the most current literature. The following report is a review and synthesis of the topic areas covered.

'Best Practices'

As stated above, this report will examine 'best practices' in relation to prevention, identification and intervention related to FAS/ARBEs among Aboriginal people in Canada. The use of the term 'best practice' has become a common reference term used by various governments and non-government bodies that deal with health care issues; however, its meaning is often varied and unclear. 'Best practices' are generally defined as "*optimal* ways of doing something, and can refer to both *individual* or *organization* functions, practices or processes" (Mable and Marriott, 2001:3). In relation to health care, the concept has been expanded to include "any initiative which makes a tangible improvement to the quality of life" (UNCHS, 1998 in Mable and Marriott, 2001:3). Health care priorities, such as "fully-implemented programs, benchmarked and tested which meet or set new standards or introduce innovations in healthcare delivery" (Best Practice Network, 2000 in Mable and Marriott, 2001:3) have been included in the definition.

Chapter 1

'Best practices' identified in this report come from a limited scope of knowledge, as they are mainly derived from scientific articles and previously defined 'best practices' identified by Health Canada. A limitation of this study in identifying 'best practices' was the lack of published evaluations and reviews for most of the programs and services currently addressing prevention and intervention of FAS/ARBEs in Canada and elsewhere. While many local programs may have identified 'best practices,' descriptions of the practices and information on how and why they would qualify as a 'best practice,' are generally absent from the current literature published on FAS/ARBEs. The 'best practices' study recently released by Health Canada attempted to address this gap by basing the determination of 'best practices' on scientific evidence *and/or* the perspective of consumers, expert practitioners and educators (Roberts and Nanson, 2000). To date, the report by Roberts and Nanson represents the most comprehensive attempt to identify 'best practices' for FAS/ARBEs in Canada and will serve as an important touchstone for this report.

'Best Practices' and Fetal Alcohol Syndrome

A recent goal of Health Canada has been to identify 'best practices' as they relate to specific health problems experienced by the Canadian population. In 1999, FAS and other ARBEs were identified as important health issues and became the focus of a Health Canada 'best practices' study completed in December 2000. The project took place under the direction of the Canadian Centre on Substance Abuse (CCSA) and was supported by a national steering committee consisting of professional and lay experts in the field of FAS and other related birth disorders.

The Health Canada report primarily reviewed scientific literature, specifically evidence-based research, to come up with a set of 'best practices' in areas of prevention, identification and intervention. 'Best practice' statements, while mainly based on scientific evidence, were also based on the perspectives of consumers, expert practitioners and educators, especially where little or no scientific research existed (Roberts and Nanson, 2000). The report distinguished between three levels of evidence - 'some', 'moderate' and 'good' - and used the following criteria:

Some evidence:

(1) 2 or more case studies or evaluations without control or comparison groups, or

(2) 1 quasi-experimental study (i.e., non-random comparison group).

Moderate evidence:

(3) 2 or more quasi-experimental studies, or

(4) 1 controlled study (i.e., random control group).

Good evidence:

(5) 2 or more controlled studies.

Chapter 1

A goal of this project is the identification of 'best practices' as they relate to FAS/ARBEs found among Aboriginal people in Canada. In order to benefit from the expertise in the Health Canada report, this project will examine the 'best practices' proposed by Roberts and Nanson and attempt to situate the identified practices within the larger socio-cultural and historical context in Canada that impacts upon the daily lives of Aboriginal people. While the report by Roberts and Nanson represents the dominant discourse among FAS/ARBEs experts, the authors point out that the identified 'best practices' are to be seen not as definitive answers, but as possibilities or directives that should be understood, implemented and critiqued according to local context (Roberts and Nanson, 2000).

This report will explore, where possible, what the 'best practices' identified by Roberts and Nanson mean in relation to the lives of Aboriginal people, specifically with regard to local geographical, cultural, ethnic, health and socio-economic realities. Barriers that may prevent certain practices from successfully being implemented will also be identified and, where possible, alternative solutions will be given. In the final two chapters of this report, each 'best practice' identified by Roberts and Nanson will be discussed as part of the review of the prevention and intervention literature.

'Best Practices' and Traditional Knowledge

The question of what 'best practices' means for Aboriginal people, specifically in relation to traditional knowledge, is an area that deserves special attention. This is particularly true when dealing with an issue as sensitive as pregnancy and substance abuse and FAS/ARBEs. However, because of the limited scope of this study, the role of traditional Aboriginal knowledge has been marginalized in the discussion. To partially address this gap, a summary of Marilyn Van Bibber's (1997) discussion of Aboriginal teachings and FAS prevention and treatment strategies is given below. Although it could be argued that Van Bibber's account is specific to her or to the members of her family, community or nation, the view she presents is one that is commonly shared in one form or another by many Aboriginal groups living in Canada.

Van Bibber (1997) writes that some Aboriginal people believe that the creator gives a child many "gifts," and these gifts are generally known as humility, respect, compassion, truth, wisdom and love. How the gifts affect a child's life depends upon the nurturing the child receives in his or her home and community. Van Bibber points out that fundamental Aboriginal teachings can be guiding principles in FAS prevention and treatment strategies. A guiding principle of respect in FAS/ARBE prevention, she suggests, will promote positive development in the community, among family members, individuals affected by FAS/ARBEs, and community workers. Similarly, caring promotes the positive energy of kindness and can be used by all prevention partners.

A hopeful attitude from care givers, family, educators and community members about the positive potential of a child with FAS or an ARBE, Van Bibber (1997) states, positively reinforce the child's image of himself and others. Humility is an important guiding principle since awareness and acceptance of what positive action can and cannot be taken in a FAS/FAE community is a learning process. The use of compassion recognizes that, contrary to the clinical, grim and narrow outlook of medical journals, people with FAS/ARBEs are real people who possess their own special, unique qualities and rightfully deserve a place in the community. Patience, Van Bibber adds, is very important when dealing with FAS/ARBEs, since parenting or teaching approaches that work for children not affected may not work for alcohol-affected children and adults. Sometimes, approaches used successfully one day may not work

Chapter 1

the next. Cooperation is essential since it takes a team effort for FAS/ARBE prevention and treatment programs to be effective in the community over the long term. Van Bibber points out that team building and teamwork are vital, no matter what the needs and resources of the community.

Van Bibber (1997) suggests that before information is presented about FAS/ARBEs in an Aboriginal community, a number of issues should be considered. The most important is that prior to the presentation of information, an informed and caring support network be put in place to receive referrals of anyone who might come forward about their own alcohol use or FAS/ARBEs. The presenters of information must be properly trained in communication and must be knowledgeable about FAS/ARBEs. Van Bibber also adds that knowledge of traditional practices relating to conception, pregnancy and birth should be recognized as a good basis on which to develop community-based prevention programs.

Chapter Descriptions

The following report covers a wide range of inter-related topic areas. Chapter two introduces the diagnostic category fetal alcohol syndrome (FAS) and discusses the evolution of diagnostic categories, which cover the range of alcohol-related birth effects identified in clinical research. A brief discussion of the current status of diagnostic assessments in Canada is also included in this chapter. Chapter three examines alcohol use among Aboriginal people in Canada from several perspectives, including historical, biological and cultural explanations. Chapter four looks at childhood abuse, specifically childhood sexual abuse and its relationship to adult problems, such as substance addiction. Chapter five examines the residential school system, including the daily operation and life at the schools. Chapter six deals with contemporary health and social issues among Aboriginal people, with specific attention paid to intergenerational links to the residential school experience. Chapter seven is a review of the epidemiology literature on FAS/ARBEs, with particular attention paid to studies among Aboriginal groups in North America. Chapter eight looks at risk and protective factors for pregnant women, specifically Aboriginal women with substance abuse problems. This chapter concludes with a discussion of intergenerational links between substance abuse and pregnancy and residential schools. Chapter nine discusses 'best practices' for prevention of FAS/ARBEs. Chapter ten discusses risk and protective factors for persons with FAS/ARBEs and includes a discussion of intergenerational links to residential schools. It also discusses 'best practices' for people with FAS/ARBEs. Chapter eleven is a brief summary of the report and includes final comments on the overall findings and best practices discussed in the report.

Chapter 2

What is Fetal Alcohol Syndrome?

Introduction

Alcohol-related birth effects (ARBEs), particularly fetal alcohol syndrome (FAS), have been identified by many Aboriginal groups in Canada as health and wellness issues that deserve special attention. However, despite a great deal of discussion and concern regarding high rates of FAS/ARBEs among Aboriginal people, along with an explosion of newly created programs and services directed toward prevention, identification and intervention, many individuals, including those who fund, create and implement FAS/ARBE programs and services for Aboriginal people, have limited knowledge of the current scientific research concerning these diagnostic categories. This is not to suggest, however, that local service providers, particularly front-line workers, do not have very complex understandings of the lives and needs of their clients. In fact, they are in the best position to identify possible avenues for research, programming and follow-up. This is also not to suggest that local service providers should or, in fact, have the time to keep up with the most recent scientific findings concerning FAS/ARBEs. What this observation is meant to suggest is that a critical review and synthesis of the FAS/ARBE literature in relation to Aboriginal people in Canada is a much needed source of information for those who are given the task of funding, creating and implementing programs and services.

This chapter attempts to contribute to this need by providing information about the evolution of FAS and other ARBEs as biomedical diagnoses. In doing so, the reader will become better informed as to why, in many instances in this report and most probably in their own experience in dealing with FAS/ARBE issues, there are no definitive answers. This chapter, as well as those that follow, are designed to encourage the reader to think critically, albeit in constructive ways, about local understandings and activities in their community related to substance abuse and pregnancy, and FAS/ARBEs more specifically. The language used in this report, where at all possible, attempts to be accessible to a wide audience, while still maintaining the intended statistical and medical meanings of the research literature reviewed.

Aboriginal people in Canada die earlier than non-Aboriginal people, on average, and sustain a disproportionate share of the burden of physical disease and mental illness (MacMillan, MacMillan et al., 1996; Kirmayer, Brass and Tait, 2000). Mainstream health care targeting Aboriginal communities has been shaped by a century of internal colonial politics that have effectively marginalized Aboriginal people from the dominant system of care (Browne and Fiske, 2001; O'Neil, 1986). Because of this, a central objective for Aboriginal people in areas of health, wellness and healing must be a re-examination of their individual and collective interaction with mainstream health and social service delivery.

One way in which any group can become more actively informed consumers of health and social services and gain maximum control over managing and monitoring those services for their people is through better understanding of the ways in which diagnostic criteria is developed, researched and standardized within the field of biomedicine. This is particularly true for Aboriginal people with regard to illnesses that have been identified as occurring more commonly among the general Aboriginal population. While this may seem like an insurmountable task, moves in this direction have been already made by some Aboriginal groups who have identified certain conditions, such as diabetes or alcoholism, as serious health problems linked to larger social and historical factors and, from this, have developed initiatives such as programs, services and research to meet the specific needs of their people.

Chapter 2

Some of these initiatives have occurred within the biomedical framework, while others have focused specifically on addressing the issue through traditional Aboriginal knowledge and practices. However, in many examples, complementary elements of both biomedical and traditional knowledge and practices have been used in the creation of successful programs and services in Aboriginal communities.

The Evolution of a Diagnosis

In 1968, researchers in France described a cluster of features observed in children of alcoholic women (Lemoine et al., 1968). This was followed by a publication by two American researchers, Kenneth Jones and David Smith (1973), who found similar anomalies in infants born to alcoholic women, and led them in 1973 to formally describe *fetal alcohol syndrome* (FAS) in the medical literature. Their description was derived from observations that suggest high rates of alcohol abuse among certain American Indian communities were linked to birth defects and developmental delays in children (Pauley, 1992). Since its initial description in 1973, FAS has been described in patient populations in most countries of the world (Stratton, Howe et al., 1996).

Fetal alcohol syndrome is marked by pre and/or post-natal growth deficiency (e.g., low birth weight and height); central nervous system (CNS) dysfunction; and characteristic cranio-facial malformations (e.g., short palpebral fissures [short eye slits], flat upper lip, flattened philtrum [the groove between the nose and upper lip] and flat mid-face) (Jones and Smith, 1973). The severity of the illness can vary greatly between individuals and specific markers of the illness, such as the facial features, can change over time or manifest themselves differently in the same individual (Stratton, Howe et. al., 1996). Stratton and colleagues write:

> ... people diagnosed with FAS can have IQs from well within the normal range to the severely mentally retarded range. The physical anomalies can be slight or quite striking. Some with FAS live fairly normal lives if given adequate and structured support throughout their lives, whereas others are severely impaired. The defects may or may not be apparent or easily diagnosed at birth. Although the manifestations of the damage might change with age, FAS never completely disappears and, as with many developmental disabilities, there is no cure, although there might be some amelioration in some individuals. FAS does not refer to signs of acute alcohol exposure or withdrawal at birth. Newborns can have blood alcohol levels high enough to affect acutely their central nervous system function and not have FAS. Newborns can also have no alcohol in their bloodstream *at time of delivery* but still have FAS. FAS is not a 'drunk' baby (emphasis in text, 1996:19).

Since the first description of FAS in the medical literature, on-going progress has been made in developing specific criteria for delineating this syndrome. However, controversy remains in key areas, including the relative boundaries of the diagnosis, as well as the markers that should be used to define those boundaries (Stratton, Howe et al., 1996). Within the medical literature, diagnostic criteria vary from study to study and, along with other methodological factors such as the method of case ascertainment and the population surveyed, has meant that estimates on the prevalence of FAS and ARBEs vary widely (Roberts and Nanson, 2000).

Chapter 2

Abel (1998a) has proposed using the term *fetal alcohol abuse syndrome* in order to emphasize alcohol abuse, rather than simply alcohol use as being responsible for the anomalies. He suggests that the use of 'averaging' (e.g., taking the total number of drinks per week consumed by a pregnant woman and then dividing that number by seven days to get the average ounces or absolute alcohol (AA) per day) in many studies has lead to a misconception that low doses of alcohol can produce anomalies. The use of averaging, Abel argues, has masked patterns of high risk behaviour, such as binge drinking by pregnant women (see Chapter eight for further discussion).

Controversy exists with regard to related classifications such as fetal alcohol effects (FAE) and alcohol-related birth defects (ARBEs), more generally. For example, FAE was originally used to refer to behavioural and cognitive problems occurring in offspring exposed to alcohol in-utero without typical FAS diagnostic features. FAE was understood to be generally less severe than the full-blown syndrome; however, some authors have stressed that FAE involves CNS dysfunction as severe as that occurring in FAS (Abel, 1998a; Streissguth et al., 1997). Others suggest that the precision of the term FAE, which has never been very exact, has been gradually reduced because of the difficulties found in measuring exposure to alcohol, coupled with the difficulties inherent in quantifying or demarcating behavioural and cognitive problems (Stratton, Howe et al., 1996). Some authors have even suggested that the term FAE be abandoned altogether (Aase, Jones and Clarren, 1995; Sokol and Clarren, 1989), which is unlikely to happen anytime soon in Canada as the term is widely used by both professionals and lay persons (Tait, 2003).

In 1996, the American Institute of Medicine (IOM) proposed a revision of the FAS and ARBE diagnostic criteria. These guidelines have been used in many recent studies and applied in clinical practice in North America and elsewhere. The diagnostic categories include five categories: *FAS with confirmed maternal alcohol exposure*, including evidence of facial dysmorphology, growth retardation and central nervous system (CNS) dysfunction; *FAS without confirmed maternal alcohol exposure*, including evidence of facial dysmorphology, growth retardation and CNS dysfunction; *partial FAS (pFAS)* with confirmed maternal alcohol exposure, facial dysmorphology and either growth retardation or CNS abnormalities; *alcohol-related birth defects (ARBD)* - presence of congenital anomalies (e.g., cardiac, skeletal, renal, ocular, auditory) known to be associated with a history of pre-natal alcohol exposure; and *alcohol-related neuro-developmental disorders (ARND)* - confirmed maternal alcohol exposure and evidence of CNS abnormalities (Stratton, Howe et al., 1996). The specific criteria for each category appears in Appendix B.

The criteria proposed by the IOM included two important changes. First, they added the category *FAS without confirmed maternal exposure,* in order to address those cases where maternal alcohol could not be confirmed (e.g., the biological mother's drinking history was unavailable) and those for whom the exposure history was unclear (e.g., differing accounts of the biological mother's drinking). This category became specifically useful for cases where children were in the foster care system, were foreign adopted children (Aronson, 2000) or adults who were fostered and adopted in their childhood years. (Roberts and Nanson, 2000). Secondly, because of the controversy surrounding the category FAE, the IOM dropped this category and replaced it with a new one, *partial FAS*, to further delineate the diagnosis of those with confirmed alcohol exposure history and some, but not all, of the anomalies (Roberts and Nanson, 2000).

Chapter 2

As Roberts and Nanson point out, the categories proposed by the IOM are not without controversy. Abel (1998a) argues that the reliability and validity of diagnostic classifications for alcohol-related effects, including the ones proposed by the IOM, are still relatively untested. He suggests testing-retesting the reliability of diagnostic categories in relation to how consistent they are in identifying individuals with FAS/ARBEs over time, as a way to address this problem. Two studies have suggested that reliability of a FAS diagnosis over time may be problematic. In a study of forty-four German children diagnosed in early childhood and who were then followed up on for the next ten to fourteen years, Spohr and colleagues found that at the time of follow-up, 70% (31/44) had only 'mild' expressions of the syndrome, whereas 20% (8/44) could no longer be identified as having FAS. Only ten per cent of the original sample (5/44) were still recognizable as having FAS (Spohr, Willms and Steinhausen, 1994 in Abel, 1998a). A second study reported that seven out of the eight children previously diagnosed with FAS during infancy no longer warranted the diagnosis at four years of age (Ernhart, Greene et al., 1995 in Abel, 1998a).

Abel's (1998a) point here is not to suggest that alcohol-related birth anomalies do not occur, but rather to point toward the possibilities of mis-diagnosis and over-diagnosis, particularly with regard to diagnostic classifications such as 'partial FAS' and FAE. Astley and Clarren also recently expressed their concern about the continued risk of mis-classification of patients. They argue that "in the absence of accurate, precise, and unbiased methods for measuring and recording the severity of exposure and outcome in individual patients, diagnoses will continue to vary widely from clinic to clinic" (2000:400). Mis-classification, they add, can potentially lead to inappropriate patient care, increased risk for secondary disabilities and missed opportunities for primary prevention. This can also lead to inaccurate estimates of incidence and prevalence rates (Astley and Clarren, 2000; Stratton, Howe et al., 1996). Astley and Clarren write:

> Inaccurate estimates thwart efforts to allocate sufficient social, educational, and healthcare services to this high-risk population and preclude accurate assessment of primary prevention intervention efforts. From a clinical research perspective, diagnostic misclassification reduces the power to identify clinically meaningful contrasts between groups. Non-standardized diagnostic methods prevent valid comparison between studies (2000:400).

Astley and Clarren (2000) describe five primary limitations in the current practice of diagnosing individuals with prenatal alcohol exposure. They include the following:

1. While there are diagnostic guidelines that physicians and medical researchers are encouraged to follow, the guidelines are not sufficiently specific to assure diagnostic accuracy or precision.

2. There is a lack of objective, quantitative scales to measure and report the magnitude of expression of key diagnostic features.

3. The term fetal alcohol effects (FAE) is broadly used and poorly defined.

4. Clinical terms like FAE, alcohol-related birth defects (ARBD) and alcohol-related neuro-developmental disorder (ARND) (Stratton, Howe et al., 1996) inappropriately imply a causal link between exposure and outcome in a given individual.

5. The terms FAS and FAE fail to convey the diversity of disability present in these individuals.

It is important to point out here that the diagnostic problems faced by experts in the field of alcohol-related birth disorders are greatly increased for general practitioners and other diagnosticians who are less aware of the diagnostic criteria and the problems associated with it. In order to address these concerns, Astley and Clarren (2000) have proposed a more precise diagnostic system that uses the numbers 1 to 4 to convey magnitude of expression in each of the four key diagnostic domains: growth deficiency, FAS facial phenotype, brain damage and pre-natal alcohol exposure. This approach, according to Astley and Clarren, is more precise in its evaluation of diagnostic categories and better characterizes the full spectrum of disabilities (2000; 2001; Astley et al., 2000a; 2000b). Initial testing of the reliability of the 4-digit diagnostic code has been promising and it has proved to be fairly easily taught to a broad array of social and health care professionals in a range of clinical settings (Astley and Clarren, 2000).

Diagnosing Fetal Alcohol Syndrome and Alcohol-Related Birth Effects in Canada

Currently in Canada, FAS/ARBEs are diagnosed at varying rates across the country, with the majority of diagnoses being made in western regions. In some provinces there remains a general reluctance on the part of diagnosticians to make a diagnosis of FAS/ARBEs; however, this appears to be changing as physicians receive more education and training in diagnostic assessment (Tait, 2003). Roberts and Nanson (2000) point out that there are several issues of concern pertaining to identification of FAS in certain ethnic populations in Canada. Of particular importance for Aboriginal people is the pattern of facial features proposed by the IOM as markers of FAS, mainly short palpebral fissures (short eye slits), flat upper lip, flattened philtrum (the groove between the nose and upper lip) and flat mid-face, as these features may overlap with racial features found in some Aboriginal groups (Roberts and Nanson, 2000; Aase, 1994; Abel 1998a). Authors such as Godel and colleagues (2000) argue for diagnostic standards that reflect ethnic variance of facial phenotypes. Roberts and Nanson caution that until these differences are reflected in diagnostic assessment, diagnosticians need to "guard against over-diagnosis by being aware of local variants in facial features that can occur, and avoid using these alone to support a diagnosis of FAS" (2000:54).

Standard growth measurements have also been identified as a possible source of diagnostic problems, as they may not reflect the growth norms among a specific population (Roberts and Nanson, 2000). For example, standard growth charts developed in the United States are generally used in FAS/ARBE assessments; however, it was found that unaffected children in an isolated Manitoba community were typically taller and heavier than standard growth curves would predict. This, Roberts and Nanson (2000) suggest, may mask growth retardation caused by prenatal alcohol exposure, as children may not appear to have retarded growth based on the universal measures but, in fact, may be small relative to other children in the community. Average head circumference in some Aboriginal groups has also been identified as being above North American averages, which may mask decreased head size caused by pre-natal alcohol exposure (Roberts and Nanson, 2000). In some instances, the exact opposite may occur; for example, where a group of children may fall below standard growth measurements, thereby falsely suggesting to diagnosticians large numbers of affected individuals in a specific community (Tait, 2003).

Roberts and Nanson (2000) point out that psychological testing for CNS dysfunction has been developed for mainstream groups and may not be appropriate for children who do not speak mainstream languages, such as English and French, or who have not been educated in mainstream cultures. They caution that when assessments are carried out, psychometric tests should first be evaluated for use with the population group of the child or adult being assessed, and that the examiner be familiar with the cultural characteristics of the specific community in relation to factors, such as response styles and other behaviours or circumstances that may influence test results.

Conclusion

Medical researchers are currently attempting to standardize diagnostic tools used by clinicians in making a diagnosis of FAS and other related ARBEs. Due to a lack of standardized diagnostic tools and, to many physicians in Canada not being trained in FAS/ARBE assessments, it is difficult for a patient to receive a medical assessment for FAS/ARBEs in most regions of Canada. Confounding factors, such as specific phenotypes (e.g., typical facial features, height, head size) among certain Aboriginal groups that are similar to those found in persons with FAS/ARBEs, have meant that the potential for mis-diagnosis or over-diagnosis of FAS/ARBEs in some Aboriginal communities exists. Standardized psychological testing for CNS dysfunction may also be inappropriate for Aboriginal children who do not speak English or French as their first language or who have been educated in remote communities. Cultural characteristics of the specific community, as well as consideration of other local factors (e.g., community integration), must be considered in the development of appropriate assessment tools. Research into the testing-retesting of the reliability and validity of FAS/ARBE diagnostic classifications and assessment tools should be undertaken, in order to determine how consistent FAS/ARBE diagnostic classifications are in identifying Aboriginal individuals with alcohol-related birth disorders over the life span. Testing-retesting could involve independent reassessment (the clinician is blind to previous diagnosis) of patients at different intervals over the life span to see if these patients still warrant the diagnostic label.

Chapter 3

Alcohol Use Among Aboriginal People in Canada

Introduction

Within the historical and scientific literature discussing health and social issues of Aboriginal people in North America, high rates of alcohol abuse among the general Aboriginal population figure is a central concern. Historical accounts indicate that alcohol use occurred in some indigenous agricultural societies in the southern regions of the Americas prior to European contact. Intoxication in this context was very rare, as alcohol was used primarily for religious ceremonies (Fournier and Crey, 1997). In northern regions, including the region now known as Canada, indigenous societies lacked a brewing tradition. It was only after contact with Europeans that these groups were introduced to alcohol (Brady, 2000).

The introduction of alcohol to indigenous groups in Canada can be traced back to the Hudson Bay region during the late seventeenth century. French fur traders, eager to obtain furs, used gifts of alcohol to entice indigenous trappers to trade with them (Brady, 2000; Waldram, Herring and Kue Young, 1995). The giving and trading of alcohol quickly gained prominence in fur trading activities, becoming a way for rival trading companies to attract indigenous trappers to their posts (Waldram, Herring and Kue Young, 1995; Ray, 1974). Several written accounts, particularly by the Jesuits, document the deleterious effects the introduction of alcohol had on indigenous people during this period.

Assault and murder were two social problems particularly noted by the Jesuits, along with problems such as sexual assaults, marriage breakdown and food deprivation (Waldram, Herring and Kue Young, 1995). However, historical records show that for some indigenous groups, first contact with alcohol was marked by an initial period of 'naive grace' and consumption of alcoholic beverages was not accompanied by anti-social behaviour (Frank, Moore, et al., 2000; MacAndrew and Edgerton, 1969). In Canada, the early contact period was generally a time when indigenous people drank alcohol only when they were at the trading posts, as it was too dangerous to drink while living on their trap-lines and alcohol was too heavy to carry over the distances they traveled. Periodic visits to trading posts were associated with festive parties, with alcohol being consumed over a day or more, generally until the supply was gone (Saggers and Gray, 1998).

Early European settlers, traders and soldiers tended to be heavy drinkers, engaging in binge drinking episodes that often led to violent and disruptive behaviour. This is expressed, for example, in the diary of one early European trader living in Canada:

> Of all the people in the world I think the Canadians when drunk, are the most disagreeable: for excessive drinking generally causes them to quarrel and fight, among themselves. Indeed I had rather have fifty drunken Indians in fort than, five drunken Canadians (quote taken from Smart and Ogborne, 1986:105).

Chapter 3

Alcohol use during the fur trade period was not limited to men, but some indigenous women[2] regularly drank alcohol alongside their male counterparts. While many indigenous women who worked on the trap-lines abstained from alcohol use, others, when at the trading posts, had patterns of alcohol use similar to those of men. Van Kirk (1980) writes that it was noted in many journals of traders that indigenous 'homeguard' women were particularly vulnerable to addiction to alcohol. For 'homeguard' women, who lived near or at the trading posts, drinking appears to have occurred with greater frequency than with other women, as they often lived in precarious situations where alcohol abuse was combined with other harmful behaviour such as prostitution (Waldram, Herring and Kue Young, 1995). The historical record indicates that indigenous women, whether they drank alcohol or not, were vulnerable to acts of violence committed against them and their children by the men around them. For example, Van Kirk (1991) writes that indigenous women, during the fur trade period, were vulnerable to sexual and physical abuse by indigenous and European traders, which increased significantly during the drunken days of the fur trade war. Maracle (1994) found numerous accounts in the historical record of Aboriginal women trying desperately to hide the weapons of their drunken husbands and sons in efforts to protect not only themselves, but also their children.

Despite alcohol becoming a social problem in the early contact period for some indigenous groups, many abstained from alcohol use and, in several regions, alcohol was recognized by indigenous leaders and their constituents as harmful for their people. For example, some indigenous leaders in the west welcomed the formation of the North-West Mounted Police in 1873 as a means of stemming the American whisky trade.[3] In other circumstances, trading captains requested that the traders not make alcohol available to band members (Waldram, Herring and Kue Young, 1995). It was also not uncommon for an entire people to reject alcohol for decades after their initial contact with settlers. These examples suggest that there was great heterogeneity in the responses to the introduction of alcohol by indigenous groups and the rise of socially harmful drinking patterns was neither uniform nor inevitable, as is suggested, for example, by genetic determinism theories (Frank, Moore et al., 2000).

At the same time as alcohol was being introduced to indigenous groups, other social and health problems were taking a toll upon the lives of indigenous people. For example, infectious diseases from Europe combined with infectious-disease loads, which were present before contact, resulted in widespread illness and, in some cases, mass loss of life among indigenous groups throughout the Americas (Waldram, Herring and Kue Young, 1995). While debate continues as to the extent to which infectious-disease epidemics shaped the post-contact demography of North America, there is no doubt that they contributed to growing widespread social, economic and demographic changes for indigenous groups.

---

[2]   European women did not accompany European men during the early contact period. During this period, it was common for indigenous women to marry European men and raise families. These women often acted as important liaisons between the European and indigenous cultures and the historical record indicates that many of the women exerted a great deal of influence over their European husbands (Van Kirk, 1991).

[3]   Daniel Francis, in *The Imaginary Indian: The Image of the Indian in Canadian Culture* suggests this claim should be read with caution as some early historians of the R.C.M.P. colourfully exaggerated Native helplessness in the face of American whisky traders in Alberta, in order to enhance the heroic image of the beginnings of the force (Francis, 1992 in Steckley and Cummins, 2001).

Chapter 3

Compelling arguments have been made that alcohol abuse was adopted by some indigenous men and women as a method of coping with vast and drastic changes in their individual and collective autonomy and in the social, environmental and political landscape.

In their book, *Dealing with Alcohol: Indigenous Usage in Australia, New Zealand, and Canada* (1998), Saggers and Gray argue that while alcohol abuse was initially viewed as a pleasurable activity by indigenous people in all three countries, many individuals and groups also adopted the use of alcohol as a means of escape. They write:

> With the coming of European colonists, indigenous populations of all three countries were decimated by introduced disease (Saggers & Gray, 1991; Kunitz 1994), and as a result of violence, as colonists and indigenous peoples struggled over possession of land and natural resources (Reynolds, 1981).Particularly in Australia and Canada, but also in New Zealand, many indigenous people were relegated to the status of dispossessed, poverty-stricken fringe dwellers. In these circumstances, the excessive use of alcohol was fueled, both as a means of solace and for its own pleasures (1998:44).

While the individual and collective use of alcohol as a means of coping will be discussed in greater detail later in this report, what this indicates in relation to colonialist strategies, such as residential schooling of Aboriginal children, is that alcohol use/abuse became recognized by some indigenous groups during the early contact period as a meaningful way to express suffering and loss, and as a way to cope emotionally, as individuals and as a collective, with negative feelings and experiences brought on by colonization (Tait, 2003). The use of alcohol as a means to cope was only one piece of a very complex and diverse landscape of drinking, which included other factors such as physiological addiction, an on-going association between alcohol use and pleasure, and the use of alcohol as an item of trade. These were all factors that have helped shape overall patterns of alcohol use/abuse among Aboriginal people today.

Levels and Patterns of Drinking: Alcohol Epidemiology Studies

Canadian studies, which look at per capita consumption of pure alcohol, have found that the average consumption rate per year in the general population is 9.5 litres, whereas in areas with large Aboriginal populations, per capita consumption generally rises. For example, Kellner and colleagues found that rates of per capita pure alcohol consumption in the Yukon, where Aboriginal people make up a significant percentage of the population, averaged 14.8 liters per person (1996 in Brady, 2000; Kellner, Webster and Chanteloup, 1998). Adrian and colleagues (1990-91 in Brady, 2000) found that the presence of First Nations reserve populations increased the overall consumption figures in a study examining alcohol consumption levels in Ontario counties. Scott (1997) points out that in Aboriginal-specific studies, a sizable portion of Aboriginal people, namely the Métis, are excluded from most data bases. She also suggests that the findings from these studies, in most cases, cannot be generalized to the off-reserve (including the urban) context, where the majority of Aboriginal people live.

Research indicates that despite excessive use of alcohol by some Aboriginal people, more Aboriginal people in Canada abstain from the use of alcohol than do individuals in the Canadian population (Statistics Canada, 1993). Brady suggests that indigenous populations in Canada, the United States, Australia and New Zealand have developed very similar patterns of alcohol consumption, characterized by there being many abstainers and many heavy drinkers but few moderate drinkers. As well, those who do drink generally consume more alcohol than those drinkers in the general population, often at levels considered harmful to their health (Brady, 2000). Daily drinking occurs less frequently among indigenous people in Canada, the United States, Australia and New Zealand. Also, the proportion of drinkers and the consequences of drinking vary significantly with age and sex, with young indigenous males being particularly at risk (Brady, 2000; Royal Commission on Aboriginal Peoples, 1996b).

Excessive alcohol consumption among the sub-groups of Aboriginal people in North America who do drink has been linked to higher incidences of homicide, child abuse, child neglect, poor health,[4] family dysfunction, violence, suicidal ideation and suicide in Aboriginal communities as compared to the general population (Kirmayer, Hayton, Malus, Jiminez, Dufour et al., 1992; Fournier and Crey, 1997; Frank, Moore et al., 2000). Between fifty and sixty per cent of illness and death among the Aboriginal population in North America is believed to be alcohol-related (Brady, 1995). For example, in Canada, death by injury among Aboriginal people has decreased over the past twenty-five years; however, it is still almost twice as common among Aboriginal people as among non-Aboriginal people. In some age groups, it is more than four times as common. The majority of these deaths are from injury as the result of motor vehicle accidents, with alcohol being a major contributing factor (Royal Commission on Aboriginal Peoples, 1996b). Alcohol-related arrests are also significantly higher among Aboriginal people than among non-Aboriginal people (Kline and Roberts, 1973). The National Native Association of Treatment Directors has estimated that approximately eighty per cent of Aboriginal people in Canada are directly or indirectly affected by alcoholism (Fournier and Crey, 1997).

In the United States, similar findings have been reported. For example, alcohol-related deaths in 1977 were twenty times higher among American Indians than the general American population (Aase, 1981). The 1992-1994 age-adjusted alcohol mortality rate for American Indians was close to six times higher than the 1993 rate for the entire American population (Frank, Moore et al., 2000). The age adjusted mortality rate from cirrhosis of the liver was found to be 2.6 times higher among American Indians than their non-American Indian counterparts and the age-adjusted mortality rate from alcoholism was determined to be twenty times higher among American Indians as opposed to the general American population (May and Smith, 1988). Factors such as cultural dislocation, poverty, racism, poor health, unemployment, boredom and sexual abuse all have been linked to alcohol abuse among Aboriginal people in North America (Fisher, 1987; May and Smith, 1988; Brady, 1995; O'Nell and Mitchell, 1996; Fournier and Crey, 1997; Frank, Moore et al., 2000).

---

[4]   Excessive alcohol abuse among Canadian Aboriginal people has resulted in increased incidences of the following health ailments: heart disease, cirrhosis, liver disease, gastrointestinal cancers and hepatitis (Fournier and Crey, 1997).

Chapter 3

Aboriginal Women and Alcohol Use

Few epidemiological studies that examine alcohol use among Aboriginal women in Canada currently exist and epidemiological data on this sub-group usually exist as part of larger data sets (Roberts and Nanson, 2000). Determining accurate levels of alcohol consumption by Aboriginal women and women, more generally, has been difficult (Poole, 1997). Canadian studies, however, indicate that Aboriginal women are more likely than men and non-Aboriginal women to abstain from alcohol use (Roberts and Nanson, 2000). Through national surveys, researchers estimate that approximately sixty-seven per cent of women in Canada drink alcohol, making it the most commonly used substance by women (Poole, 1997; Addiction Research Foundation of Ontario 1996; Health Canada, 1996). The National Population Health Survey (NPHS) found that half of the women in Canada between 25 to 44 years of age are regular drinkers; twelve per cent drink 7 to 13 drinks per week and four per cent drink 14 or more drinks per week (1999). Regular heavy drinking patterns are more common among younger women than older women. Regular heavy drinking rates were found to have doubled among young women 20 to 24 years of age between 1994/95 and 1996/97 (NPHS, 1999), which has led some to argue that this may indicate particular risk for alcohol-related birth effects (ARBEs) among this age cohort of women (Federal, Provincial and Territorial Advisory Committee on Population Health, 1999 in Roberts and Nanson, 2000).

The Aboriginal Peoples Survey (APS) reported the use of alcohol by Aboriginal women fifteen years and older, with a breakdown between First Nations on-reserve, First Nations off-reserve, Métis and Inuit (Statistics Canada, 1993). The survey found that 60.6% of Aboriginal women drank during the year prior to the survey, with the percentage being greatest for Métis (67.5%) and off-reserve First Nations women (65.1%) (Statistics Canada, 1993).[5] When looking at abstention by Aboriginal identity, the Inuit have a significantly higher abstinence rate than either First Nation or Métis groups. Scott (1997) argues that this finding may suggest that the greater polarization pattern is more evident in the North. She further suggests that the patterns of use by indigenous grouping found in the APS "lend greater evidence to the notion that there is something significant about community" (Scott, 1997:145). Scott goes on to state:

> When questioned about whether or not they perceived alcohol abuse as a problem in their community, Indian groups on and off-reserve were more likely to perceive alcohol abuse as a problem in their community than either Métis or Inuit groups. Inuit, on the other hand, were more likely to believe that alcohol abuse is not a problem (Scott, 1997:145; see Statistics Canada, 1993).

Collectively, these studies suggest that the widely held belief that most Aboriginal people consume excessive amounts of alcohol on a regular basis is incorrect (Royal Commission on Aboriginal Peoples, 1996b).

---

[5]   The APS was based on self-reports and, therefore, should be considered with some caution. However, most data describing substance abuse in Canada (and elsewhere) are self-reported data (Royal Commission on Aboriginal Peoples, 1996b:159, fn 138:331).

Chapter 3

In a review of the literature on substance use among Aboriginal groups in Canada, Scott (1997) suggests that gender differences are apparent between Aboriginal women and men in relation to substance abuse. Scott states that, generally, substance abuse is inferred from social indicators, such as death due to injury and poisoning. However, Aboriginal men are more likely than Aboriginal women to die violently, suggesting gender differences in experiences related to substance abuse. Scott argues that this difference does not necessarily suggest Aboriginal women do not suffer from addiction to the same extent as their male counterparts, but that the physical consequences of their addictions are not as frequently fatal as for Aboriginal men.

This conclusion, she adds, is supported by findings that suggest Aboriginal men and women are more similar to each other than they are to non-Aboriginal people when considering, for example, opportunities for social reinforcement of substance use and adolescent use patterns (Scott, 1986; 1997; Health and Welfare Canada, 1989; Gfellner and Hundelby, 1995).

Explanations For Contemporary Alcohol Abuse Patterns Among Aboriginal People

> The view that tribal people have a predisposition or genetic weakness to alcohol is a racist response to a serious national problem. The notion that tribal people drink to relive their past memories as warriors will neither explain nor mend the broken figures who blunder drunk and backslide through cigarette smoke from one generation to the next. Separations from tribal tradition through marriage or acculturation do not explain the behaviour associated with drunkenness. Tribal cultures are diverse and those individuals who are studied at the bar, or on the streets, are unique, alive and troubled, not entities from museums or the notebooks of culture cultists (Vizenor, 1990: 307-308).

A general consensus exists among researchers that high rates of alcohol abuse among certain sub-groups of Aboriginal people in North America, which are often marked by specific harmful behavioural patterns, is the result of collective experience that is multi-faceted and diverse. This is further complicated when the added dimension of individual life experiences is factored into explanations for why some Aboriginal people abuse alcohol, while others do not. The following discussion will review various theories, which have been put forth to account for contemporary alcohol abuse and alcohol-related behavioural patterns among Aboriginal groups and individuals in North America.[6] The aim of this discussion, however, is not to come up with an explanation of why Aboriginal people drink. It will be shown that, not unlike people in other cultural and ethnic groups, Aboriginal people drink alcohol for various reasons. This discussion seeks to look at some of the explanations for the higher rates of harmful alcohol consumption and related harm among Aboriginal people, compared to non-Aboriginal people in Canada[7] (Saggers

---

[6]   While this is not a comprehensive review of the literature on indigenous people and alcohol, this section reviews the key arguments that have been put forward in various fields of research. The review structure used here will follow the one put forth in Chapter 5: Dealing with Alcohol: Indigenous Usage in Australia, New Zealand and Canada, by Saggers and Gray (1998) and will incorporate some of the more recent literature not included in their review.

[7]   This section does not discuss, in detail, alcohol abuse among Aboriginal people with regards to the question of gender differences. This will be dealt with in more detail later in the report, in discussions of alcohol abuse and pregnant women.

Chapter 3

and Gray, 1998). This section also aims to illustrate how difficult it is to answer the question of why a particular individual or group of individuals, such as pregnant Aboriginal women, may or may not abuse alcohol. This will then be discussed later in the report in relation to literature written on the prevention of substance abuse and pregnancy, and understandings of alcohol use/abuse by pregnant women.

Biology

The connection between alcohol abuse among Aboriginal people in North America and racial susceptibility reaches as far back as the days of the fur trade in Canada (Brody, 1988; Royal Commission on Aboriginal Peoples, 1996b; Steckley and Cummins, 2001). Biological vulnerability to alcohol was tied into larger notions that Europeans held about indigenous people, particularly that they were a vanishing inferior race doomed to extinction (Steckley and Cummins, 2001). While alcohol became a key trade item used by European traders to access furs from indigenous traders, the hypocrisy of turning alcohol into a highly sought-after trade item and then blaming the results on the 'nature' of indigenous people was not lost on nineteenth-century Ojibwa writer George Copway:

> The ministry of this country, and the sluggards in the cause of humanity, say now: **There is a fate or certain doom on the Indians, therefore we need do nothing for them.** How blasphemous! First you give us rum by the thousand barrels, and, before the presence of God and this enlightened world, point to God, and charge him as the murderer of the unfortunate Indians. (Copway, 1972:264-5 in Steckley and Cummins, 2001:181, emphasis in text).

While the destructive influence of alcohol abuse was very real for some indigenous groups, as stated earlier, there are numerous examples of indigenous groups resisting alcohol, which has often been downplayed or ignored in the literature (Steckley and Cummins, 2001).

Scientific research has long been interested in racial classifications, with indigenous people figuring prominently as research subjects in many of the studies. For example, Samuel George Morton's *Crania Americana,* published in 1839, was a 'treatise on the inferior quality of Indian intellect.' Gould states that Morton's study, while highly respected at the time, was incorrect in measurement and mathematics and wrongheaded in its conception of "racial intelligence" (Gould, Stephan and Jay, 1981:57 in Fisher, 1987:83). Early racial classification schemes, such as those adopted by Morton, were based on common racist views, even in scientific circles, right through to the 1950s. In this framework, racial classifications were invoked by scientists as objective classifications derived from 'natural' divisions of the human species. Racial classification schemes not only saw the races as inherently different, but some races as inherently inferior to others (Gould, 1981 in Fisher, 1987). Racial typology was also central in 19th and 20th century eugenics movements, the most extreme form of these being Nazism (Saggers and Gray, 1998).

For the most part, biological race as a scientifically useful concept has been discredited. One of the most influential studies to debunk biological racial classification was conducted by Lewontin, who studied intra-group versus inter-group variation. Lewontin set out to find how much variation there is within populations and whether the degree of variation within and between human populations can be estimated (1972 in Fisher, 1987). Beginning with 'mostly classical racial groupings,' Lewontin estimated diversity within populations, among populations, within races and among races. In the end, he concluded that, based on blood type data, only 6.3 per cent of human difference is accounted between differences among racial groupings.

Somewhere between 90.7 per cent and 67.4 per cent of human variability is to be found within these populations (1972 in Fisher, 1987). Lewontin sums up his findings: "Human racial classification is of no social value ... Such racial classification is now seen to be of virtually no genetic or taxonomic significance either, no justification can be offered for its continuance" (1972:397 in Fisher, 1987:83).

Despite positions such as that taken by Lewontin, race remains a research category for some alcohol studies. Race and metabolism, for example, were the focus of a number of studies during the 1970s. The most well known of these was a study by Fenna and colleagues in 1971. In this study, Inuit and Indian hospital patients from two Edmonton hospitals and in the community of Inuvik, NWT, were compared to Euro-Canadian volunteers. To examine the rate of metabolism of alcohol, rates of sobering up were compared between Aboriginal and non-Aboriginal participants. Alcohol was administered intravenously to each participant and blood alcohol levels were measured by breathalyzer. Fenna and colleagues (1971) found that Inuit and Indian patients had slower rates of disappearance of blood alcohol. This differential response persisted even after stratifying for individual patient histories of typical alcohol consumption (categorized as light, moderate and heavy drinkers). In a critique of the implications of the Fenna study, Waldram and colleagues write: "This study lent credence to the impression that Aboriginal drinkers took a longer time to 'sober up'. The Alberta study, however, was not corroborated by subsequent studies in other Aboriginal groups, some of which actually showed the opposite trend" (1995:95).

For example, a later study by Bennion and Li (1976) found no significant difference in alcohol metabolism between Indians and Caucasians. In a comparative study of Euro-Canadians, Chinese and Ojibwa, Reed (1985) enumerated nine categories of alcohol response where ethnic differences had been shown to occur: consumption rate, absorption rate from the digestive tract, metabolism rate, prevalence of variants of the enzymes alcohol dehydrogenase (ADH) and acetaldehyde dehydrogenase (ALDH), alcohol sensitivity, cardiovascular changes, psychological changes and alcohol abuse. The data showed that, in tandem with the fastest decline in blood-ethanol concentration among the three groups, at various times after the ingestion of ethanol, the Ojibwa participants also showed the highest levels of acetaldehyde, the metabolic by-product of alcohol believed to be responsible for such symptoms of intolerance as facial flushing (Reed, Kalant, Griffins, Kapur and Rankin, 1976 in Waldram, Herring and Kue Young, 1995). Reed concluded that enzyme differences were most probably due to single genes, while rates of absorption and metabolism were likely under the control of many genes (Reed, 1985 in Waldram, Herring and Kue Young, 1995). Waldram and colleagues write:

> Sensitivity to alcohol and its metabolic by-products would appear to be a 'protective' mechanism in populations with deficient or abnormal enzymes. Even if this were the case with Aboriginal people, and the evidence is by no means consistent, it would appear that socio-economic and cultural factors could overcome this physiologically base aversion to alcohol such that some members of this group appear to experience significant social and health problems related to alcohol abuse. Even if there are substantial genetic differences in alcohol metabolism among ethnic groups, it remains to be seen if such differences are in reality translated into differences in social response, the frequency of abuse, and

the potential for successful interventions. On the other hand, the demonstration of metabolic differences does not mean that the problem of alcohol abuse is immutable and that broader strategies addressing social and economic determinants are necessarily futile (1995:95-96).

Hanna conducted a study in Hawaii among Caucasians, Chinese and Japanese, and found that Chinese and Japanese subjects (who are genetically more closely related to indigenous Americans than to Caucasians) metabolized alcohol more rapidly than Caucasians, which supports the findings of Reed and colleagues (Hanna, 1978 in Saggers and Gray, 1998). An Australian study of a small group of Aboriginal and non-Aboriginal prisoners found that, although there were wide differences in the rates of alcohol metabolism between individuals, there was no significant difference in the mean rates in each group (Marinovich, Larsson and Barber, 1976). They write: "Considering these factors we must conclude that there appears to be no genetically determined difference in blood alcohol degradation between Aboriginals and whites" (1976:46 in Saggers and Gray, 1998:70).

A number of studies set out to examine if genetic differences existed that affected responses to alcohol. Data were collected from individuals who appeared to be from one of the popularly accepted racial groupings. Fisher writes:

> Clinical studies of alcoholism overlap with fundamental psychiatric or pharmacological research, and they rely on twin studies and family studies. In clinical genetic/racial alcoholism research the object has been to find a genetic marker for problems with alcohol in racial populations. Recent research into genetics and alcoholism has looked for traits or markers of susceptibility to compulsive drinking or to find a 'genetically determined dysfunctional state' which produces alcoholism (McConnell 1984:9). While not specifically mentioning race, contemporary studies of genetics of alcoholism emphasize the organic origins of the disease entity, attempting to exclude or eliminate environmental forces (1987:84).

Alcoholism, however, is similar to other diseases such as hypertension, coronary heart disease, schizophrenia and diabetes in which the triangular aspect of the illness, person and social milieu makes it especially tricky to sort out genetic-familial from family-environment in the presence or absence of alcohol (Fisher, 1987).

A group of studies have looked at variations in dopamine D^2 receptors in the brain[8] (Blum, Noble, Sheridan, Ritchie, Jagadeeswaran et al., 1990; Noble, 1992). Noble hypothesized that individuals who had a lower number of receptors "*may* need a very strong stimulation of their fewer receptors" (Noble, 1992:27 in Saggers and Gray, 1998:70, emphasis in text) and, therefore, seek the stimulation provided by alcohol. In his study, Noble examined brain samples from deceased persons and found that the allele, which genetically codes for few receptors, was more common in deceased 'alcoholics' than in

---

[8]   Dopamine is a neuro-transmitter, the release of which is stimulated by alcohol (among other chemical compounds). It has various effects, one of which is to induce feelings of pleasure when it attaches to D^2 receptors in certain brain cells. The number of these receptors is determined by one of two alleles (variants of a gene) (Saggers and Gray, 1998).

non-alcoholics. However, he found no differences based on racial categories between Caucasian and Black subjects (Noble, 1992). Some similar studies appear to have confirmed this result, while others failed to do so (Karp, 1992). In summing up the studies, Saggers and Gray write:

> Setting aside the major issue of what constitutes 'alcoholism', as Saunders and Phillips (1993) point out, the relationship between 'alcoholism, and the presence of the D^2 receptor remains simply an association, that is, no causal relationship has been demonstrated ... [While] there are biochemical and physiological factors which influence individual responses to alcohol and its metabolites ... popular prejudice to the contrary, there is no firm evidence that these differences cause the misuse of alcohol or that they explain differences between populations in either patterns of alcohol consumption or its consequences (1998:70).

Racial susceptibility to alcoholism and the effects of alcohol consumption has also been discussed in relation to pregnancy and substance abuse. In an article discussing risk factors for FAS in American Indian populations, Aase speculates about "some of the poorly understood factors of maternal physiology which might contribute to an increased risk for FAS in American Indian children" (1981:154). Referring to several of the studies discussed above, she writes:

> While conflicting results were obtained, and none of the studies is completely satisfactory, the majority point to an *increased* rate of alcohol degradation in Indians. If this is true, a more rapid fall in alcohol levels might constitute a protective effect after exposure for the fetus in utero. Unfortunately, none of the studies to date have yielded information on women with chronic and severe alcohol abuse, but rather on 'social drinkers'. The possibility remains that some metabolic difference in the handling of alcohol in truly alcoholic Indian women may place their babies in increased peril. One interesting discovery along these lines is that many American Indians share with Orientals a deficit in the breakdown of acetaldehyde, the first product of alcohol degradation. This may imply a genetic basis for altered alcohol metabolic pathways in these two racial groups (Aase, 1981:155).

In this example, Aase suggests that differences in the metabolism of alcohol by different racial groups could impact negatively on fetal development, producing differing outcomes with regard to ARBEs, with Aboriginal and 'Orientals' being at greatest risk. However, despite her speculation, no such studies exist to support this. Furthermore, May points out that, to base this type of study on racial classifications, seems mis-directed in its concern. He writes:

> No state-of-the-art study published in mainstream journals to date has verified any major peculiarity in alcohol metabolism among Indians. Existing studies have examined the metabolism of ethanol, acetaldehyde, and liver phenotype in Indians. No physiological variables have been identified to date that are substantial enough to explain major differences in Indian drinking and intoxicated behaviour from that of whites, blacks, or Asians (Bennion and Li, 1976; Farris and Jones, 1978a, b; Lieber, 1972; Reed, Kalant, Griffins, Kapur and Rankin, 1976; Rex, Bosron, Smialek and Li, 1985; Schaefer, 1981; Zeiner, Parades and Cowden, 1976). In fact, most of these studies conclude by stating

that the reasons for the differences between Indian and non-Indian drinking behaviours should be sought in sociocultural variables (Bennion and Li, 1976, for example).

Therefore, the currently accurate, scientific conclusion is that there is no major or consistent, racially based physiological difference in alcohol metabolism between Indians and others, and that there is as much variance among individual Indians as there is between Indians and others. The alcohol metabolism rates of particular Indians are affected by common human factors, such as drinking style, prior drinking experience, and body weight, as is generally true of all major racial groups (Reed, 1985; May, 1991:240).

Biological racial susceptibility to alcoholism and alcohol abuse (and more recently ARBEs) has long been associated with the Aboriginal population. May and others, in attempts to re-educate scientific and lay communities, have reviewed the scientific literature and shown that not only is a link between biological race and alcoholism or behaviour resulting from alcohol abuse not proven in the scientific literature, but racial classifications based on biology are impossible to apply to empirical research. Despite this, a scientifically constructed image of Aboriginal people as biologically susceptible to alcohol and alcohol abuse is a commonly held belief among some professional and lay groups (Tait, 2003). This perception, Waldram and colleagues argue, is in keeping with a similar belief that Aboriginal people have a special susceptibility to tuberculosis. They write:

> This [special susceptibility to alcohol and tuberculosis] stands in stark contrast to the supposed resistance of Euro-Canadians to both. In this we see quite clearly the outlines of the discredited notion of racial traits and all that this implies about treatment policy. Equally important, the effects of this construction reach far beyond the academic domain and 'the biological explanation maintains its strongest existence in the realm of folk belief' (May, 1984:15), with the potential to serve as an explanation for individual problems with alcohol abuse for Aboriginal and non-Aboriginal people who accept the belief (Waldram, Herring and Kue Young, 1995:266).

As pointed out by Waldram and colleagues, the hypocrisy spoken about in the nineteenth-century by George Copway continues to the present day.

The 'Drunken Indian' Stereotype

The detrimental impact that alcohol abuse has in many Aboriginal communities and the significant amount of public attention it has received through the media has resulted in a negative association between Aboriginal people and alcohol use within the general public. The stereotype of the 'drunken Indian,' which has been greatly exaggerated within Canadian society, is the clearest and most common example (Royal Commission on Aboriginal Peoples, 1996b). At a very basic level, this stereotype implies that individually, Aboriginal people are biologically incapable of engaging in 'responsible' consumption of alcohol and are prone to acts of reckless abandon, often with tragic results (May, 1988). For Aboriginal people collectively, this stereotype has implications on both social and political levels (Maracle, 1994).

Chapter 3

The 'drunken Indian' stereotype resonates not only within every level of non-Aboriginal society in North America, but there is evidence to suggest that it resonates within some Aboriginal communities as well. For example, an American study by May and Smith (1988), which looked at opinions about alcohol abuse held by members of the Navajo population, found that only 30 to 42% of Navajo adults drank, compared with 71% of the general population. Despite this, study participants cited alcoholism to be the number one health problem on their reserve. Sixty-three per cent of the study participants felt that Aboriginal people, in general, have a physical weakness to alcohol that does not exist among the non-Aboriginal population. It is not clear from the discussion by May and Smith what factors influenced study participants to respond this way, but knowledge of the history of Aboriginal-white relations indicates that this response was likely shaped by the dominant historical and social discourse about Aboriginal people and alcohol.

Alcohol Dependence as 'Disease' or 'Dysfunction'

Alcohol abuse, alcohol dependence and alcoholism are strongly associated with one another and, in many instances, are terms used interchangeably in professional and lay discussions on alcohol, women and FAS/ARBEs. However, it is important to distinguish the specific meaning of each term as, in certain contexts, they imply very different things. Abel writes:

> ... to drinking behaviour that adversely affects an individual's health, behaviour, or the society in which he or she lives, but does not necessarily involve impaired control over drinking ... If alcohol abuse progresses to the point that it does become obsessive/ compulsive as well, it is called alcoholism or alcohol dependence (Abel, 1998a:11; U.S. Department of Health and Human Services, 1993).

As no reliable 'biological markers' for alcohol consumption exist, clinicians and researchers rely on self-reports given by patient-subjects about their drinking habits (Abel, 1998a). Relying on self-reports of drinking patterns raises concern in areas of research as several problems can arise, such as under or over-reporting and recall failure. For example, the Royal Commission on Aboriginal Peoples (1996b) expressed concern that lower consumption rates of alcohol use among Aboriginal people, as reported in the Aboriginal Peoples Survey (APS) (Statistics Canada, 1993), could reflect present day circumstances in which Aboriginal people are beginning to achieve higher levels of sobriety or may reflect under-reporting of alcohol consumption due to fears held by research participants about possible breaches of confidentiality and anonymity. This concern is important as each hypothesis suggests different strategies for future research, development of health and social policy and funding allocation.

Alcohol dependence or alcoholism are generally central issues in any discussion of alcohol abuse and problem drinking. However, understandings of alcohol dependency are not without controversy, particularly as they apply to Aboriginal people. Saggers and Gray (1998) point out how excessive use of alcohol had changed in the early part of the 20th century. Where prior to the early 20th century, excessive use of alcohol in the Western world was generally perceived as a moral problem, in that individuals who abused alcohol were seen to be doing so by choice and, thus, were held to be morally culpable for that choice. This perception shifted in the early 20th century to a disease model. In this framework, individuals were believed to be 'sick,' rather than 'immoral,' as the problem situated within individual physiology. Characteristically, alcohol as a sickness or disorder was characterized by a craving for alcohol and loss of the ability to control the level consumed. Saggers and Gray point out that, within the disease model, two explanations of alcohol dependency emerged:

> The first [explanation] saw this loss of control primarily as the manifestation of a physical disease, 'alcoholism'. While there are some variations in definition, generally those who view it as a disease characterise it as occurring among individuals who, among other things: are genetically predisposed; are physiologically dependent upon alcohol (that is they are so accustomed to its intake that they suffer withdrawal symptoms on cessation of drinking); and suffer alcohol-related brain damage which further impairs their ability to control their level of consumption (Jurd, 1996:2-4). The second approach viewed the excessive consumption of alcohol … which was often a manifestation of underlying psychopathology. It should be noted, however, that these were primarily differences in emphasis, for proponents of both views usually acknowledged elements of the other approach (1998:71).

Even though there has been wide acceptance of the disease model, concepts such as alcoholism, alcohol dependency and alcohol misuse are contested categories. For example, in the 1970s, the term 'alcoholism' was removed from the International Classification of Diseases because agreement could not be reached as to its definition. It was replaced by 'alcohol dependence syndrome,' "defined in terms of observable physical aspects and separating these from behaviour and affective factors whose aetiology is more controversial" (Saggers and Gray, 1998: 71-72).

The application of concepts, such as alcoholism, to populations has been even more difficult and problematic. Conceptually, diseases should have cross-culturally valid diagnoses and treatment, regardless of cultural differences (Fisher, 1987; Vaillant, 1983; Levy and Kunitz, 1973). However, a straightforward application with regard to alcoholism and Aboriginal groups does not seem to exist. Even *within* the culturally diverse population known as 'Indian' or 'Aboriginal,' the disease model is difficult to apply consistently (Fisher, 1987). For example, Leland (1976) examined the ethnographic accounts of thirty-three North American Indian groups and found that nineteen of the ethnographies examined concluded that alcohol addiction was 'absent or rare' among their subjects. This suggests that nearly sixty per cent of these Aboriginal groups did not manifest the supposedly universal symptoms of alcoholism (Leland, 1976). O'Connor (1984) argues that excessive alcohol consumption by indigenous Australians cannot be explained by the same theories used to explain alcohol dependence in the non-indigenous population. His study found that some indigenous Australians who might be classified as heavy drinkers demonstrated, depending on the social environment, an ability to abstain from or control their drinking in ways that are inconsistent with the described behaviours of persons who are believed to be alcohol-dependent (O'Connor, 1984 in Saggers and Gray, 1998). Similar observations of individuals belonging to an indigenous group and who appear to meet the criteria for alcoholism, but who completely abstain from drinking for periods of weeks and sometimes months, has also been described by several authors (Levy and Kunitz, 1974; Saggers and Gray, 1998; Shkilnyk, 1985).

The disease model of alcoholism has been adopted by many alcohol addiction treatment programs, some of which are based on traditional Aboriginal healing approaches, Alcoholics Anonymous or a combination of both. Waldram and colleagues suggest that the strength of these programs comes from their focus on individuals, thereby setting aside biological and cultural explanations (1995). Along with others researchers (Fischer, 1987; May and Smith, 1988; Brady, 1995; O'Nell and Mitchell, 1996; Fournier and Crey, 1997; Frank, Moore et al., 2000), Waldram and colleagues suggest that Aboriginal communities appear to be disproportionately experiencing the negative effects of alcohol abuse not because of biological or cultural factors, but rather because of the "fairly uniform negative effects of poverty, racism, and marginalization stemming from colonization" (1995:269). However, they stress that it must be recognized that only a minority of Aboriginal people experience alcohol-related problems, despite the widespread attention alcoholism among Aboriginal people receive (Waldram, Herring and Kue Young, 1995).

Whitehead and Hayes (1998) move away from debates concerning definitions of alcoholism and alcohol dependence and, instead, focus on the question of what alcoholism is. In this discussion, the concept of alcoholism is an assumed category and the question for Whitehead and Hayes is what that category represents, either a primary social problem or a symptom of poor mental health. Determining what 'alcoholism' is, they contend, will have significant implications for public policy with respect to prevention and treatment of the problems of alcoholism and alcohol abuse. As a primary social problem, alcoholism is understood as a condition that contributes to a wide variety of other harmful social, economic and health-related conditions (Whitehead and Hayes, 1998; Scarpetti and Anderson, 1989). While there is debate among researchers as to precisely how alcoholism contributes to the generation of negative outcomes, proponents of this view believe that "resources addressed directly at the treatment and prevention of alcoholism constitute a frontal attack on a long list of problems and damaging consequences that, if unchecked, will continue to exact a high toll" (Whitehead and Hayes, 1998:7; Fitzpatrick, 1974; Brill, 1970; MacAndrew and Edgerton, 1969).

Proponents of the view that alcoholism is a symptom of poor mental health also have varying ideas as to the precise pattern of causality; however, most agree that the relationship between alcoholism and other problem behaviours and conditions are based on pretense. For example, alcohol abuse is not believed to generate aggressive behaviours, but both are seen to be brought on by underlying conditions of poor mental health (Timpson, McKay, Kakegamic, Roundhead, Cohen et al., 1988; Potter-Efron, 1989). In terms of treatment, this understanding suggests treatment and prevention of alcohol abuse will provide symptomatic relief only and will have, at best, no impact on the prevalence of other social problems, such as family violence, suicide and crime (Whitehead and Hayes, 1998). Eradication of alcohol abuse, without equal or greater effort being directed toward more fundamental issues of mental health, may result in an actual increase in the prevalence of other problems (Whitehead and Hayes, 1998).

Whitehead and Hayes take the position that alcohol abuse is a primary social problem and they criticize the Royal Commission on Aboriginal Peoples (RCAP) for arguing that alcohol abuse among Aboriginal people is a symptom of poor mental health. While this distinction will be discussed later in this report in relation to prevention and treatment strategies for pregnant women who abuse substances, it is important to further outline the two arguments.

The section on alcohol in the RCAP report criticizes the Canadian government as having taken a 'half-hearted' approach to Aboriginal mental health issues generally (1996b). The Commission states:

... we would like to see the insights of Aboriginal addictions workers applied to social and emotional health problems more broadly. In our view, the failure to do so reflects the half-hearted approach taken by the Canadian governments to Aboriginal mental health issues generally. Alcohol addiction is seen by most health authorities-and by many of those who work in the treatment field-as a stand-alone problem with treatable causes. Some see it as a disease. Moreover, it is funded as a stand-alone problem with treatable causes. The most successful alcohol treatment programs developed by and for Aboriginal people have gone far beyond this restricted understanding of addictions; they have tackled related problems of physical and sexual abuse, loss of self-esteem and cultural identity, lack of personal opportunity and exclusion from Canadian society. Counsellors have found that Aboriginal addictions are part of a circle of oppression, despair, violence and self-destructive behaviour that must be addressed as a whole. For most of their clients, tackling addictions is like grabbing the tail of the tiger-family violence, suicide, self-injury, accidental injuries and deaths all being stripes on the same animal (Royal Commission on Aboriginal Peoples, 1996b:161-162).

The stance taken by RCAP reflects an approach that is grounded in a notion of 'holistic' wellness and locates individuals, in all their complexity, within the family, community and natural environment, as well as within historical and cultural context. "Physical, emotional, spiritual and environmental health are all essential aspects of well-being. When they are in balance, health and wellness prevail. When they are out of balance, ill health and social discord predominate" (Royal Commission on Aboriginal Peoples, 1996b:164). While one could argue that this is not the understanding of all Aboriginal people in Canada, it does represent a commonly shared belief among many Aboriginal groups. Furthermore, this view is not unlike that taken by some mental health professionals who have worked extensively in Aboriginal communities. For example, in a literature review for RCAP, Kirmayer and colleagues take the following position:

The fragmentation of mental health programs into substance abuse, violence, psychiatric disorder and suicide prevention ... does not reflect the reality of great overlap among the affected individuals, the professional expertise needed ... and the appropriate interventions. In many cases, it is not helpful to single out a specific problem as ... a focus ... because focusing attention exclusively on the problem without attending to its larger social context can do more harm than good. A comprehensive approach to mental health and illness should therefore be integrated within larger programs ... (Kirmayer, 1994 in Royal Commission on Aboriginal Peoples, 1996b:163-164).

Therefore, whether referred to as 'wellness' or 'peace of mind' (Royal Commission on Aboriginal Peoples 1996b) by Aboriginal groups or 'mental health' by mental health professionals, a common understanding of the need for a broader scope of understanding, *vis à vis* the individual, is seen to be necessary.

In a review of the literature, which contends alcohol is a primary social problem, Whitehead and Hayes (1998) found that, other things being equal, Aboriginal communities that experience low rates of alcoholism tend to experience relatively low rates of a broad range of other social, legal and health-related problems. These communities also tend to experience lower rates of drug abuse, injury and death from accident, violence and poisoning. While Whitehead and Hayes support the hypothesis that alcohol is a primary social problem, they conclude that there is insufficient data to lay to rest the debate between those who argue that alcohol is a primary social problem and those who argue that it represents little more than a symptom of poor mental health. However, they add, support for alcohol as a primary social problem "requires far less reliance on assumptions that are difficult to test" (1998:63). They write:

> It is more likely, therefore, that alcoholism is at the nexus of a broad range of social problems rather than mental illness. For some individuals, the experience may well be one of dual disorders. From a public policy perspective, however, the implications of reducing the extent of alcoholism (and its causes) in the population are difficult but less daunting than reducing the amount of mental illness (and its causes) (Whitehead and Hayes, 1998:63).

While Whitehead and Hayes may be right in their assessment of how daunting the task is of reducing mental illness and its causes, their conclusions seem to provide little consolation for both Aboriginal addiction workers and their clients, as seen in the following two statements made to the Royal Commission on Aboriginal Peoples:

> In a Native-run [alcohol and drug] treatment center, we get clients that come in, and they have multiple problems. We have only a limited three weeks to work with clients, and they have so many problems. It is really overwhelming what to do with these people that come in. For example, I myself have had to deal with an individual who had five family members die in one year, and she was contemplating suicide. I had to try to deal with her prescription drug problem and also her grieving. It was really overwhelming ... We need workers that can practice a generalist approach, where they be able to deal with all problems, with the many issues of the clients (as cited in 1996b:162).

> One recommendation I would suggest is [holistic] Native treatment centres that not only cover alcohol treatment but the other issues we face, such as being ACOA [adult children of alcoholics], co-dependency, the [impacts of the] mission schools, the sexual abuse and all that. I went to a treatment center ... in 1990. I dealt with my alcoholism, but when I came back [to my community] I had a lot of other issues to face, because everything else [surfaced] for me. It was quite a struggle.

> We badly need treatment centers to deal with these other issues, not just alcohol. You are not better just because you deal with your alcohol abuse (as cited in 1996b:163).

These accounts point to a need for increased training and support for front-line, addiction and after-care workers, including better integration of addiction and mental health services for Aboriginal communities.

Chapter 3

Psychological Distress

Psychological distress has been a central theme in discussions of Aboriginal drinking. For most authors who examine links between alcohol abuse and psychological distress, an individual's distress is believed to directly contribute to their abuse of alcohol. In this framework, distress is believed to be brought on by various factors, including those which impact upon the group to which the individual belongs (e.g., processes of colonization, social, political and economic marginalization) and by factors that affect the individual specifically and are not necessarily shared by the collective (e.g., sexual abuse). In studies that have examined psychological distress and alcohol abuse among Aboriginal people, the cause of distress is generally explained equally in terms of collective and individual experiences and responses. Saggers and Gray write:

> As a result of colonization, indigenous cultures were regarded as having irretrievably broken down and been lost. As a consequence, indigenous people were seen as having lost traditional roles, and as having no social rules to guide their behaviour, nor institutions that could exercise effective social control over behaviour. It was argued that this supposed breakdown of culture was manifested psychologically in loss of individual autonomy, identity and self-esteem, and in alienation from both traditional and colonial cultures (1998:74).

A more specific example is the experiences of Aboriginal people who attended residential schools. In this example, collective and individual experiences of those who attended the schools is believed to have jointly contributed to psychological distress that led many individuals to alcohol abuse as a way to block out the distress they felt (Fournier and Crey, 1997).

Studies that have examined psychological distress brought on by acculturation have drawn on the concept of 'anomie,' first postulated by Emilé Durkheim (1951). "Anomie refers to a state of normlessness or for the individual a sense of powerlessness over one's life that inevitably leads to depression and, in some instances, suicide" (Waldram, Herring and Kue Young, 1995:265). Central to the development of the concept of anomie was the notion that, with few exceptions, Aboriginal people had 'lost' their culture.

Aboriginal people experienced loss either as a state of anomie (or normlessness) or as a state of stress, as a consequence of difficulties acculturating (or assimilating) to the supposedly homogeneous wider society (Saggers and Gray, 1998). For example, for Levy and Kunitz, the concept of anomie, as applied to Aboriginal drinking, suggests that Aboriginal drinking was a type of retreatism in the face of culture contact and the loss of autonomy following colonization (1974 in Waldram, Herring and Kue Young, 1995). Dozier suggests alcohol was the easiest and quickest way to deaden the senses and to forget the feeling of inadequacy (1966 in Waldram, Herring and Kue Young, 1995).

Acculturative stress is believed to occur when indigenous people accept the goals and values of the wider society and attempt to assimilate into them. In their attempts, however, they generally face numerous problems that restrict their ability to assimilate, such as poverty, discrimination and lack of skills (Saggers and Gray, 1998). A number of writers have argued that high levels of alcohol consumption has become a meaningful way for Aboriginal people to deal with psychological distress caused by either anomie or the frustrations caused by numerous obstacles that prevent Aboriginal people from easily obtaining the goals they have adopted from the wider society (Albrecht, 1974; Eckermann, 1977; Kamien, 1978; Graves, 1967).

Waldram and colleagues (1995) point out that the picture of the Aboriginal alcoholic as victim looms large in this scenario. Other authors suggest that the explanation of anomie does not hold up in some sub-groups. Levy and Kunitz found that, among members of the group they studied, the highest intensity of involvement with drinking and greatest use of alcohol was found among the least acculturated group (1971 in Saggers and Gray, 1998). Saggers and Gray argue that the cultures of indigenous people, like all cultures, change through time in response to broader social, political and economic environments. While distinct and shared characteristics of 'traditional' indigenous cultures remain, as do the cultures of the colonizing societies, cultures are living, dynamic and ever changing. Others argue that accounts of anomie fail to account for resistance and resilience by Aboriginal people (Nöel and Taché, 2001; Tait 2003). While there is no doubt that psychological distress felt by many Aboriginal people contributes to their use of alcohol, it should be pointed out that not all Aboriginal people who experience psychological distress resulting from negative collective and/or individual experiences turn to alcohol abuse as a means of dealing with their feelings. Why some people do and others do not will be further examined throughout this report.

Cultural and Historical Explanations for Alcohol Abuse Among Aboriginal Groups

Characteristics of Traditional Indigenous Cultures

Alcohol abuse has been directly linked to the intersection of cultural and historical factors in several studies on Aboriginal people. As stated above, indigenous people in Canada prior to contact with Europeans did not possess alcohol. This historical context has been used to explain why excessive drinking patterns developed among some Aboriginal groups. Authors contend that because no social rules or conventions existed to control the use of alcohol when it was introduced, consumption was largely unregulated and people drank, and continue to drink, excessively (Saggers and Gray, 1998). Saggers and Gray point out that this position has been refuted on two levels.

First, historical evidence indicates that at least some indigenous groups did have access to psycho-active substances, including naturally fermented alcoholic drinks, and no evidence has been found to suggest the response to large quantities of alcoholic beverages was any different between those indigenous groups who did and those who did not possess alcoholic drinks prior to contact with Europeans. Second, this view suggests cultures are static and unchanging, rather than dynamic and, thus, possessing the ability to successfully incorporate a range of new ideas and material goods over time, as suggested by the archeological record (Saggers and Gray, 1998; Flood, 1995; Rowley, 1974). Saggers and Gray (1998) further point out that studies, such as those completed by Collmann (1979) and Sansom (1980), illustrate that indigenous groups have incorporated the use of alcohol into their societies in regulated ways.

Anthropologists have frequently contributed to the body of research literature on traditional indigenous cultures and alcohol abuse. One such body of literature argues that the small-scale nature of indigenous communities required members to suppress their emotions and personal feelings in the interest of social harmony, to an extent not required in larger-scale societies, and that excessive drinking provided an opportunity to escape from such restrictions (Hallowel, 1955; Saggers and Gray, 1998). One of the most famous of these studies was done by Rubel and Kupferer (1968) who studied alcohol consumption among the Inuit in northern Canada. They suggested 'normative' interpersonal relationships outside of the nuclear family were characterized by underlying contention, suspiciousness and hostility. These underlying tensions, according to Rubel and Kupferer, were suppressed by other cultural norms, thereby ensuring a certain degree of societal harmony. Under the influence of alcohol, suppressed tensions rose to the surface, resulting in arguments, fighting and violent behaviours. Balicki argued that, among the Kutchin, some individuals harboured 'an intense desire' to become drunk in attempts to free themselves from the normal behavioural constraints of their culture (1963 in Waldram, Herring and Kue Young, 1995).

Other studies have argued that the value placed on personal individual autonomy in indigenous societies facilitates excessive consumption, as individuals and communities are reluctant to impose on the personal autonomy of others and, thereby, fail to place individual or societal pressure on individuals who drink in excess (Brady, 1995). Levy and Kunitz (1974) in their study of problem drinking among the Navajo of the southwestern United States, argue that drinking behaviour reflects traditional forms of social organization and cultural values, rather than reflecting societal disorganization. Drinking alcohol, they argue, is less a consequence of the pathological aspects of indigenous culture and more a reflection of positively valued forms of expression.

Learned Behaviour

A number of studies argue that current patterns of alcohol abuse among some Aboriginal groups may reflect learned patterns of behaviour stemming from cultural and historical roots (Honigmann, 1979; Smart and Ogborne, 1986; Brady and Palmer, 1991). Many of these studies contend that some drinking behaviours were learned from Europeans during the early contact period. For example, Honigmann (1979) suggests that the northern 'frontier' culture in which European men binged (drinking large quantities of alcohol in short spans of time) excessively on alcohol, while paying little concern to their disruptive and uncontrollable behaviour, was adopted by indigenous people in their attempts to identify with the frontier culture, resist concession of superiority to European culture and maintain some autonomy and spontaneity.

Some authors argue that a pattern of binge drinking, which became typical behaviour for Aboriginal men and women who drank alcohol during the fur trade period, was due to the nature of fur trapping. They argue that Aboriginal trappers abstained, for the most part, from becoming intoxicated while on the trapline because it was too dangerous and because it was difficult to transport large quantities of alcohol in the bush. Only when they came to the trading posts did Aboriginal trappers consume alcohol, typically in large quantities over a few days. Mohawk author Brian Maracle (1994) argues that a pattern of binge-drinking became a typical way for Aboriginal people to consume alcohol during the fur trade period, a pattern reinforced in 1868 when the Canadian Parliament passed legislation through the *Indian Act*, which made it illegal for status Indians to buy or possess alcohol. Indian prohibition lasted 117 years, surviving in one form or another in Canada until 1985. Maracle writes that thousands of First Nations people were arrested and jailed because of this law and it acted as a form of social control, which allowed Indian agents and the police to arbitrarily arrest and detain Aboriginal people. He writes:

Chapter 3

Of course the law didn't stop or prevent Indians from drinking, but it did change the way they drank-for the worse. Since Indians were forbidden to buy liquor, they frequently resorted to drinking other far more dangerous intoxicants. The law also reinforced a destructive drinking culture that Indian people evolved after their first contacts with hard-drinking soldiers and scheming fur-traders. Since they were not allowed in bars or taverns and since they were not permitted to possess alcohol in their homes, the law forced them to become furtive and drink in bushes and back alleys.

More ominously, Indians also had to guzzle their beer, wine or liquor as quickly as possible to keep from being arrested (Maracle, 1994:44-45).

Some researchers argue that, under the imposed conditions of prohibition, Aboriginal people formed patterns of drinking that are still part of present day drinking cultures among some groups (Beckett, 1964; Smart and Ogborne, 1986). Explanations such as these have recently been linked to high rates of alcohol-related birth effects (ARBEs) among Aboriginal people in Canada, as binge-drinking has been shown to be exceptionally harmful to the developing fetus (Tait, 2003). This connection will be explored in further detail later in this report.

Saggers and Gray (1998) argue that, while general patterns of alcohol use by Aboriginal people can be linked intergenerationally to the experiences of Aboriginal people who lived during the fur trade and prohibition periods, these experiences as an explanatory reference imply a rather static view of Aboriginal cultures in which once a pattern of behaviour has been adopted, such as binge drinking, it remains unchanged. Rather, they contend that this type of explanation does not stand on its own and needs to be "linked to others that show how and why such patterns have been maintained" (Saggers and Gray, 1998:78-79). Similarly, Maracle (1994) suggests present day alcohol abuse among Aboriginal people can only be understood and addressed by considering the full historical and social context of Aboriginal and non-Aboriginal relations in Canada and cannot be reduced to the development of drinking patterns in the early contact period.

Alcohol in Contemporary Aboriginal Communities

Several studies have looked at the role alcohol plays in contemporary indigenous communities. These studies have typically focused on cultural meanings associated with drinking. For example, some authors stress the valued nature of drinking within local communities, which is seen by those who drink as opportunities for socializing and enjoyment and as a means of relieving boredom (Beckett, 1964; Brody, 1977; Thomas, 1981; Watson, Fleming and Alexander, 1988; O'Nell and Mitchell, 1996; Spicer, 1997). Based on research among American Indian men and women in Minneapolis in the early 1990s, Spicer concluded that research that approaches drinking as either *good* or *bad, functional* or *dysfunctional*, fails to see the complexity of drinking behaviour. He writes:

> For the men and women I interviewed, drinking is quite obviously and simultaneously both good *and* bad, functional *and* dysfunctional. There is some benefit in even the most pathological of drinking, of course. But equally, my research shows that there is an important element of harm and injury in much of what we have represented as socially integrated and culturally patterned drinking. The fact that drinking can be

simultaneously functional and dysfunctional suggests that we should be suspicious of attempts to cast it purely as one or the other. Even the use of alcohol that is well integrated in a society can nevertheless cause considerable harm, which is as relevant to drinkers' experience as is the way in which their drinking is socially and culturally patterned (Spicer, 1997:318).

O'Nell and Mitchell (1996) argue that a shift from ethnographic to survey-based approaches in research methodology of studies that examine alcohol and drug abuse among American Indian adolescents has occurred in the past three decades. While survey studies[9] have provided population-based data illustrating high rates of alcohol and drug abuse among American Indian adolescents, they have failed to answer important questions about how substance use is conceptualized and meaningfully integrated into the lives of Indian teens. O'Nell and Mitchell argue that, within survey studies, the emphasis is on quantity/frequency measures of alcohol use with teens being cast "as 'biological beings' whose behaviours while drinking reflect a putatively natural, biological response to a biochemical substance; conventional patterns of alcohol use and their social significance remain peripheral to the issue" (1996:565-566). They add:

> Additionally, with its emphasis on measures of psychological dysfunction and deviance, the field casts teens as 'distressed actors' whose patterns of drinking reflect a pan-human 'tension-reducing' response of the individual to stress and distress; peripheral to this model is cultural variation in the definitions of normal and pathological uses of alcohol. The 'distressed actor' model is, of course, related to the 'biological being' model to the extent that the effects of alcohol as temporarily palliative, or tension-reducing, are assumed to be universal. In either model, however, the alternate interpretation of teen drinking as culturally and socially rooted has been precluded through the oversimplification of culture (O'Nell and Mitchell, 1996:565-566).

O'Nell and Mitchell stress that neither 'biological' nor the 'distress' models are sufficient explanations for American Indian teen drinking. They refer to two studies, one by Kemnitzer (1972) and the other by Medicine (1969), who both describe Oglala Lakota group drinking as consisting of conventional stages - from conviviality to maudlin sentimentality, to bellicosity and hostility, to 'forgetting.' Interestingly, these stages are only vaguely related to the amount of alcohol ingested by participants. Kemnitzer goes so far as to suggest that certain changes in effect are absolutely unrelated to the biochemical properties of alcohol, since they occur even before alcohol is ingested, such as when individuals in a group shift into a 'party mode' (Kemnitzer, 1972 in O'Nell and Mitchell, 1996).

O'Nell and Mitchell argue that the 'distress' model is also problematic "given the degree to which ethnographers have been able to identify a congruence between drinking style and social role; in other words, in ethnographic accounts, drinking habits frequently seem to reveal more about an individual's social location within a culturally defined context than they do about his or her psychological motivations" (1996:566). For example, Maynard argues that individuals frequently change their drinking style to

---

[9] See, for example, Mohatt (1972), Topper (1974), Beauvais et al. (1985, 1989), Holmgren et al. (1983), Liban and Smart (1982), Oetting and Beauvais (1984), Oetting et al. (1989), Okwumabua and Duryea (1987), Powless-Sage (1987).

match the drinking situation in which they find themselves, suggesting that individuals drink according to social norms of the situation and, thereby, that psychological distress may not be reflected in their 'choice' of drinking style (Maynard, 1969 in O'Nell and Mitchell, 1996; Hill, 1974; Topper, 1980).

The image that emerges from ethnographic accounts, according to O'Nell and Mitchell (1996) is that greater understanding of drinking behaviours come from an analysis of cultural norms, rather than narrow exploration of individual characteristics. They go on to state:

> First, normal and pathological must be understood as concepts of value rather than as concepts of "objective" reality. Rather than by biochemical imperatives or knee-jerk responses to stress, the normal and the pathological are framed by cultural definitions of 'the good life.' An individual, and/or his/her family, will perceive pathology, when there is an alteration of the normal, according to value-laden qualities that have been constructed as important in his/her cultural world ... Until the cultural context of normative drinking and non-drinking has been ethnographically investigated, pathological drinking will remain an unknown quantity (O'Nell and Mitchell, 1996:567).

The normal and pathological, O'Nell and Mitchell add: "must also be understood as political concepts, inextricably linked with relations of power as certain social actors are credited with the authority to define behaviors as problematic" (1996:567). They suggest that questions concerning power-relations—What is 'the problem'? Whose problem is it? And, who benefits from the problem and certain ways of defining it?— need to be asked in order for researchers not fall victim to the spread of hegemonic Euro-American values and problem definitions into less-powerful communities. The unwarranted pathologization of American Indian adolescents and their societies more generally, O'Nell and Mitchell add, is a potential danger that inheres in the naive application of Euro-American judgements to American Indian drinking. It is a danger that can only be avoided by the rigorous ethnographic investigation of the normal and the pathological within each community (O'Nell and Mitchell, 1996).

Political and Economic Factors

Research that examines political and economic factors that contribute to alcohol abuse among Aboriginal groups suggests that dispossession and the resulting on-going economic and political marginalization of Aboriginal people has contributed to alcohol abuse and related harm among this group (Hunter, 1993; Moore, 1992). Dispossession and its consequences has also been adopted as an explanation by Health Canada[10] as high rates of alcohol use and abuse have been correlated with low income, education and occupational status (Health and Welfare Canada, 1989). Gray and colleagues found that social and economic indicators clearly link inequalities to alcohol and drug use among young indigenous people in Western Australia (Gray, Morfitt, Williams, Ryan and Coyne, 1996).

---

[10] Although Health Canada may adopt this as an explanation, typical government responses, in terms of policy, programming and funding, has meant that issues such as poverty, poor education and chronic unemployment in Aboriginal communities have not been adequately considered or addressed by both federal and provincial governments.

Chapter 3

Some authors argue that low socio-economic status, rather than Aboriginal identity per se, is important when considering alcohol abuse by Aboriginal people. Brody (1977 in Saggers and Gray, 1998), for example, suggests that the Inuit and Dene communities are subject to the same negative impacts of industrial expansion as non-indigenous groups, with similar results, including high rates of alcohol misuse. Smart and Ogborne (1986) point out that heavy drinking patterns are found in Canadian society amongst sections of the non-Aboriginal population that are similar to those recorded among some northern Aboriginal people. However, as Saggers and Gray point out, few studies exist that examine comparable non-Aboriginal communities (1998; McKenzie, 1993).

Saggers and Gray (1998) pose the question as to how dispossession, political and economic marginalization, and discrimination 'cause' alcohol misuse. They list several factors, including psychological pain caused by a barrage of assaults, rejections, the break-up of families, institutionalization and consequent low self-esteem. Saggers and Gray also suggest alcohol abuse is a way to cope with poverty, including limited or no access to other recreational activities for enjoyment.

A few authors have argued that alcohol abuse is, in some contexts, a form of resistance by Aboriginal people (Sackett, 1988; Brady and Palmer, 1984). Lurie (1979), for example, has referred to drinking patterns of indigenous people in North America as 'the world's oldest on-going protest demonstration.' However, equating alcohol abuse and its associated consequences to a form of resistance and protest is suspect, as it suggests those 'protesting' are aware of their actions. It is also highly unlikely that Aboriginal leaders or their constituents would make this analogy, particularly given their publicly expressed concerns about the widespread health and social problems alcohol abuse has generated in their communities (Tait, 2003). Saggers and Gray (1998) adopt a 'political economy' approach to explain differences in patterns of alcohol consumption and related harm between indigenous and non-indigenous people. They write:

> The political economy approach is similar in some respects to others that emphasise the role of political and economic factors. However, it differs from such approaches in that it does not treat those factors as discrete variables; and it treats current political and economic systems not as givens, but as shaped by history and differential power relationships. Thus, for example, differences in the distribution of wealth between indigenous and non-indigenous peoples are not viewed as the outcome of abstract 'market forces', but as the outcome of differential power relations between those peoples (Saggers and Gray, 1998:85).

Saggers and Gray (1998) argue that a review of the literature on drinking across Aboriginal groups suggests a shared commonality of drinking patterns and a broad similarity of experiences that become evident when they are compared. If only particular characteristics, cultures or histories, or particular individuals, groups or indigenous populations are considered, these shared patterns and similar experiences do not become apparent in the same way. Furthermore, they add, seeking an explanation for drinking patterns) within the culture of particular groups ignores the fact that such groups do not exist in a vacuum. Since most Aboriginal groups have had contact with Europeans for over 150 years, their lives have been shaped partially in response to colonial societies and, therefore, cannot be adequately understood apart from this contact. Saggers and Gray go on to write:

Given this similarity, it is unlikely that it [patterns of drinking among indigenous people] has arisen from unique circumstances within indigenous societies. In our view, explanation of this phenomenon requires consideration of what is common to them all. That is, the experience of colonialism, the destruction of traditional economies, exploitation and marginalization, the loss of power entailed in these processes, and the responses of indigenous peoples to them. A model of indigenous drinking must take this as the starting point, and other factors need to be considered in the context of these political and economic relationships (1998:86).

Saggers and Gray (1998) argue that colonization for indigenous societies in Canada, Australia and New Zealand was a disaster of catastrophic proportions. Even though the timing and pattern of colonization was different between and within the three countries, the outcomes have been strikingly similar. Saggers and Gray cite the appropriation of the most valuable land and resources by the colonialist regime and the decimation of populations due to violence and introduced diseases as central factors in undermining the economic base of traditional societies. Added to this was the influx of non-indigenous migrants who monopolized the labour market, while indigenous people were relocated on reserves or reservations, or left to live on the fringes of European towns and cities. Saggers and Gray go on to state:

> They [indigenous people] were provided with only meagre education, or denied access to it altogether, and their access to vocational training was similarly restricted. Non-indigenous people regarded them as inferior, took their impoverishment as evidence of that supposed inferiority, and actively discriminated against them. Indigenous people were regarded as a 'problem'; and when that 'problem' did not disappear as anticipated, an attempt to solve it was made through policies of assimilation. In the attempt to assimilate indigenous people, children ... were taken from their indigenous parents and placed in institutions and foster care, causing untold psychological trauma for both parents and children (1998:86-87).

Saggers and Gray (1998) point out that despite the tragic consequences of colonization, indigenous people in Canada, Australia and New Zealand have not been passive, helpless victims. On-going struggles with, and resistance to, processes of colonization by Aboriginal people in Canada have occurred from the time of contact and continue to occur daily by contemporary Aboriginal people throughout Canada (Brody, 1988; Brady, 2000; Fournier and Crey, 1997; Maracle, 1994; Royal Commission on Aboriginal Peoples, 1996a; 1996b; Waldram, Herring and Kue Young, 1995). Authors, such as Culhane, argue against the notion Canada has entered a 'post-colonial' period and suggest that processes of colonization are a daily reality for Aboriginal people (personal communication, 2001). In many countries, such as Canada, alcohol remains a central tool in the on-going colonization of indigenous people.

Chapter 3

This is summed up, for example, by Kahn and colleagues in their discussion of the continued colonization of indigenous Australians:

> … the exploitation of Aborigines as an economic resource through alcohol certainly continues, via sale and taxation, via 'grog-running' to remote communities, and perhaps the growth of bureaucratic structures set up to service alcohol-affected Aborigines (1990:359 in Saggers and Gray, 1998:87).

Saggers and Gray (1998) suggest that, despite the multi-faceted reasons behind alcohol use/abuse by indigenous people, based on individual and collective experience underlying this entire complexity, are inequalities between indigenous and non-indigenous people that exist throughout the broader web of political and economic relationships. Interventions, they argue, aimed solely at the symptoms—while alleviating some of the pain—will not address the underlying cause and the symptoms will continue to re-emerge.

Conclusion

The above discussion outlines current debates concerning alcohol abuse among Aboriginal people. Especially evident is the complexity involved in accounting for why some individuals or groups of individuals abuse alcohol, while others do not. Important re-occurring themes in accounting for substance abuse among Aboriginal groups in Canada are the devastating effects of colonization upon Aboriginal people and the on-going economic and social marginalization experienced by these groups over a number of generations. In relation to literature written on alcohol abuse and pregnancy, a clear distinction in the two bodies of literature exists, with the body of literature on substance abuse and pregnancy taking a much narrower view of alcohol abuse (May, 1998). Attempts to understand maternal drinking in the FAS-specific literature has, for the most part, a narrower focus than the overall literature on alcohol and women, as it has tended to identify a limited range of variables, focus on information that is mostly medical in nature and collect data primarily in prenatal or obstetric clinical settings (May, 1998). Although the focus in pregnancy and alcohol abuse studies is widening, intergenerational and collective trauma, which have proved to be of great significance in understanding alcohol abuse generally among Aboriginal groups, has received very limited attention (Tait, 2003).

Chapter 4

Child Abuse

Introduction

Child abuse and neglect have received increasing attention over the past fifty years in Canada and, more generally, North America. Sexual, physical and emotional abuse have been identified as harmful to childhood development, particularly if the abuse is experienced by the child on more than one occasion and over an extended period of time. This chapter begins with a brief discussion of child physical abuse and neglect, and then looks more closely at child sexual abuse, specifically, research involving Aboriginal children. This is followed by a discussion of child abuse and the development of adult alcohol dependency. Pregnancy and substance abuse are then considered in relationship to child and adult abuse. The chapter concludes with a brief discussion of institutional child abuse in Canada, with a specific focus on how child abuse in institutions differs from child abuse that occurs in domestic settings. This will set the stage for a discussion in the following chapter on the residential school system and the abuse of students who attended the schools.

Child Physical Abuse and Neglect

Child physical abuse is a category easily defined by most Canadians in its most extreme forms, but becomes much more difficult to define as we move away from extreme acts of violence. Spanking a child, for example, while not seen by the courts to be illegal, draws a great deal of moral criticism from many people as they see it as improper behaviour on the part of a care giver. Similarly, physical neglect presents the same problem. Linda Gordon (1988) suggests that neglect has generally been divided into two categories: physical and moral. Physical neglect includes, for example, lack of supervision, dirtiness, lack of proper food and clothing, and lack of attention to needed medical care. Moral neglect involves deviation from sexual norms and from norms of proper family life, such as frequent alcohol abuse and the promotion of 'unchildlike' activities (1988 in Swift, 1995:71). Both child physical abuse and neglect are categories used by professionals, such as social workers and health care practitioners, but also have common usage among para-professionals and lay groups. In both cases, these definitions are often ill-defined and in the less obvious cases involving child welfare services, for example, would fall to the discretion of individual social workers.[11] Poor families, in general, and specifically poor Aboriginal families, are under a greater amount of surveillance and scrutiny in Canada by child welfare agencies than higher income families for signs of child abuse and neglect. This greater surveillance contributes to perceptions that child physical abuse and neglect are more common among poor Aboriginal families (Swift, 1995).

Examining rates of child physical abuse is difficult from a research perspective, as there are several methodological problems, such as the specificity of abuse definitions (e.g., inclusion of a wider range of activities will give higher rates) and problems with self-reports (over or under-reporting, memory recall) (Langeland and Hartgers, 1998). Rates of child physical abuse in the research literature vary greatly, from 5% to as high as 34% among certain sub-populations (Langeland and Hartgers, 1998).

---

[11]   Although of great importance, a discussion of the use of these categories in relation to families on social assistance, particularly Aboriginal families, is beyond the scope of this report. For further discussion, see Swift, 1995.

Chapter 4

Possible long-term effects of child abuse have been identified as self-destructive behaviours, anxiety, depression, poor self-esteem, difficulty trusting others, anger and hostility, and substance use disorders (Langeland and Hartgers, 1998; see reviews by Beitchman, Zucker, Hood, DaCosta, Akman and Cassavia, 1992; Herman, 1992; Wyatt and Powell, 1988). However, in relation to substance abuse, Langeland and Hartgers caution that:

> Although the association between child abuse and subsequent alcohol and/or drug problems has a great deal of plausibility, a greater incidence of many DSM-III-R (American Psychiatric Association 1987) Axis I diagnoses has been found to be associated with CSA [childhood sexual abuse] and CPA [child physical abuse]. Therefore, it is assumed that child abuse may be a general, nonspecific factor that contributes to psychopathology, including substance use disorders. An important question is whether there are other factors, such as family dysfunction, childhood neglect or parental substance abuse problems, rather than the abuse per se, that laid the foundation for later psychiatric disturbance (Beitchman, Zucker, Hood, DaCosta, Akman and Cassavia, 1992; Cicchetti and Carlson, 1989; ... Herman, 1992; Wyatt and Powell, 1988). Both the adult disorder and the child abuse could originate in a disturbed family environment that failed to nurture and protect the developing child. Child abuse would not then be causal but would share a common cause with substance use disorder (1998:336-337).

For some Aboriginal families, child physical abuse and neglect are part of a larger picture of family dysfunction and violence (Jacobs and Gill, 2002). The Royal Commission on Aboriginal Peoples points out that family violence in Aboriginal communities is distinct:

> ... in that the unbalanced power relationships that structure the lives of Aboriginal people are not found primarily in the relationships between men and women. The imbalance lies in the powerlessness of Aboriginal people relative to society as a whole, including the social institutions that dominate every aspect of their lives, from the way they are educated and the way they earn a living to the way they are governed (1996b:73).

However, the Commission goes on to add that family violence originating in imbalances of power is not to excuse it and individuals must take responsibility for their actions (Royal Commission on Aboriginal Peoples, 1996b; LaRocque, 1993). The Commission writes:

> In looking for solutions, we begin by drawing attention to the structured origins of violence in relations between Aboriginal and non-Aboriginal societies. We do so because without changing these power relationships and without alleviating poverty and powerlessness, measures to reduce family violence will be patchwork solutions at best. Solutions based on individual therapy may even be destructive in an unrelentingly oppressive political, economic and social environment, because they can reinforce the perception Aboriginal people have of themselves as being weak and morally inadequate (1996b:74).

Chapter 4

The Commission (1996b) goes on to point out that some Aboriginal communities have lost their sense of cohesion to an extent that can be described as collective trauma. Because of this, many families in these communities have lost confidence in their ability to parent their children. In urban settings, Aboriginal families face the challenge of building a community from people of diverse Aboriginal nations with varied cultural and community experiences. Without a sense of community cohesion, urban Aboriginal families who struggle with issues such as violence and substance abuse can be cut off from much needed support networks, which can help them to restore their capacity to care for their family members (Royal Commission on Aboriginal Peoples, 1996b; Jacobs and Gill, 2002).

Child Sexual Abuse

Child sexual abuse became a topic of western scientific inquiry at the end of the nineteenth century through the work of Sigmund Freud (1890), who found that a number of his adult patients had been sexually victimized or molested by adults or older siblings. Through his new psycho-analytic treatment method, Freud demonstrated how hysterical and neurotic symptoms of his patients could be traced back to these traumatic sexual experiences during childhood (Green, 1993). The 1940s and 1950s saw several surveys of adults indicating a substantial prevalence of child sexual abuse experiences; however, the abuse of children remained virtually unexamined by medical researchers until the 1962 publication of a paper by Kempe and colleagues, entitled the "Battered Child Syndrome" (Kempe, Silverman, Steele, Droegemuller and Silver, 1962). This paper focused attention on the physical abuse of children by their parents and led to the enactment of child abuse reporting laws in the United States and other western countries, including Canada (Green, 1993). A decade later, child care and mental health professionals began to describe case reports of sexually abused children and descriptions of incest began to appear in the literature with greater frequency. Child sexual abuse in North America is generally defined as:

> ... sexual contact between an adult and a child less than 18 years old in which the child is used for the sexual gratification of the adult. A parent or caregiver who allows another person to have sexual contact with a child also is deemed sexually abusive. Incest refers to the sexual exploitation of a child by a family member. However, in its common usage incest also includes sexual abuse by stepparents and relatives by marriage. Acts defined as sexually abusive include genital, anal intercourse; oral genital contact, fondling of the genitalia, anus, or breasts; and genital exhibitionism (Green, 1993:890).[12]

It has been estimated that approximately one of every three adult women in Canada has been the victim of some form of sexual abuse during her lifetime. A large percentage of reported life-time abuse happens to victims during their childhood. For example, a study by Bagley and Ramsay (1986) found that 22 per cent of 377 women interviewed in Calgary had been sexually abused before reaching their sixteenth birthday. In a review of the literature on child sexual abuse, Green (1993) found that several childhood problems were reported as occurring more often in abused children than non-abused children. Some

---

[12]   Definitions of sexual abuse vary, particularly with regard to the age of the person. Many studies take the age of sixteen, as the age between childhood and adulthood. Others, such as Green, take the age eighteen as the distinguishing age.

of the problems found were anxieties, fears, depression, angry destructive behaviour, phobic reactions, deficits in intellectual, physical and social development, sleep disturbances, insomnia, nightmares, somatic complaints, eating disorders, guilt, shame, increased psychiatric diagnosis, impairment of memory or identity, forgetfulness, excessive fantasizing and daydreaming, sleepwalking and blackouts. While the nature of the links between sexual abuse and childhood problems, such as those listed above, is difficult to precisely pinpoint, several factors, such as the child feeling powerless, betrayed and exploited and feeling a loss of trust have been suggested as important variables. Studies also suggest that individuals may experience several different problems at different stages in childhood, adolescence and adulthood. Adults who experienced sexual abuse as children were found to have increased anxiety, including anxiety attacks and anxiety-related symptoms, such as sleep disturbance and somatic complaints, guilt feelings of detachment, sexual dysfunction, delayed or chronic post-traumatic stress disorder, behavioural re-enactments, depression, impulsivity, dissociation, low self-esteem, suicidal behaviour, substance abuse and personality disorders. Women who were sexually abused in childhood were also at risk of revictimization as adults. The studies reviewed by Green also suggested that adults who sexually abuse children are more likely to have been abused themselves as children (Green, 1993).

Sexual abuse is not a single, unitary phenomenon that has been linked to any particular recognizable syndrome, nor does it necessarily lead to later psychological disturbance (Hussey and Singer, 1993). Factors that are believed to contribute to fewer psychological problems for victims of child sexual abuse are the strength and availability of social supports available to the victim, particularly good, supportive relationships with parental figures, family and friends (Hussey and Singer, 1993; Frank, Anderson, West and Lando, 1988; Mann and Gaynor, 1980; Straus, 1981; Tsai, Feldman-Summers and Edgar, 1979).

Child Sexual Abuse Studies Among Aboriginal Groups

Child sexual abuse in some Aboriginal communities in Canada and the United States is estimated to be significantly higher than national averages (LaRocque, 1993; Nechi Institute, 1988). Canim Lake in British Columbia and Hollow Water in Manitoba, two communities that have conducted systematic research among their members, found that 75 to 85 per cent of people in the communities reported that they had been the victims of unwanted sexual contact as children (Fournier and Crey, 1997). Haig- Brown (1988) and Fournier and Crey (1997) have argued that the increased incidence rates of child sexual abuse in some Aboriginal communities is directly linked to the sexual abuse of students at residential schools.

Barker-Collo (1999) points out that research focusing on child sexual abuse assumes relative homogeneity in the sequel of abuse; however, the body of research on child sexual abuse is generally based on studies involving Caucasian men and women from mainstream North American society. Studies, including the experience of ethnic minorities, have only recently started to appear (e.g., Wyatt, Newcomb and Notgrass, 1991); however, limited effort has been made to differentiate on the basis of ethnicity, despite its known salience in the construction and interpretation of human experience (Barker-Collo, 1999; McEvoy and Daniluk, 1995).

Chapter 4

Robin and colleagues (1997) examined the prevalence, characteristics and impact of childhood sexual abuse in a southwestern American Indian tribe. Participants who were identified as sexually abused as children were required to be younger than sixteen years of age when the abuse occurred, and direct physical contact was a necessary criterion for child sexual abuse. Robin and colleagues found that children were most likely to be sexually abused in the family environment and by persons known to them (95%). This rate is high compared to rates of 8% to 26% of abuse occurring in family environments for females less than 18 years of age in the general American population (Robin, Chester et al., 1997; Boney-McCoy and Finkelhor, 1995; Bushnell, Wells and Oakley-Browne, 1992; Fink, Bernstein, Handelsman, Foote and Lovejoy, 1995; Russell, 1983). Robin and colleagues suggest:

> In the community we studied, the practice of extended family members (grandparents, aunts and uncles, cousins) to reside in high density households may have increased opportunities for child sexual abuse to occur in the home environment. Poverty also contributes to an environment where the daily supervision of children by working mothers is reduced. At times, caretaker responsibilities are shifted to unemployed males, many of whom are alcoholic (1997:782).

Robin and colleagues (1997) found that males who were sexually abused were more likely to report early behavioural problems as compared to males who did not report abuse. Males were also more likely to be expelled from school, break rules, be arrested, appear in juvenile court, lie, steal, break and destroy property, run away from home and have voluntary sex at a young age. Females who were abused as children demonstrated similar behaviours as abused males, as well as being more likely to skip out of school and to drink excessively. Robin and colleagues found that both males and females who were sexually abused as children continued to have behavioural problems after the age of fifteen. Compared to individuals who were not sexually abused as children, they were more likely to attempt suicide, have difficulties with personal debts, and have no close personal relationships. Sexually abused females also reported a greater frequency of drunkenness than females who were not abused. There were no significant differences between the two groups in terms of employment, felony arrests, fighting, divorce or separation (Robin, Chester et al., 1997).

Among males who were sexually abused as children, anti-social personality disorder, lifetime drug use disorders and lifetime affective disorders were among the most common diagnosed psychiatric disorders. Abused females were more often diagnosed than non-abused females with anti-social personality disorders lifetime alcohol disorders, lifetime drug use disorders, lifetime affective disorders, lifetime anxiety disorders and lifetime post-traumatic stress disorder (PTSD). Males and females who reported histories of child sexual abuse were more likely to be diagnosed with 3 psychiatric disorders, including alcohol dependency or abuse, than were non-abused subjects, after controlling for parental alcoholism and age. Sexually abused males were over two times more likely to have at least one alcoholic parent than were non-abused males. Parental alcoholism was also associated with an increased likelihood of PTSD in abused females, even after controlling for child sexual abuse (Robin, Chester et al., 1997).

In the study by Robin and colleagues (1997), severity of sexual abuse was measured by sexual penetration (55%) and multiple perpetrators per subject (50%). It was more common for males to be perpetrators (96%); however, severity of sexual abuse, unlike findings of other studies, was not significantly associated with juvenile and adult problems. Robin and colleagues conclude by stating that child sexual abuse among American Indian children is an element and index of family and community dysfunction (Bechtold, 1994; Piasecki, Manson, Biernoff, Hiat, Taylor et al., 1989; Rodenhauser, 1988; Swanson, Bratrude and Brown, 1971), and a predictor of future problems. They suggest that high rates of child sexual abuse and psychiatric disorders may correspond with an accelerated deterioration of the social structure and cultural traditions in the study population (Robin, Chester et al., 1997). This supports similar conclusions of studies among other American Indian and cultural groups, which reported a relationship between urbanization of rural areas, acculturative stress, increased violence against women and children, and the increase of psychiatric disorders (Kettle, 1993; Kirmayer, 1994).

Robin and colleagues point out that, traditionally in Aboriginal communities, the family has acted as a conduit for cultural transmission, "providing an environment in which traditions were passed from one generation to the next, lending stability, support, guidance, and direction to family members" (1997:783; McCubbin, Thompson, Thompson, McCubbin and Kaston, 1993; Red Horse, Red Horse, Neubeck and Decker, 1981). In contrast, the tribal community in which they conducted their research had discontinued most traditional ceremonies and rituals before the turn of the century and, therefore, these traditions were unknown to the vast majority of tribal members. The traditions that were still practiced were basically ignored by the younger generations who were increasingly consumed with more mainstream influences and behaviours (Robin, Chester et al., 1997).

Barker-Collo (1999) examined the reported symptomatology of Aboriginal and Caucasian females who were sexually abused in childhood. The study suggests that Aboriginal and Caucasian women report significantly different levels and types of symptomatology following sexual abuse, with Aboriginal women reporting higher overall levels of symptomatology. The three general categories that symptoms fell into that contributed to this difference were somatic symptoms, sleep disturbances and sexual difficulties. Aboriginal women also reported significantly higher frequency of episodes of uncontrollable crying. Barker-Collo writes:

> In light of reports of increased prevalence of sexual abuse in Native Canadian populations (e.g., LaRocque, 1994), these findings point toward the existence of a cultural group that is not only at greater risk of experiencing sexual abuse but is likely to experience greater negative symptomatology following abuse than those in the cultural majority ... Because [treatment for childhood sexual abuse] interventions are grounded on research that assumes relative homogeneity in response to abuse, they are not sensitive to differences in response to abuse based on race, class, and so forth. The results of this study would seem to indicate that this assumed homogeneity does not exist. Specifically, the results of this study suggest that factors unique to the experience of Native Canadians influence severity symptom presentation following sexual abuse. These differences may limit the generalizability of existing treatment approaches to Native Canadian populations (1999:756-757).

While the study by Barker-Collo (1999) points to important differences between Aboriginal and non-Aboriginal women in the manifestation of symptoms, the study does not provide information on why these differences may exist. Barker-Collo points out that the study is also limited by its inability to account for other factors such as deprived socio-economic status, incidence of revictimization, exposure to other forms of trauma, reduced accessibility to social service and education.

Chapter 4

In her study, Barker-Collo draws on the work of Savishinsky (1991) to suggest that cultural factors play a significant role in responses by Aboriginal women to sexual abuse. Savishinsky identified values held by Aboriginal people in Canada that could impact on responses following sexual abuse, including, for example, a value of inter-dependence, whereby behaviours that strain inter-dependence are avoided (1991 in Barker-Collo, 1999). Savishinsky suggests that inter-dependency may influence an individual's willingness to accuse another member of the community with sexual abuse. A second value identified by Savishinsky is non-intervention in which, in the cases where sexual abuse is apparent, there is a concerted effort by the victim to avoid the enlistment of others to assist in coping.

In addition, other community members may be likely to refrain from injecting themselves into the situation. Outside interventions (e.g., rape crisis centres and mental health services), according to Savishinsky, could also be mistaken as intrusive and, therefore, under-utilized (1991 in Barker-Collo, 1999). The third value put forth by Savishinsky is self-restraint, meaning that feelings and thoughts are not expressed overtly and it is believed that they are explicitly understood by others. This would then impact on an individual's ability to respond to sexual abuse in an emotional way that is consistent with what is expected in mainstream culture. This value may have implications for assessment and treatment of Aboriginal women who have been sexually abused (Barker-Collo, 1999). Finally, Savinshinsky suggests that personal responsibility is the value that underlies the interpretations and beliefs of Aboriginal people in Canada in reference to sexual abuse.

While it is important to draw attention to the role of cultural influences in shaping an individual's and community's response to child sexual abuse, both Savishinsky and Barker-Collo wrongly assume that *all* Aboriginal people in Canada share one set of cultural values and, therefore, would have similar individual and collective responses to their experiences. Secondly, they assume that the 'values'— 'interdependency,' 'non-intervention,' 'self-restraint' and 'personal responsibility' they refer to—are 'cultural values' and, in doing so, fail to consider these characteristics within a local, historical context. For example, the level of dysfunction in a community or family is left out of their account, even though it is more likely that these factors greatly influence local 'values' and responses to issues such as child sexual abuse. Issues such as power relationships between the victim and perpetrator, how isolated or dispersed a community may be, what support services are available to victims and the level of poverty and despair in the community also significantly influence responses by victims and their families within a local context. Therefore, to suggest that 'cultural values' are generating responses is far too simplistic an explanation (see discussion of LaRocque below).

Child Abuse and Alcohol Dependency/Abuse Studies

Child sexual abuse and lifetime sexual abuse have been identified as possible risk factors for problems, such as adult alcohol dependency/abuse, the disruption of normal developmental processes, self-destructive behaviour, anxiety, poor self-esteem, anger, hostility and suicide (Kirmayer, Hayton, Malus, Jiminez, Dufour et al., 1992; Chandy, Blum et al., 1996; Langeland and Hartgers, 1998; Jasinski, Williams et al., 2000; DiLillo, Tremblay et al., 2000). Research examining the links between sexual abuse and the subsequent development of alcohol abuse problems have found it difficult to determine if sexual abuse is an independent predictor of adult alcohol dependency/abuse. However, research has clearly shown that sexual abuse is a confounding factor of adult alcohol dependency/abuse (Fleming, Mullen et al.,

45

1998). Langeland and Hartgers (1998) point out that other causal factors include concomitant family dysfunction, childhood neglect, parental substance abuse and adult victimization experiences.

In an American study examining the inter-relationships between experiences of childhood victimization and the development of women's alcohol problems, Miller and colleagues (1993) found that two-thirds of the alcoholic women in their study had experienced some form of childhood sexual abuse, which was significantly higher than two comparison groups, first-time drinking and driver offenders[13] (20%), and a random household sample of women (33%). Alcoholic women reported experiencing greater levels of each type of sexual abuse (exposure, touching, penetration) than did women in the other two samples. Miller and colleagues write:

> Penetration represents a type of sexual abuse that portrays the most physically invasive behaviors that are perpetrated against children. It is when this type of sexual abuse is examined that the differences between alcoholic women and the other two samples are the greatest, with nearly half of the alcoholic women as compared to less than 7% of the drinking drivers and 9% of the household sample reporting this type of childhood sexual abuse (1993:111).

Alcoholic women were also found to have the highest levels of violence meted against them by their fathers (verbal aggression, moderate violence and severe violence). Nearly half (45%) of the alcoholic sample, as compared to 18% of the drinking drivers and 13% of the household sample, reported severe abuse by their fathers (Miller, Downs et al., 1993). Severe violence by their mother was also more prevalent among alcoholic women (46%) as compared to the drinking drivers (27%) and the household sample (28%). Miller and colleagues (1993) point out that when the percentage of each of the three samples that have experienced neither childhood sexual abuse nor severe parental violence are compared, alcoholic women are significantly less likely to have escaped either form of childhood victimization: 13% (alcoholic women) compared to 57% (drinking drivers) and 41% (household sample).

Miller and colleagues (1993) also compared women with alcohol problems who were in therapy with women who were in therapy but without alcohol problems, and with a household sample (no alcohol problems). The study found that when women in different types of therapy who have alcohol problems are compared to women without alcohol problems in the same types of treatment, women in treatment who have alcohol problems are significantly more likely to have experienced childhood sexual abuse. Seventy per cent of women in therapy with alcohol problems had experienced some form of child sexual abuse, as compared to approximately half (52%) of the women in these same treatment settings without alcohol problems and one-third of the household sample (35%). Again, women with alcohol problems reported sexual abuse involving penetration (44%) to a greater degree than women in the other samples (27% of the therapy sample without alcohol problems and 9% of the household

---

[13]   The DWI sample in this study represented women with a lower level of alcohol problems, as compared to the group of alcoholic women. Women in the original household sample were screened for alcohol problems and those with problems were removed from the analysis so that this group represented a group without alcohol problems. These comparisons were designed to provide a test of whether the relationship between childhood victimization and alcohol problems in women is important for any level of alcohol problems or whether this relationship is predominately found in women with the most serious alcohol-related problems (Miller, Downs et al., 1993).

sample). Similar patterns of father and mother violence were reported as in the previous comparison, with women with alcohol problems reporting higher levels than the other two groups. Alcoholic women in the study were more likely to have a parent with alcohol problems (55% vs. 27%) and to belong to an ethnic minority (39% vs. 24%). Miller and colleagues write:

> The high rates of childhood victimization for women with alcohol-related problems suggest that there is a link between victimization and the development of women's alcohol problems, specifically ... The strength of the interrelationships between childhood victimization and the development of women's alcohol-related problems when holding the treatment condition constant is of particular interest in this study. In our second set of comparisons, we found that the rates of childhood victimization were significantly greater for women in treatment with alcohol-related problems as compared to women in treatment without alcohol-related problems. Thus, even when holding the treatment condition constant, childhood victimization has a specific connection to the development of women's alcohol-related problems. These findings remained significant even when controlling for demographic and family background differences, including parental alcohol-related problems (1993:115).

Miller and colleagues (1993) suggest that the theoretical connections between childhood abuse and alcoholism in women may be facilitated by feelings of low self-esteem that, in turn, contribute to a pattern of alcohol or drug use as a means to cope with these negative feelings. Use of substances are also linked to pejorative labels, which may further diminish the woman's sense of self-value and self-esteem. A second possible connection between childhood victimization and women's alcohol-related problems, according to Miller and colleagues:

> ... is that childhood victimization often results in women feeling as though their experiences (particularly sexual) have made them distinctly different from other girls their age. This may result in young girls withdrawing from the more normative circles of friends and seeking alliances with the fringe groups where they perceive that they will not be judged harshly or fail to win acceptance (1993:115).

Fringe groups may be more likely to value heavy alcohol and/or drug use, leading young girls to develop a pattern of heavy drinking, which can lead to further problems. Young women who drink heavily may also be given pejorative sexual labels, thus further alienating them from other juvenile groups who do not engage in heavy drinking on a regular basis (Miller, Downs et al., 1993).

While a combination of physical abuse by the father and childhood sexual abuse by a male perpetrator were common in the histories of women with alcohol problems, Miller and colleagues (1993) found that most of the women were not sexually abused by their fathers, but were abused by someone other than their father. This, they suggest, raises the question of the impact upon female children and adults who have been abused by two (or more) violent male perpetrators as children.

Chapter 4

Hussey and Singer (1993) studied a group of sexually abused adolescent psychiatric in-patients, with a control group of in-patient counterparts, on measures of social competence, self-esteem, depression, substance abuse and perceptions of family characteristics and functioning. Sexually abused and control groups were similar on standardized measures of psychological distress and family functioning; however, there were statistically significant differences between the two groups on substance abuse measures. Hussey and Singer speculate that similarities between groups on measures of self-esteem, depression, social competence and family structure were probably due to the homogeneous nature of adolescent psychiatric in-patients, a population generally thought to be seriously emotionally and behaviourally impaired. On almost every measure of substance abuse, the trend was for the group who had been sexually abused to have scores indicative of more serious substance abuse than those in the control group. The sexually abused group were found to be more likely to engage in drug use, to use marijuana and stimulants more often, to report more frequent use of drugs, to be younger when they initiated drug use and to get drunk more often. Hussey and Singer go on to write:

> If we look closer at underlying explanations for abused youngsters increased substance abuse, they evidenced higher scores on scales designed to measure use patterns reflecting self-medication and rebellious motivations for drinking behavior. Abused youngsters also reported greater perceived benefits from both alcohol and drug use. Specifically in regard to drinking, these benefits included drinking to relax, to feel good, and to be friendly ... Whether this pattern of suspected self-medication was actually beneficial in achieving this end is unclear ... Perhaps substance abuse was effective in reducing levels of depression and improving feelings of self-esteem and social competence in the abuse group. On the other hand, increased levels of substance abuse to deal with psychological distress may have exacerbated psychiatric symptomatology in the abuse group (1993:958-959).

Hussey and Singer go on to suggest that the relationship between sexual abuse and substance abuse for a sub-set of the sexually abused group may be that substance abuse partially contributed to their victimization experience: "The contribution of decreased inhibitions, poor judgement, and reduced ability to protect oneself due to intoxication and chemical use may have exacerbated the potential for sexual victimization to occur" (1993:959).

Jasinski and colleagues (2000) found that, among African-American women in their study (n=113), all of whom had a documented history of sexual abuse in childhood, women physically abused in childhood were almost 2.5 times more likely to drink heavily compared to women with no history of physical child abuse. Women who experienced more than one sexual assault as a child were almost four times more likely to engage in heavy drinking behaviour than those women who experienced child sexual abuse by one perpetrator. Women who were first sexually abused at an older age were significantly more likely to engage in heavy drinking behaviour (Jasinski, Williams et al., 2000). Jasinski and colleagues suggest that these girls may have had more vivid and intrusive recollections of the abusive incident and use alcohol to self-medicate (2000; Simpson, Westerberg, Little and Trujillo, 1994; Young, 1992). This is supported by a post-hoc analysis, which revealed that women in the sample who remembered their victimization were more likely to be heavy drinkers than women who did not remember (Jasinski, Williams et al., 2000). Other research suggests alcohol may be used to relieve feelings of guilt or discomfort (Wilsnack,

Chapter 4

Klassen, et al., 1991), feelings that older girls may be more likely to have because they were unable to prevent the abuse from occurring (Jasinski, 2000).

Sexual abuse of older girls is more likely to involve greater levels of force, a characteristic associated with greater levels of symptomatology (Briere and Runtz, 1987; Browne and Finkelhor, 1986; Russell, 1986) and, consequently, associated with higher levels of alcohol use (Jasinki, Williams et al., 2000).

Jasinski and colleagues (2000) found that women who were physically abused as a child were 6.5 times more likely to engage in binge drinking and those who experienced multiple sexual victimization were at greater than four times the risk for binge drinking behaviour. Jasinksi and colleagues conclude that multiple incidents of child sexual abuse, more than the characteristics of the abuse, is an important predictor of adult heavy alcohol use and binge drinking at the bivariate level. They write:

> After controlling for the effects of parental drinking behaviour and negative parental relationships, multiple victimizations and youngest age at first sexual assault emerge as a significant predictors of heavy drinking and child physical abuse emerges as a significant predictor of binge drinking behaviour ...Women who were victimized multiple times as children may have greater feelings of guilt and shame, and perhaps be more likely to remember the incidents because the sexual abuse occurred more than once ... this could be associated with heavy drinking as an attempt to self medicate to relieve feelings of shame or discomfort. Binge drinking behaviour may be more likely to be related to some type of trigger event or recollection of the sexual abuse incident, whereas, heavy drinking may be an attempt to reduce a more general feeling of stress or discomfort (2000:1069).

Jasinski and colleagues (2000) also point out that women in their sample may have experienced continued abuse as adults or additional traumas subsequent to their childhood sexual abuse that, in turn, may have contributed to their alcohol abuse. They also suggest that, because children who are sexually abused are often removed from their homes in order to protect them, the trauma of this action may also be related to later drinking habits. Jasinski and colleagues add that the experience of childhood sexual abuse may also impact upon other areas of women's lives, such as their ability to form attachments, hold down a job or perform other daily activities that may play an instrumental role in the development of problematic drinking behaviour.

In a Swedish study, Spak and colleagues (1998) found that women who experienced sexual abuse prior to the age of thirteen were at greater risk for developing drinking problems than those experiencing abuse between the ages of 13 to 17. Child and/or adult sexual abuse was found to be a risk factor for a life-time anxiety diagnosis, with those experiencing child sexual abuse before the age of thirteen being seven times more likely to have an anxiety diagnosis and five times more likely to have a life-time alcohol dependency. This conflicts with the conclusions of Jasinski and colleagues (2000) discussed above, who argue that sexual abuse occurring later in life represents a greater risk factor in the development of adult alcohol abuse. However, a variable that was consistent in both studies was children neglect or children who perceived their parents to be cold and uncaring, as in both studies these individuals were found to be at greater risk for adult alcohol dependency/abuse.

Chapter 4

Spak and colleagues (1998) found significant statistical associations between child sexual abuse and certain problems, including life-time alcohol dependency or abuse, psychological or psychiatric problems during childhood or adolescence, and life-time alcohol dependency and "early deviant behaviour" (frequent truancy before 18 years of age; shoplifting or participation in other criminal activities before 18 years of age; started smoking tobacco before the age of thirteen years or smoked regularly before the age of 15 years; and stayed away from home a whole night without telling anyone before 18 years of age).

In a review of the literature on child abuse, Langeland and Hartgers (1998) found that there is a higher likelihood for a woman to develop alcohol problems if she was sexually or physically abused as a child. Only a few prospective studies in their review did not support a relationship between childhood abuse and adult alcohol problems among females; however, these studies were found to have serious methodological problems, which may have affected their research findings. Langeland and Hartgers argue that an important factor is the severity of sexual abuse, as greater severity is associated with increased levels of alcohol abuse in adulthood. For example, women who report child sexual abuse involving penetration show significantly higher rates of excessive alcohol use than do control groups. Among males, Langeland and Hartgers found that there was a dearth of information in the research literature on the effects of childhood abuse, despite the amount of public interest given to this topic.

Fleming and colleagues (1998) found that, among a group of women who reported child sexual abuse, no direct relationship between child sexual abuse and adult alcohol abuse was found. Some aspects of child sexual abuse that were more prevalent in women with alcohol abuse problems were child sexual abuse involving intercourse, the use of force and child sexual abuse lasting more than two years. Although child sexual abuse alone did not predict alcohol abuse, it increased risk of abuse, especially when in combination with having an alcoholic partner and high expectations of alcohol as a sexual disinhibitor or experiencing sexual problems arising from child sexual abuse and combining drinking alcohol with sexual intercourse for self-medication purposes. Perceiving one's mother as uncaring and overly controlling, combined with child sexual abuse, increased one's risk of adult alcohol abuse, as did violence in the home (Fleming, Mullen et al., 1998).

Pregnancy, Substance Abuse and Sexual/Physical Abuse

There are very few studies that looked at substance abuse during pregnancy and its relationship to sexual/physical abuse. However, studies that examined 'high risk' women have found that experiences of child and adult abuse are common among this group. For example, an American study profiling eighty birth mothers of children diagnosed with fetal alcohol syndrome and fetal alcohol effects found that 95% of study participants reported being sexually and/or physically abused during their lifetime (Astley et al., 2000b). Seventy-two per cent of the women reported that they did not want to reduce their alcohol use because "they were in an abusive relationship" or "they were too depressed to do anything about it" (79%) (Astley et al., 2000b:516).

Tait (2000a) found that, being a victim of sexual assault and abuse was a common experience among a group of women (n=74) in Manitoba, the majority of whom were Aboriginal (70%), who reported having past or present problems with substance abuse. Seventy-one per cent of the women reported being the victim of extreme physical, emotional or sexual abuse at some point in their lifetime. Some of the women reported that violence increased in their relationship after they became pregnant. Many of the women reported that substance abuse, including binge drinking, helped them to deal with the trauma of being abused, even during times when they were pregnant (Tait, 2000a). This is supported by other researchers who argue that alcohol is often used by many former victims of physical and sexual abuse to self-medicate and cope with the trauma of being abused (Miller, Downs et al., 1993; Astley et al., 2000b; Jasinski, Williams et al., 2000; Jacobs and Gill, 2002).

Nanson (1997) reported that the women she sees at a fetal alcohol syndrome clinic in Saskatoon, Saskatchewan, many of whom are Aboriginal, frequently report that their pregnancies are unplanned, unwanted and, in some cases, the result of sexual assault. Victims of violence during pregnancy, whether by cause or effect, are more likely to be heavy drinkers, including engaging in binge drinking behaviour (Abel and Hannigan, 1995). Amaro and colleagues (1990) found that a woman's alcohol use during pregnancy and her partner's substance use were independently associated with an increased risk of being a victim of violence during pregnancy. Berenson and colleagues (1991) found that battered women were more likely to smoke, use alcohol and/or illicit drugs than women who were not battered. Despite this, variables, such as violence, have not been included in most studies on substance use and pregnancy (Theidon, 1995).

Low-birth weight babies have been linked to violence during pregnancy. In one study, private patients in an American hospital, who had been battered, were four times more likely than non-battered private patients to give birth to low-birth weight infants (Bullock and McFarlane, 1989). Theidon (1995) points out that, in addition to partner violence, other dimensions of violence, such as women living in a state of constant fear in their communities, must be considered. A study in Chile found that after adjusting for potential confounders, it was determined that high levels of socio-political violence were associated with an approximately five-fold increase in risk of pregnancy complications (Zapata, Rebolledo, Atalah, Newman and King, 1992 in Theidon, 1995).

LaRocque writes that a "direct relationship between racist/sexist stereotypes and violence can be seen, for example, in the dehumanizing portrayal of Aboriginal women as 'squaws', which renders all Aboriginal female persons vulnerable to physical, verbal and sexual violence" (1993:74). She points to the obstacles that Aboriginal victims of violence face in small communities: lack of privacy; fear of further humiliation through community gossip; and fear of ostracism and intimidation from supporters of the perpetrator. The victim can be confronted with disbelief, anger and family denial or betrayal, and secrecy is often expected and enforced. This type of scenario, LaRocque (1993) adds, is indicative of small communities, Aboriginal and non-Aboriginal; in effect, acts as a type of censorship against those who would report sexual assault or even other forms of violence. In cases where the victim is poor, Aboriginal, pregnant and struggling with substance abuse, the chances of her coming forward to report violence are even slimmer, likely because of her pregnancy and abuse problem that she does not want to draw the attention of social service workers to her situation. Furthermore, for pregnant women, reporting violence by a partner may be reason enough for child welfare to place a 'birth alert' on the pregnancy, which will result in the woman's baby being apprehended from her care at birth if the agency feels there is a threat of violence to the baby.

Chapter 4

This factor may further dissuade pregnant women from reporting abuse. Aboriginal women in urban settings, particularly if they are poor, may have few supports they feel they can trust and may face a barrage of racist/sexist obstacles that prevent them from reporting abuse (Tait, 2003). If a woman does come forward and report abuse, several problems can occur. LaRocque writes:

> ... if a victim does proceed with reporting, who will want to hear? And if she goes out of the community, she faces racism/sexism in the form of judgement, indifference or disbelief. Many non-Aboriginals in positions of social service or power either have little knowledge of what circumstances confront the victim, or they do not take complainants seriously. The stereotype that Aboriginal women are sexually promiscuous is still quite prevalent. Also, in many communities women cannot trust policemen since some policemen, especially in previous generations, were also doing the attacking! This is not to mention that the entire process of reporting is itself a formidable challenge (1993:77).

LaRocque adds that considerably less than ten per cent of Aboriginal victims report violence and the conviction rate of accused perpetrators that go to trial are dismal. The courts are also wantonly lenient in their sentencing: "as a rule, thieves and minor drug dealers receive way stiffer penalties than do child molesters, rapists or even rapist-murderers" (1993:77-78).

Institutional Child Abuse

> After a lifetime of beatings, going hungry, standing in a corner on one leg, and walking in the snow with no shoes for speaking Inuvialuktun, and having a stinging paste rubbed on my face, which they did to stop us from expressing our Eskimo custom of raising our eyebrows for 'yes' and wrinkling our noses for 'no', I soon lost the ability to speak my mother tongue. When a language dies, the world dies, the world it was generated from breaks down too (cited in Law Commission of Canada, 2000:29).

> By the time Emily Rice left Kuper Island in 1959, at the age of eleven, she had been repeatedly assaulted and sexually abused by Father Jackson and three other priests, one of whom plied her with alcohol before raping her. A nun, Sister Mary Margaret, known for peeping at the girls in the shower and grabbing their breasts, was infuriated when Emily resisted her advances. "She took a big stick with bark on it, and rammed it right inside my vagina," recalls Rice. "She told me to say I'd fallen on the stick and that she was trying to get it out." The girl crawled into the infirmary the next day, too afraid to name the perpetrator. Nevertheless, when Emily returned to the dorm a few days later, the beatings by Sister Mary Margaret and the other nuns resumed without pause. In the years that followed, Emily would have to twice undergo reconstructive vaginal surgery, and she suffered permanent hearing loss. Father Jackson also wanted to make sure no one would talk. On the sisters' [Emily and Rose] first trip home at Christmas, he suspended Rose by her feet over the side of the boat, threatening to release her into the freezing waves unless she promised to stay silent (Fournier and Crey, 1977:48).

Chapter 4

In 1997, the Minister of Justice, the Honourable A. Anne McLellan, asked the Law Commission of Canada to prepare a report to address processes for dealing with child physical and sexual abuse. The scope of the report was to examine abuse that took place in residential schools for Aboriginal children and in institutions such as orphanages, schools for the deaf, long-term mental health care facilities, and sanitoria and training schools. The goal was to identify "what types of processes would best address wrongdoing, while affording appropriate remedies, and promoting reconciliation, fairness and healing" (Law Commission of Canada, 2000:12). In the report, institutional child abuse is defined as "abuse inflicted on a child residing in an institution, as distinguished from abuse occurring at home, or 'domestic child abuse'" (Law Commission of Canada, 2000:20). Currently, the Law Commission's report represents the most comprehensive review of institutional child abuse in Canada.

Canada has a wide variety of institutions for children that can be described as *total institutions*, targeting different communities and regions of the country. The term 'total institutions,' according to the Law Commission, refers to "institutions that seek to re-socialize people by instilling them with new roles, skills or values. Such institutions break down the barriers that ordinarily separate three spheres of life: work, play and sleep. Once a child enters, willingly or not, almost every aspect of his or her life is determined and controlled by the institution" (2000:24).

A total institution is a world unto itself, where those in charge hold all formal power and rules govern almost every aspect of daily life. Residents have little input into those rules and, in cases where abuse occurs, there is generally little effective recourse for victims and usually no independent procedure for handling complaints from children. Contact with the outside world—family, friends, community—is tightly controlled and infrequent (Law Commission of Canada, 2000).

In a total institution, children lack outside supports to offset the abuse. The Commission writes that children may live in fear of arbitrary or excessive punishment directed toward them. Added to this may be the fear of a form of abuse that has nothing to do with the rules and discipline, but everything to do with the arbitrary exercise of power: sexual abuse. Sexual abuse, the Commission writes, "is an intensely private form of abuse, and a singularly potent expression of power and domination that totally undermines a person's autonomy" (2000:27). Importantly, the Commission adds:

> Once that sense of the unchecked power of those in authority is firmly established, an atmosphere of insecurity and fear pervades an institution. Children do not have to experience arbitrary or excessive punishment to want to avoid it—they just have to witness enough of it to understand that they could be next (2000:27).

An in-depth discussion of the residential school system, including child abuse that occurred at the schools, will be given in the next chapter of this report; however, certain unique characteristics that set apart the residential school system from other child institutions will be briefly discussed here. The Law Commission's report points out that unlike other child institutions, the residential school system was intended to undermine a culture. It was one component in a loosely integrated set of statutes and programs aimed at controlling and re-orienting Aboriginal behaviour (Law Commission of Canada, 2000).

Chapter 4

While the Commission suggests individual acts of physical and sexual abuse cannot be attributed to the general government policy of assimilation, the policy did set the framework that was "used [in the schools] to denigrate and erase all aspects of Aboriginal heritage and justify a number of harmful practices that were undertaken in the name of instilling non-Aboriginal values in Aboriginal children" (Law Commission of Canada, 2000:48). The Commission concludes that there was little doubt the overall effect of this policy was to engender a sense of cultural and spiritual alienation among the children, which typically led to psychological disorientation and spiritual crisis for the children. The Commission writes:

> Denial of access to family and culture and other forms of emotional abuse, including, for some students, physical and sexual assaults, characterized the experience of Aboriginal children at residential schools. The effects on their mental and physical health were both immediate and long-lasting. Even today, many former residents are still coming to terms with their childhood experiences (2000:50).

The Commission found that, of all the institutions in Canada where children have been placed, the residential school system has done the greatest damage. This was due to a number of factors, including: the children being very young when they entered the schools (some as young as six years old); their removal from their families for ten months of the year or longer; their on-going experience of physical deprivation; in many cases, various forms of abuse while at the schools; the children being forbidden to speak the only language they knew; and their being taught to reject their home, heritage and, by extension, themselves (Law Commission of Canada, 2000). In this way, the children were deprived of any emotional and support resources that could have assisted them in resisting physical and sexual abuse. For these reasons, the Commission concluded: "It cannot be emphasised too strongly that, for all the elements of similarity with abuse in other types of institutions, Aboriginal children suffered in a unique way in residential schools" (2000:28).

Conclusion

Child abuse is an important factor when considering intergenerational links between the residential school system and current rates of substance abuse during pregnancy among Aboriginal women. Research shows that child abuse is linked to a number of mental health problems, including adult alcohol abuse. Studies also show that severity and multiple-episodes of abuse increase the risk for these problems. Child sexual abuse, in some Aboriginal communities in Canada, is believed to be significantly higher than national averages and some research suggests that Aboriginal women may experience higher levels of certain symptomatology related to child and adult sexual abuse, such as somatic symptoms, sleep disturbances, sexual difficulties and alcohol abuse.

Aboriginal victims of abuse and their families may face numerous barriers, which prevent them from reporting the abuse. Furthermore, they may have limited support if they do report abuse and it is likely that their perpetrators will not be prosecuted or, if convicted, will not receive appropriate sentencing. Studies involving pregnancy and substance abuse have failed to fully address the question of violence, even though women at risk of producing affected children report high rates of child and adult abuse. Some studies report that violence may increase in some instances during pregnancy and that violence has been linked to poor pregnancy outcomes, such as low-birth weight babies.

Chapter 4

Institutional child abuse occurs within an institutional setting where children are placed in the care of a group of people who control almost every aspect of the children's lives. Within this setting, children are made particularly vulnerable because they are cut off from family supports and there are generally few or no avenues for them to report abuse. The residential school system was identified by the Law Commission of Canada (2000) as causing the most amount of damage to a group of children than any other institution in Canada. The residential school system was unlike other institutions, as it was intended to undermine a culture; because of this, Aboriginal children suffered in a way distinct from children placed in other types of institutions.

Chapter 5

Residential Schools

Introduction

The full impact of the residential school system on the collective and individual health and wellness status of Aboriginal people in Canada is becoming increasingly clearer. First-hand personal accounts by former students, as well as information found in academic and lay publications, illustrate that the residential school system had a devastating effect upon the lives of many of those who attended the schools, as well as upon subsequent generations of Aboriginal people. The central goal of this report is to examine intergenerational links between the residential school experience and current rates of alcohol-related birth effects (ARBEs) among Aboriginal people.

This chapter will deal directly with the history of the school system and the experiences of individuals who attended them. It will discuss how Aboriginal communities and Nations responded to the removal of their children from their care to accommodate the government's plan to assimilate their children. Specific attention will be paid to intergenerational impacts in relation to health and social issues which are either directly or indirectly related to the residential school system. However, a discussion of intergenerational links between the experience of residential school students and current rates of fetal alcohol syndrome (FAS) and ARBEs will not be specifically dealt with in this chapter, but will be discussed in the chapters on risk and protective factors for FAS/ARBEs (see Chapters 8 and 10).

While this report is written in a way that distances the experience of individuals and, instead, privileges scientific research and the opinions of academic experts, the following chapter will try to break somewhat away from this approach by including several explanations and accounts by individuals who attended residential school as children. These individuals have agreed to record their experiences for the public record in various publications and, for this report, have been adopted to serve an important role: that of bringing the reader closer to the 'lived' experience of those who attended residential schools. In this way, a discussion about intergenerational impacts of residential schools can, albeit in a limited manner, remain in the hands of those who have experienced them and their voices will not be lost entirely in scientific method and analysis.

Situating Residential Schools In Historical Context

> ...it is to the young that we must look for a complete change of condition (as cited in Royal Commission on Aboriginal Peoples 1996a: vol. 1:337).[14]

> Our Sto:lo life was stolen away. Our children were removed by priests, social workers and police to residential schools, foster care and jail. My own family was at the eye of the hurricane, and we are only now beginning to regain our bearings. All over North America, the experiences of other First Nations families parallel my family's trials and triumphs (as cited in Fournier and Crey, 1997:22).

---

[14]   NAC RG 10, volume 3647, file 8128, MR C 101113, To Indian Commissioner, Regina, from J.A. Macrae, 18 December 1886.

Chapter 5

The first known boarding-school arrangements for Aboriginal youth in Canada began in 1620 under the control of the Récollets, an order of Franciscans who had settled in New France. The primary objective of the school was the evangelization of indigenous people through the education of children (Miller, 1996). Several boarding schools were opened throughout the seventeenth and eighteenth centuries by other religious orders, such as the Friars and the Jesuits, and were characterized by intense competition between religious orders. This trend continued throughout the duration of the residential school system.

The *Bagot Commission Report* (1844) formalized early assimilation policy and solidified the place of the residential school system in post-Confederate Canada (Bagot Report, 1844 in the Royal Commission on Aboriginal Peoples, 1996: Volume 1). After a two-year review of reserve conditions, the Commission asserted that indigenous communities were in a "half-civilized state" and further progress by communities would be realized only if indigenous communities were 'civilized' and imbued with the primary characteristics of civilization: industry and knowledge (Milloy, 1999:12-13). Manual labour schools, such as the Mohawk Institute (1834) and Mount Elgin (1850), were established in Ontario with hopes that pupils would "imperceptibly acquire the manners, habits and customs of civilized life" (Bagot Report, 1844 in Milloy, 1999:13; Furniss, 1992; Grant, 1996; Miller, 1991; 1996; Graham, 1997). Subsequently, Governor Sir E. Head's commission of 1856, *Report of the Special Commissioners Appointed to Investigate Indian Affairs in Canada*, concluded that "any hope of raising the Indians as a body to the social and political level of their white neighbours, is yet a glimmering and distant spark" (Milloy, 1999:12).

From 1830, the newly formed Department of Indian Affairs[15] took the position that *all* indigenous people—men, women and children—could be civilized, and collectively they were to receive ameliorative attention (Milloy, 1999). However, following the *Bagot Commission Report*, the Department decided Aboriginal adults could make only limited 'progress' toward this goal. To maximize the potential of assimilating indigenous people, the Department decided Aboriginal children should become its central focus. This was based on the belief that children possessed malleable identities that could be shaped by colonialist education. Indigenous children, rather than their parents, were, therefore, held by government leaders to be the logical focus for assimilation strategies (Grant, 1996; Graham, 1997; Milloy, 1999; Miller and Danziger, 2000). Indigenous adults, in particular, elders, were believed to be a threat to this process as indigenous traditional ways of life were seen to be merely remnants of dying cultures and a vanishing race, and held no place or value in the newly formed Canada (Miller, 1996; Fournier and Crey, 1997; Milloy, 1999).

Removal of children to residential schools, where they could be imbued with European values and culture, was an early strategy adopted by colonialist forces to Christianize (the goal of the church) and assimilate (the goal of government) indigenous people (Miller, 1996; 1987; 1989; Ing, 1991; Furniss, 1992; Armitage, 1995; Feehan, 1996; Grant, 1996; Milloy, 1999; Johansen, 2000). However, by 1858

---

[15]   The Department of Indian Affairs was created in 1830 by Sir George Murray, the Secretary of State for the Colonies in the British Imperial government. This marked a radial change in the long-standing policy pertaining to the First Nations of Upper and Lower Canada initiated by the Imperial government with the Proclamation of 1763. The Department was directed to ameliorate the condition of Aboriginal communities "by encouraging in every possible manner the progress of religious knowledge and education generally amongst the Indian Tribes" (Murray, 1830 in Milloy, 1999:11).

the Department of Indian Affairs and the churches found that the system of manual labour schools was largely ineffective in achieving assimilation. This was partially due to difficulties with enrollments and runaways and, more importantly, to the behaviour of school graduates. Milloy points out:

> Much more problematic ... was the behaviour of the graduates. On returning to their communities, supposedly re-socialized as non-Aboriginal people, they became cultural backsliders. They were not infected with industriousness, and they did not take a leading role in community development ...The blame for this situation, which for the commissioners [of the Bagot Commission] was "discouraging in the extreme", did not in their analysis rest in the schools but in the conditions that graduates returned to on the reserves (1999:18).

The Department particularly blamed the influence of parents and elders for the 'backslide' of graduates (Miller, 1987; Furniss, 1992; Grant, 1996; Milloy, 1999).

After Confederation, the newly formed Conservative government, led by Prime Minister John A. Macdonald, took several steps to diminish indigenous control over land and resources, as well as political and social infrastructures. Parliament abolished self-government and replaced traditional government with "municipal government," giving extensive control of reserves to the federal government and its representative, the Department of Indian Affairs.

Subsequent legislation, the *Indian Act* of 1876 and 1880, and the *Indian Advancement Act* of 1884, allowed the government to "mould, unilaterally, every aspect of life on the reserve and to create whatever infrastructure it deemed necessary to achieve the desired end - assimilation through enfranchisement and, as a consequence, the eventual disappearance of First Nations" (Milloy, 1999:21). The government could and did, in ensuing years, determine who was and was not considered an Indian; control the election of band councils; manage reserve resources, developmental initiatives and band funds; impose individual land-holdings; and make and enforce regulation affecting all aspects of public and private life in communities (Milloy, 1999). Milloy adds:

> While the acts related solely to Indian First Nations, the assumption behind them was the same for all Aboriginal people. Men, women, and children-Métis, "non-status and status" Indians, and Inuit-each in their own time and place, as their homeland was encompassed by the expanding Canadian nation, would be expected to abandon their cherished life ways, to become "civilized" and thus to lose themselves and their culture among the mass of Canadians. This would be an unchanging federal determination, justified in the minds of Confederation policy makers and successive generations of politicians and Departmental officials by their sincere, Christian certainty that the nation's duty to the original people of the land was to prepare them "for a higher civilization by encouraging" them "to assume the privileges and responsibilities of full citizenship" (1999:21).

Milloy (1999) points out that, of all the initiatives undertaken by colonialist forces in the first century of Confederation, none were more ambitious or central to the civilizing and assimilation strategies of the Department of Indian Affairs than the residential school system.

Chapter 5

A new strategy to re-socialize Aboriginal children through off-reserve residential schools led the federal government to consider the American Indian boarding school system (Deiter, 1999). Nicholas Flood Davin of Regina, a Member of Parliament backbencher, was sent to the United States to evaluate the American system and then make recommendations on Indian education to the federal government. The American Indian boarding school system, still in existence today, was initially devised by the American government to solve the 'Indian problem' by preparing American Indians for enfranchisement, as well as to acculturate them into American ways of 'thinking' and 'being' (Adams, 1995; Carroll, 2000; Colmant, 2000). Impressed with its perceived effectiveness and efficiency, Davin strongly recommended the establishment of a similar system of education in Canada. He implored the Canadian government to entrust missionaries, because of their commitment to 'civilizing' the indigenous population, with the task of running the schools (Milloy, 1999).

The *Davin Report* was accepted by the Department of Indian Affairs in 1879, marking the beginning of one of the most damaging and destructive forms of assimilation strategies in the history of Aboriginal and non-Aboriginal relations in Canada (Milloy, 1999; Deiter, 1999). The report suggested that the 'Christian' obligation to Aboriginal people could be realized "only through the medium of children." Aboriginal adults, the report argued, could not be rescued from "their present state of ignorance, superstition and helplessness [because they were] physically, mentally and morally ... unfitted to bear such a complete metamorphosis" (Davin, 1879 in Fournier and Crey, 1997:55-56). Furthermore, Department bureaucrats advised Macdonald that residential schools were a "good investment" to prevent indigenous children from becoming "an undesirable and often dangerous element in society" (Fournier and Crey, 1997:55-56).

Following the acceptance of the *Davin Report* (1879), the federal government began the construction of church-run residential schools across Canada. The preference was for large industrial residential schools located away from reserves in order to minimize parent-child, elder-youth contact (Miller, 1987; 1996; Ing, 1991; Armitage, 1995; Grant, 1996; Milloy, 1999). The federal government entrusted various branches of the church with the task of educating, assimilating and 'civilizing' Aboriginal youth. The residential school system was dependent upon a tripartite relationship between the federal government, branches of the church and Aboriginal people. The federal government provided economic support, the church provided manpower and instruction, and Aboriginal people provided the children. This relationship was unevenly balanced and was dominated largely by the churches and the federal government (Kelm, 1996). For the federal government, the residential school system represented a cost-effective system of education as it enabled the Department to sub-contract schooling to missionaries, which was both cost-effective and less labour intensive (Fournier and Crey, 1997; Satzewich and Mahood, 1995; Grant, 1996; Milloy, 1999). For various branches of the church, the residential school system represented a regular source of revenue to supplement their organizational activities. The residential school arrangement also ensured missionaries a means by which they could solidify their institutional status within Aboriginal communities (Satzewich and Mahood, 1995).

An examination of current commentary on the Canadian residential school system highlights how destructive and damaging the system has been for Aboriginal people, past, present and future. Much of the contemporary discord in Aboriginal communities, such as increased prevalence rates of substance abuse, family dysfunction and suicide, have been linked to intergenerational impacts brought about by residential schooling (Tait, 2003). It must be noted, however, that some Aboriginal groups initially thought this system of education would be beneficial and lobbied for the extension of educational opportunities to their children (Knockwood and Thomas, 1992; Armitage, 1995; Miller, 1996; Milloy, 1999). However, their motives in doing so were very different from those of the Canadian government and the churches. For many Aboriginal leaders and their constituents, residential schooling was seen as a mechanism through which they could obtain knowledge about the customs and practices of the rapidly expanding settler society (Miller, 1987; 1996; Furniss, 1992; Knockwood, 1992; Grant, 1996; Graham, 1997; Miller and Danziger, 2000). Assimilation of their children into the colonialist society, however, was not something they expected, nor wanted, as part of the education process (Miller, 1987; 1996; Milloy, 1999; Miller and Danziger, 2000), and was a point on which Aboriginal leaders and their communities clashed with government and church leaders throughout the residential school era (Deiter, 1999).

Traditional Indigenous Education

The structured school curriculum and highly formalized nature of residential education contrasted greatly with traditional forms of indigenous education. Traditional education, throughout Aboriginal Nations, has been generally characterized as being based on values such as respect, humility, sharing, caring and cooperation (Grant, 1996). Elders were the primary educators of children in the pre-contact period and until the Canadian government created legislation requiring Aboriginal children to attend colonialist schools (Johnston, 1988; Ing, 1991; Knockwood and Thomas, 1992; Grant, 1996; Miller, 1996; Milloy, 1999). Observing, listening and learning were the basic educational tools used in traditional teachings (Miller, 1996). These teachings provided indigenous children with cultural and pragmatic skills that were needed to participate in the lifestyle of the community. Education and skills taught in residential schools were, for the most part, of limited benefit to students once they were living back in their home communities (Haig-Brown, 1988; Bull, 1991; Knockwood and Thomas, 1992; Feehan, 1996; Grant, 1996; Miller, 1996; Milloy, 1999).

Across Canada, numerous indigenous languages were spoken and were central to the ways in which indigenous people perceived and interacted with the world around them. For example, storytelling was a common teaching tool of traditional education and these stories were shaped and altered to illustrate aspects of daily life and cultural values (Haig-Brown, 1988; Ing, 1991; Furniss, 1992; Knockwood and Thomas, 1992; Grant, 1996). By forbidding students to speak their indigenous languages, the residential school system threatened not only the transmission of indigenous languages to younger generations, but also the transmission of cultural and pragmatic knowledge through processes such as storytelling. The assault on indigenous languages, through the residential school system, created distance between parents and their children and between elders and the younger generations who attended the schools (McLeod, 1998).

Gender Differences

> And you couldn't speak to your brother on the other side or your cousin, whoever. If you were caught talking to a boy, any boy, you'd get your hair cut right off. What was wrong with talking to the boys? It's a darn wonder we, any of us even got married. Because it was a sin to talk to a boy. Good grief (cited in Deiter, 1999:46).

Chapter 5

Very little is written about the differing experiences of male and female students who attended residential schools; however, it has been argued that differing experiences did exist based on gender division (Fiske, 1996; 1981). This is reflected in the underlying goals of the state and the church, which were to prepare female students to become wives and members of nuclear households located in reserve communities (Fiske, 1996). This strategy was meant to undermine extended family and corporate kinship organizations within Aboriginal communities, as well as the traditional leadership roles of women and, instead, establish self-sufficient, patriarchal, nuclear families, headed by men (Fiske, 1981).

Control of sexual morality was central, and religious and moral instruction was shaped by negative assumptions about the psychology and character of Aboriginal girls (Fiske, 1996). This resulted, in many instances, in stricter rules and surveillance of the female students, as well as strict sexual segregation. Furthermore, in some instances, the church, in its 'moral obligation' to protect Aboriginal females from the 'vices of frontier and indigenous societies,' frequently requested that the girls remain at school until a marriage was arranged for them. In many cases, this meant that female students remained at the schools, often as full-time unpaid labour, until they were over eighteen years of age (Fiske, 1996).

Reasons For Enrollment

Prior to 1894, Aboriginal children were sent to residential schools for a variety of reasons. Decisions to send a child to a residential school could be made by a child's parents or the local Indian agent.[16] In most cases, economic factors were behind parental decisions to send children to the schools. Aboriginal parents believed that residential schools were places where their children would be provided with adequate food, clothing and housing in a safe environment. However, the reality of the situation often fell short of their expectations (Milloy, 1999).

In many instances, Indian agents decided which children would be sent to residential schools, a decision that was often based on how the agent perceived the home environment of the child (Milloy, 1999; Miller and Danzinger, 2000). Truancy, alcoholism and violence were common factors invoked by Indian agents to declare parents unfit and were justification enough to result in the removal of a child from their family.

An 1894 amendment to the *Indian Act* paved the way for compulsory education and attendance, solidifying the role of residential schools as the federal government's primary tool of education and assimilation. Further amendments to the *Indian Act* in the early part of the twentieth century ensured compulsory education. As a result, parents no longer had the option of withholding their children from residential schools without facing legal consequences. In order to ensure the successful enrollment and attendance of children, RCMP officers were employed to act as truant officers (Miller, 1996).

After World War II, the federal government decided that the residential school system was no longer a viable mechanism to educate Aboriginal people. A special joint committee of the Senate and the House of Commons deemed the system a failure, as very few students graduated and those who did rarely

---

[16]   The Indian agent was an appointed government official who was responsible for the implementation of the *Indian Act* (1876) in reserve communities.

found the skills they learned to be helpful in gaining employment on or off the reserve. As a result, the federal government began orienting Indian education policy towards integration. This shift was arguably a bureaucratic response to fiscal problems (Miller, 1987; 1996).

The residential school system became an administrative and economic headache, one which the federal government believed could be alleviated with the integration of Aboriginal children into provincial and on-reserve day schools (Miller, 1987; 1996; Milloy, 1999). Despite the marked shift in education policy, the underlying motivation remained the same. A 1951 revision of the *Indian Act* left the inadequate education structures intact and the assimilative purpose of the school system remained a part of education offered to Aboriginal students (Miller, 1987; 1996).

The shift in education policy and the construction of on-reserve day schools, however, did not mark the end of all residential schools in Canada. Residential schools remained a part of the lives of some Aboriginal people until approximately 1984; however, these schools were largely reserved for orphaned and destitute children, children whose parents voluntarily enlisted them, and children whose community did not have a day school.

Daily Operations and Life at Residential Schools

> In the residential school I was not really allowed to speak Cree, but they didn't know 'cause we just switched to English every time we saw a supervisor coming or something like that.

> There was not one single native tradition in the school. They just took you away from home, where you left everything, all the Indian- ness back there. They took you where all the supervisors were all white people (cited in Deiter, 1999:40).

> The Sisters didn't treat me good - they gave me rotten food to eat and punished me for not eating it - the meat and soup were rotten and tasted so bad they made the girls sick sometime. I have been sick from eating it ... I used to hide the meat in my pocket and throw it away. I told the Sisters to look at the meat as it was rotten, and they said it was not rotten and we must eat it. The Sisters did not eat the same kind of food as they gave the girls. If we didn't eat our porridge at breakfast, it was given to us for our dinner, and even for supper, and we got nothing else till it was eaten (cited in Milloy, 1999:143).[17]

During the period 1910 to 1932, the residential school system expanded rapidly and amendments to the *Indian Act* made school attendance mandatory for at least ten months of the year for First Nations children older than six years of age. By 1930, throughout Canada, roughly seventy-five per cent of all First Nations, as well as significant numbers of Métis and Inuit children between the ages of seven and fifteen, attended the schools (Fournier and Crey, 1997). The philosophy of the residential school system was that expressions of Aboriginal culture and individuality were to be suppressed.

---

[17]   At the Williams Lake inquest, a woman explained why she had run off twice from the school.

Chapter 5

From the moment Aboriginal children entered the schools, physical and cultural markers (e.g., clothing, long hair[18]) were removed and replaced by European equivalents (Fiske, 1996; Gresko, 1986; Haig-Brown, 1988; Miller, 1987; 1996). As well, each child was assigned a number and a European name, and was forbidden to speak his or her language. Severe punishment was handed out to those who resisted or disobeyed (Fournier and Crey, 1997; Miller, 1996).

In many cases, residential school buildings were hastily constructed, clear evidence of the federal government's intense obsession with the economics of Indian education (Graham, 1997; Milloy, 1999). Reports indicate that school buildings were generally over-crowded, poorly ventilated and lacking proper safety equipment, such as fire escapes. These features, along with Aboriginal children being overworked and poorly nourished, made residential schools sites for widespread disease and illness (Kelm, 1996). The practice of strict confinement of school attendees allowed infectious diseases, such as tuberculosis, scabies, influenza, pneumonia and whooping cough, to spread rapidly through school dormitories (Armitage, 1995; Feehan, 1996; Grant, 1996; Kelm, 1996; Miller, 1996; Graham, 1997; Milloy, 1999). The heavy disease load at many of the schools often resulted in the death of a significant number of children. Mortality rates at residential schools were so high by the late nineteenth and early twentieth centuries that the federal government commissioned an investigation in 1907 to determine why. The *Bryce Report*, named after principal investigator Dr. Peter Bryce, concluded that every residential school student should be considered a potential tuberculosis sufferer (Bryce, 1907).

The response to the *Bryce Report* by the Department of Indian Affairs, headed by Duncan Campbell Scott, was to state that the recommendations of the report did not apply to the school system. As a result, Aboriginal families and communities continued to see their children taken away to the schools, which they increasingly associated with disease and death. In reaction to these dangers, many parents tried to resist compulsory education by keeping their children at home; however, under government legislation, it was illegal for them to do so. Kelm (1996) points out that, ironically, the residential school system was based on the belief that the state and church were 'saving' Aboriginal children from unhealthy home environments. This is clear in government descriptions in the late nineteenth and twentieth centuries, which described Aboriginal communities as 'backwards' and 'dirty,' their children unhealthy because of the inability of their 'uncivilized' parents to care for them (Kelm, 1996; Million, 2000). In actuality, residential schools were increasingly responsible for disease, illness and death among Aboriginal children and for establishing a legacy of poor health that continues to affect Aboriginal people today (Kelm, 1996).

The federal government was a firm believer in the notion that a combination of industry and knowledge were the only means by which Aboriginal children could be turned into successful, contributing Canadians (Furniss, 1992; Milloy, 1999). Until the middle of the twentieth century, most residential schools operated on the 'half-day' system (Johnston, 1988; Haig-Brown, 1988; Miller, 1996; Milloy, 1999). One half of the day was dedicated to academic subjects, while the other half of the day was spent practicing a trade, such as sewing (for girls) or working on the school farm (for boys). Residential schools were characterized by strict regimentation (Bull, 1991; Feehan, 1996; Grant, 1996; Kelm, 1996;

---

[18]   In many indigenous cultures, a person 's hair held great symbolic significance and the shearing of the hair upon entering a residential school was the cause of great shame and degradation of individual and collective identity for these Aboriginal children (Grant, 1996).

Miller, 1996; Milloy, 1999). Eating, working, learning, sleeping and cleaning were all done according to a rigid schedule. Failure to comply with the imposed schedule resulted in punishment. Reports indicate that it was not unheard of for students to spend more time labouring in the fields rather than in the classroom (Milloy, 1999).

The curriculum of residential schools was designed to provide Aboriginal children with a basic knowledge of reading, writing and arithmetic (Miller, 1996). It was also constructed to act as a means of assimilation by bridging the gap between the conditions of 'savagery,' in which the children were perceived by the government and church to be raised, and the 'civilized' colonialist society that, hopefully, they eventually would enter (Milloy, 1999; Grant, 1999). However, residential schools were inadequate in their ability to educate students. Standards of education were significantly lower than those of neighbouring provincial schools for non-Aboriginal children (Haig-Brown, 1988; Bull, 1991; Knockwood and Thomas, 1992; Miller, 1996; Fournier and Crey, 1997; Milloy, 1999).

School curriculums ignored and denigrated the cultural heritage of Aboriginal people. This differed from strategies taken in some American Indian boarding schools, where aspects of Indian language and culture were adopted to alleviate the pressure on students (Carroll, 2000). Throughout the twentieth century, calls were made by some school investigators for curriculum reform to address the life needs of the child and reflect their cultural heritage (Milloy, 1999). School investigators argued that the inclusion of Aboriginal history and cultural heritage in school curriculum would foster enthusiasm for learning (Milloy, 1999). Recommendations for curriculum reform were consistently ignored by government and the churches, and curriculum continued to be based on racist, ethnocentric and Eurocentric values.

Between 1890 and 1950, it is estimated that approximately sixty per cent of residential school students failed to advance beyond grade three. In some decades, that number increased to approximately eighty per cent (Milloy, 1999). Academic failure was attributed to factors such as under-funding, poorly qualified staff and the 'stunted mental capacity' of Aboriginal children. Under-funding was an excuse adopted by both the federal government and the church to account for the poor performance of residential school students. Under-funding contributed to the hiring of poorly qualified staff as wages were low and the geographic locations of most residential schools were often undesirable for qualified teachers. Under-funding was also behind students being forced to spend a significant amount of time in labour, in order to provide a supplementary income for the schools (Grant, 1996; Miller, 1996; Milloy, 1999).

Discipline, Control and Punishment

> One day I got caught by one of the staff when I was passing notes … I was taken into a locked room and there I was left all day with nothing to eat. I couldn't get to a toilet or bathroom, so I wet myself. I was about nine or ten years old. I dried my undies on the radiator and, of course, they gave off quite an odour. When the matron came to get me at night she smelled the odour and slapped me around for wetting myself, but I couldn't help it; there was no place to go.

Chapter 5

She then took me up to the dormitory where the rest of the girls were in bed. She told me to get into my nightgown and lie across the bed on my stomach. Then she got a strap and strapped me on the back. Finally I go so numb that I couldn't cry anymore. But she kept on strapping me and telling the other girls that she was making an example out of me (cited in Dieter, 1999:28).

The creation of colonial reality that occurred in the New World will remain a subject of immense curiosity and study—the New World where the Indian and African *irracionales* became compliant to the reason of a small number of white Christians. Whatever the conclusions we draw about how that hegemony was so speedily effected, we would be unwise to overlook the role of terror. And by this I mean us to think-through-terror, which as well as being a physiological state is also a social one whose special features allow it to serve as the mediator *par excellence* of colonial hegemony: the space of death where the Indian, African, and white gave birth to a New World (Taussig, 1987:5).

Residential schools were a type of *total institution* (Goffman,1961), a social institution that is 'walled off' from the world at large and breaks down the barriers that exist in mainstream society between places of work, sleep and play; and enforces and maintains an extreme power disparity between a large 'inmate' population and a smaller supervisory staff that continues to be integrated in the outside world (Chrisjohn and Young, 1997; Law Commission of Canada, 2000). Strict regimentation of student activities, along with severe punishment for students who broke the rules, were employed by school educators to control and re-socialize students (Johnston, 1988; Haig-Brown, 1988; Bull, 1991; Ing, 1991; Knockwood and Thomas, 1992; Feehan, 1996; Fournier and Crey, 1997; Milloy, 1999; Colmant, 2000; Johansen, 2000). To prevent insubordination by students, many schools adopted disciplinary practices, such as food deprivation, strapping and solitary confinement, as ways to punish children who 'misbehaved' (Milloy, 1999). Punishment of children was regularly handed out in front of other students as a way to warn them about the consequences of insubordination. Acts deemed to be insubordinate in many of the schools included bed-wetting, communicating with children of the opposite sex, speaking an indigenous language, stealing food, running away, talking back to staff and being outside of school grounds (Haig-Brown, 1988; Bull, 1991; Knockwood and Thomas, 1992; Feehan, 1996; Miller, 1996; Graham, 1997; Milloy, 1999).

The intention behind such excessive discipline and punishment of students was to cause pain and humiliation. Humiliation, such as that caused by public strapping, sought to diminish the student's sense of dignity and value of self and identity (Graham, 1997). Public humiliation has been reported by former students as one of the most devastating aspects of their experience while they attended residential school (Grant, 1996; Graham, 1997). At some schools, such as the Mohawk Institute and Mount Elgin, abuse was so frequent that students were classified based on the number of punishments they received and the reasons why they received them (Graham, 1997).

The Canadian federal government officially discouraged corporal punishment at the schools; however, it is clear that they believed strict rules and severe punishment for breaking those rules were needed to successfully assimilate Aboriginal children. While Duncan Campbell Scott, Deputy Superintendent of Indian Affairs, proclaimed that it was the right and duty of the Canadian federal government to protect Aboriginal children against ill treatment, there were no formal guidelines outlining the range of permissive disciplinary actions and corporal punishments that could be used by school staff (Miller, 1996; Milloy, 1999).

Indian agents were responsible for evaluating the conditions under which the students in their charge were living and learning. Indian agents had a significant amount of power in the early twentieth century: for example, to determine which children were sent to residential schools; to recommend to the Department of Indian Affairs the dismissal of unsatisfactory teachers, principles and staff; and to discharge students. Numerous reports filed by Indian agents attesting to the cruel and inhumane conditions at many residential schools can be found in federal archives (Satzewich and Mahood, 1995; Milloy, 1999; Johansen, 2000). This does not mean, however, that these reports led to school reforms and it should be noted that, in most cases, the excessive disciplinary actions and severe punishment experienced by students went unreported. Although local Indian agents had the legal authority to recommend the discharge of staff and students, there is very little evidence that Indian agents used this power to any great extent.

Some complaints about excessive disciplinary actions and severe punishment by members of the church who ran the schools did come to the attention of the Department of Indian Affairs; however, in these cases, little was done to address the problem. Reasons for the inaction by the Department of Indian Affairs were rooted in the intense power struggle over residential schooling between the churches who ran the schools and the federal government. Reports of abuse were also easily covered up by government officials (Satzewich and Mahood, 1995) and the federal government was particularly unwilling to disclose to the Canadian and international public the real conditions that children were living in at the schools.

Sexual Abuse and Residential Schooling

> The nightmare began as soon as Emily [eight years old] and her sister Rose, then eleven years old, stepped on the small boat that would bear them away. "I clung to Rose until Father Jackson wrenched her out of my arms ... I searched all over the boat for Rose. Finally I climbed up to the wheelhouse and opened the door and there was Father Jackson, on top of my sister. My sister's dress was pulled up and his pants were down. I was too little to know about sex; but I know now he was raping her" (as cited in Fournier and Crey, 1997:47).

> I was first sexually abused by a student when I was six years old, and by a supervisor, an ex-Navy homosexual, when I was eight ... I learned how to use sexuality to my advantage, as did many other students. Sexual favours brought me protection, sweets (a rarity in the school) and even money to buy booze. But this had its long-term effects ... including alcoholism, the inability to touch people, and an 'I don't care' attitude (former residential student as cited in Haig-Brown, 1988:17).

In recent years, former residential school students have come forward in alarming numbers to report being child victims of sexual abuse at the hands of those who were entrusted to educate, care and protect them while they were in the schools (Haig-Brown, 1988; Knockwood and Thomas, 1992; Satzewich and Mahood, 1995; Feehan, 1996; Grant, 1996; Miller, 1996; Chrisjohn and Young, 1997; Fournier and Crey, 1997; Milloy, 1999; Johansen, 2000; Million, 2000). The prevalence of sexual abuse and the

Chapter 5

range of experiences of victims is shocking and horrifying, as are accounts of how abuse affected the lives of those who experienced and witnessed it. Those who abused children in the schools included priests, nuns, teachers and other students (Haig-Brown, 1988; Miller, 1996; Milloy, 1999). As more became known about the extent of sexual abuse within the school system, some have suggested that the residential school system was nothing short of "institutional pedophilia" (Fournier and Crey, 1997).

While a fairly comprehensive record of the range of physical abuses meted against students at the schools was filed with the Canadian government by former Indian agents and government officials, these accounts virtually excluded all accounts of sexual abuse. Incidents of sexual abuse found in official government archives are deeply encoded in a language of sexual repression that marked Canadian discourse on sexual matters (Milloy, 1999; Johansen, 2000). Sexual behaviour that was identified by officials as deviant and in need of attention by authorities were acts that occurred between students, such as intercourse between boys and girls and between members of the same sex. These accounts are highlighted in official files and accounts of sexual abuse by caretakers of the schools are virtually absent (Haig-Brown, 1988; Milloy, 1999). For many school officials and caretakers, Aboriginal children were perceived to be sexually abnormal, an abnormality that they located in the 'natural' physical and mental makeup of the students. For example, one principal stated that Indians were simply "unmoral ... nature is very strong in them ...The problem of course is that these people with regard to sex mature much earlier than the whites [making it necessary] to guide that part of their emotional make-up along sound and safe channels" (Milloy, 1999:296).

Million argues that the failure of the Canadian government to address issues of sexual abuse in residential schools is a reflection of nineteenth and twentieth century colonialist understandings of Aboriginal people, which proclaimed Aboriginal people to be less 'civilized,' less 'mentally developed' and deeply lacking in Christian morals. Christian institutions portrayed Aboriginal people as sexually immoral (Million, 2000) and Aboriginal children as having been contaminated by their 'Indianness' (Graham, 1997). The residential school system was seen as a means to reform the immoral sexual predisposition of Aboriginal people through their children. As such, residential schools were structured in a manner consistent with the highly gender segregated structure of most western European societies (Haig-Brown, 1988; Knockwood and Thomas, 1992; Miller, 1996; Graham, 1997; Milloy, 1999; Million, 2000). Contact between boys and girls was restricted and heavily monitored by school staff. The penalties for communicating with members of the opposite sex were often severe and frequently resulted in physical punishment and/or loss of some, or all, of the few individual freedoms children had in the institutions (Grant, 1996; Miller, 1996; Milloy, 1999).

Sex and sexuality were not spoken about at the schools, nor was sexual abuse spoken about in political or public debates concerning residential schools. Prior to former students coming forward to tell of the abuse they experienced, a public facade existed that maintained residential schools were institutions that repressed expressions of sexuality under the moral guidance of the church. However, recent accounts illustrate that sex and sexuality were very much a part of the residential school environment. Many children quickly learned that sexual relations were dictated by power and some even used their own sexuality to gain special status with supervisors and other students (Haig-Brown, 1988).

Chapter 5

Arguments have been made that certain forms of physical punishment given to students were actually covert forms of sexual gratification. Furniss (1992) suggests that sexualized punishments of residential school students was similar to practices in Victorian England, where, for example, the act of whipping another person served as a means of sexual arousal for some individuals. Jonathan Benthall, a British social anthropologist, argues that whipping, flogging and caning by teachers and headmasters formed a 'ritual of abusive authority' and a covert form of sexual gratification (in Scheper-Hughes, 1998). Milloy argues that the practice of whipping served several purposes in the residential school environment, physical punishment and sexual arousal being the two most common, which is illustrated in a first hand account by a former student:

> First thing Father wanted me to go to his office so I did. He asks me a few questions. And then he brought me to the other office. He told me to kneel and then he pulled my skirt up and pulled my pants down. He put my head between his legs and started to give me the strap (cited in Milloy, 1999:297).

Specific qualities of residential schools, notably that the student population was almost entirely isolated from the outside world, allowed sexual predators access to hundreds of children. Million (2000) suggests that the collective silence about sex and sexual abuse at residential schools created a discursive void that allowed predatory sexual behaviour to persist over extended periods of time. School officials, particularly those who were involved with the church, are, in one way or another, implicated in this silence. This helps to explain why the Canadian public remained ignorant to the widespread and systematic physical and sexual abuse of Aboriginal students. Because government archives and official files are bereft of accounts of sexual abuse at the schools, most information has come from special inquiries into the problem and from the personal testimonies of those who experienced and witnessed the abuse.

Older students, socialized primarily in the system, commonly became perpetrators of sexual abuse themselves and preyed on younger students (Haig-Brown, 1988; Piatote, 2000). Sexual abuse was not limited to the confines of the school and, in some cases, occurred in Aboriginal communities when the children returned home (Haig-Brown, 1988; Fournier and Crey, 1997). In some smaller Aboriginal communities, an estimation of upwards to eighty per cent of community members have been victims of sexual abuse at some point in their lives (Fournier and Crey, 1997). While not all the abuse can be attributed to the residential school system, there is an undeniable direct link between sexual abuse of children in residential schools and sexual abuse by these students, either in the schools or as adults living outside of the school system.

At the peak of the residential school system, almost one-third of Aboriginal children between the ages of six to fifteen years attended a residential school (Armitage, 1995). Many of these students were the victims of, or exposed to, forms of physical, sexual and emotional abuse. While the literature fails to generate solid statistics on the number of students sexually abused at residential schools, the estimated numbers are very high, particularly in certain schools (Haig-Brown, 1988; Knockwood and Thomas, 1992; Satzewich and Mahood, 1995; Feehan, 1996; Grant, 1996; Miller, 1996; Chrisjohn and Young, 1997; Fournier and Crey, 1997; Milloy, 1999). One estimate given in an article in the *Globe and Mail*, quoting a special advisor to the Minister of National Health and Welfare on child sexual abuse, suggests that at some schools, one hundred per cent of the children were sexually abused (Milloy, 1999:298).

Chapter 5

Considering the ages that most students were apprehended and that the residential school system was their primary socializing influence in their childhood years, it is not surprising that dysfunctional relationships, based on power, control and domination, were recreated once the students were back in their community. According to Bull (1991), many former students internalized and normalized the systematic physical and sexual violence perpetrated against them. This arguably accounts for higher than average prevalence rates of physical violence and sexual abuse found among some Aboriginal groups today.

Resistance and Survival

Student resistance to their living circumstances at the schools took many forms and was common throughout the history of the residential school system. Running away was perhaps the most practiced form of resistance (Haig-Brown, 1988; Johnston, 1988; Furniss, 1992; Knockwood and Thomas, 1992; Grant, 1996; Miller, 1996; Milloy, 1999; Johansen, 2000). The frequency of runaways alarmed many school officials and government agents, particularly because students were aware of the severe punishment they would receive if they were caught (Furniss, 1992). Most student runaways were also unsuccessful, but despite students knowing of the low success rates and the severe punishment awaiting them if they were caught, alarmingly high numbers of children attempted to run away each year (Johnston, 1988; Haig-Brown, 1988; Furniss, 1992; Knockwood and Thomas, 1992; Grant, 1996; Miller, 1996; Milloy, 1999). Tragedy met some students who tried to escape and federal archives document several instances in which a runaway student perished in the attempted escape (Furniss, 1992; Milloy, 1999; Johansen, 2000). The federal government investigated cases of runaways who died before being found and, in the majority of instances, an on-going history of abuse and mistreatment at the school was uncovered (Furniss, 1992; Johansen, 2000), suggesting these were more acts of survival on the part of the students than simply acts of resistance. The federal government responded to their investigations with neither condemnation nor closer scrutiny of the school administration and practices. Instead, they adopted a benevolent stance towards the role played by the schools in student runaways. Rather than punishing school administrators for their systematic mistreatment of students, government officials stated that running away was an example of the inherent 'wild' nature of Aboriginal children (Furniss, 1992).

Speaking indigenous languages, while strictly prohibited by school officials, has been reported by former students as a very important way in which students dealt with being away from their families and communities, and served as a form of resistance against their total assimilation (Haig-Brown, 1988; Knockwood and Thomas, 1992). In most schools, breaches of this rule were met with severe punishment (Haig-Brown, 1988; Knockwood and Thomas, 1992; Grant, 1996) and, in one instance, it was reported that students were punished for speaking their language by having sewing needles pushed through their tongues (Haig-Brown, 1988). Despite the risks, many students still sought out unsupervised spaces where they could speak their indigenous languages (Haig-Brown, 1988; Johnston, 1988; Knockwood and Thomas, 1992); however, not all students were able to retain their language skills and many former students no longer have the skills to communicate in the language of their Nation.

Chapter 5

Many former students report being continually hungry while at the schools. Stealing food represented a response to both the poor quality and limited quantity of food served to them (Haig-Brown, 1988; Johnston, 1988; Knockwood and Thomas, 1992; Grant, 1996). One former student stated that hunger was so pervasive at the St. Peters Claver boys school (Spanish) that the words "I'm full" were not a part of the student vocabulary (Haig-Brown, 1988).

Resistance to the strict rules and regimentation at the schools took many forms, with some having a more serious outcome than others. Common forms of resistance included sneaking outside of school dormitories (Haig-Brown, 1988), communicating with members of the opposite sex (Haig-Brown, 1988; Knockwood and Thomas, 1992; Grant, 1996) and refusing to cry during punishment (Haig- Brown, 1988; Johnston, 1988; Knockwood and Thomas, 1992; Feehan, 1996). Other forms of resistance that resulted in more serious outcomes were the burning down of school buildings (Knockwood and Thomas, 1992) and attempts (sometime successful) at suicide (Haig-Brown, 1988).

An extreme example of students trying to resist or escape their circumstances occurred in 1920 when nine boys at the Williams Lake Indian Residential School in British Columbia made a suicide pact with one another. Each boy consumed poisonous water hemlock, resulting in the death of one of the boys. Despite resounding evidence supporting the claim that the boys had planned and attempted suicide together, a federal government investigation concluded that the boy's death was accidental. Student testimony uncovered a disturbing tale of abuse and neglect, which supported the belief of some that the boys attempted suicide as a way to escape the horrible conditions in which they were forced to live and learn (Furniss, 1992; Milloy, 1999).

Parents and Communities

> Our parents too were quite powerless in those times. They did not wish us to go to boarding school but they were threatened by the law if they didn't comply; we were all victims (cited in Deiter, 1999:64).

Traditional First Nation communities were structured around the family, with the extended family being of particular importance. In the pre-residential school era, the extended family played a prominent role in child-rearing (Haig-Brown, 1988; Bull, 1991; Ing, 1991; Grant 1996), which contrasted greatly with the emphasis on the nuclear family found in the settler society. Government officials, including local Indian agents, generally failed to understand the role of the extended family and the community in the rearing of children, which lead them also to misunderstand the role of biological parents. Breaking up Aboriginal families by placing children in residential schools removed the traditional role for child-rearing from the community and placed it in the hands of the church and the government. Changes in the social structure of indigenous communities, bereft of their children, occurred, in some instances, shortly after the children were taken away and, again, as the students returned to their communities. For example, a central and drastic change occurred in parenting practices between those traditionally used in the community and those of former students who brought home differing values they learned at the schools (Ing, 1991). This is illustrated in an account by a former student, when contrasting the treatment of children at home and in the schools: "The priests taught us to respect them by whipping us, [while] our mothers and fathers, aunts and uncles and grandparents, failed to represent themselves

Chapter 5

as a threat, when that was the only thing we had been taught to understand" (Manuel and Posluns, 1974:67 in Milloy, 1999:43).

Removal of Aboriginal children from their homes led, in some instances, to increased levels of alcohol consumption by parents (Haig-Brown, 1988; Feehan, 1995). Haig-Brown (1988) argues that increased alcohol consumption by many parents may have been the result of them feeling they were no longer needed by their children, or parents feeling that their children blamed them for being sent to the schools. Haig-Brown found that, among many families she spoke with whose children had been taken to a residential school, alcohol had become a major problem after the children were removed. She argues that alcohol was used by parents to cope with feelings of guilt and worthlessness, and to deal with their continued oppression at the hands of the colonialist society.

Initially, many Aboriginal parents were enthusiastic about their children having the opportunity to receive the "white man's" education (Miller, 1987; 1996; Knockwood and Thomas, 1992; Armitage, 1995; Grant, 1996; Graham, 1997; Milloy, 1999). Enthusiasm quickly waned, however, as parents became increasingly disappointed with the lack of academic progress by their children while at the schools. Many parents voiced concern directly to the schools and to the Department of Indian Affairs, questioning why their children were spending the majority of the year at the schools and yet were still unable to read and write in the colonialist language (Milloy, 1999). Several other issues also alarmed parents: specifically, the frequency at which their children were running away from the schools; rumours of starvation, overwork and abuse; and the alarmingly high mortality rates among the students (Furniss, 1992; Kelm, 1996; Miller, 1996; Milloy, 1999). At the extreme, some Aboriginal families and communities were forced to helplessly watch the transformation of generations of innocent children into victims of severe sexual, physical and emotional abuse (Milloy, 1999).

Due to the significant amount of power the colonialist government had over Aboriginal people, there was very little parents could do to prevent their children from being taken away to the schools. However, many Aboriginal parents across Canada tried to withhold their children from going to the schools, which was met with little sympathy by the government and churches involved. In most cases, withholding children meant that sanctions, penalties and sometimes violence were meted out against the parents (Deiter, 1999; Furniss, 1992; Grant, 1996; Miller, 1996; Milloy, 1999). Some parents were even imprisoned for their resistance (Grant, 1996; Miller, 1996; Milloy, 1999). Once their children were at the schools, some Aboriginal parents wrote letters to school principals and officials within the government asking to have their children released from the schools or, at least, that the conditions of the schools be closely monitored to ensure the safety and health of their children (Grant, 1996; Kelm, 1996; Miller, 1996; Milloy, 1999). Some parents directly confronted school staff about problems their children were having at the school, while others sent traditional foods to their children in an attempt to combat disease and illness they associated with the poor school diet (Haig-Brown, 1988; Furniss, 1992; Knockwood and Thomas, 1992; Grant, 1996; Kelm, 1996; Miller, 1996; Milloy, 1999). In general, the efforts of Aboriginal parents made little difference. Furthermore, the loss of their children came at a time when many communities were simultaneously experiencing severe social and health problems, such as famine and accelerated social and economic dissolution (Miller, 1996). This greatly added to the inability of Aboriginal parents and communities to resist the removal of their children to the schools.

Chapter 5

At the peak of the residential school system, roughly seventy-five per cent of First Nations children, as well as a significant number of Métis and Inuit children, between the ages of six to fifteen, were attending a residential school (Fournier and Crey, 1997; Armitage, 1995). Children were at the schools for approximately ten months out of the year and many were sent to schools located far from their communities. This made it very difficult for families to visit their children, leaving the primary mode of communication between parents and children to be letter-writing. In many schools, staff read letters sent to parents by students to ensure that complaints about the quality of care and education they were receiving were not brought to the attention of parents (Haig-Brown, 1988; Miller, 1996; Milloy, 1999). However, letter writing was not an available option for many families, meaning there was minimal communication between parents and their children during the school year.

In the final years of the residential school system, the schools functioned mainly as welfare institutions rather than places of academic learning. As early as 1947, the Canadian Welfare Council and the Canadian Association of Social Workers argued that Aboriginal children who were 'neglected' by their parents lacked the protection afforded to non-Aboriginal children under social legislation (Fournier and Crey, 1997). Schools, in many instances, became part of the expanding federal-provincial welfare system, housing children who were removed from their families because of 'neglect.' Neglect was based upon non-Aboriginal values and social factors contributing to neglect of children were commonly identified by Indian agents and social workers as alcoholism, 'illegitimacy,' 'excessive procreation' and poverty (Milloy, 1999). Unlike welfare strategies in non-Aboriginal communities that sought to improve care within the family, including prevention family counselling services, Aboriginal families were given no assistance to improve their circumstances and maintain custody over their children. In this way, the residential school system set the stage for the large scale apprehension of Aboriginal children under welfare reforms in subsequent decades. Once again, many Aboriginal communities were left bereft of their children at the hands of the government.

Assault on Aboriginal Identity and Cultures

The institutional violence and sexual abuse that was pervasive throughout the history of the residential school system has been linked to much of the current discord in Aboriginal communities. Often overlooked and minimized by the courts and the Canadian state is the overwhelming assault on Aboriginal identity and culture that students were forced to endure while at the schools. Some scholars have concluded that this attack was so severe at residential schools that it should more appropriately be examined as a form of cultural genocide (Haig-Brown, 1988; Grant, 1996; Chrisjohn and Young, 1997). The most profound examples are those pertaining to attacks on overt expressions of Aboriginal identity and culture. Indigenous languages, for example, were the focal point of the federal government's assault as they were perceived to be an example of 'cultural backwardness' and, within the residential school system, speaking one's indigenous language represented one of the most punishable offenses for students (Miller, 1987; 1996; Haig-Brown, 1988; Johnston, 1988; Bull, 1991; Ing, 1991; Knockwood and Thomas, 1992; Feehan, 1996; Grant, 1996; Fournier and Crey, 1997; Graham, 1997; Milloy, 1999; Colmant, 2000; Johansen, 2000).

The intense suppression of indigenous languages and cultures at residential schools resulted in several generations of Aboriginal people being unable to speak and/or understand their indigenous language (Haig-Brown, 1988; Ing, 1991; Knockwood and Thomas, 1992; Feehan, 1996; Grant, 1996; Fournier and Crey, 1997; Graham, 1997). Many parents, themselves the product of the residential school system, refused to teach their children their indigenous language as they were conditioned to believe that 'speaking' and 'being' 'Indian' was something to be ashamed of and to be punished for (Haig-Brown, 1988; Ing, 1991; Knockwood and Thomas, 1992; Feehan, 1996; Grant, 1996).

The inability to communicate in an indigenous language created an immediate communication gap between Aboriginal elders and youth. This gap greatly diminished the chance for Aboriginal children to gain respect for their elders, their language and their culture, and often lead to a rejection on the part of younger generations of all things Aboriginal (Ing, 1991). Many former students internalized the inferiority and shame they associated with being Aboriginal, which was then passed on to subsequent generations. The inability to understand their indigenous language and participate in cultural practices often meant students were caught between two cultures, unable to fit comfortably into either. The practical skills they were taught at residential schools prepared them for little more than menial jobs in a world that was not ready to accept them as equals.

Despite government rhetoric, residential school education did not prepare Aboriginal children to live equally with their non-Aboriginal counterparts, but, instead, the schools provided education and skills that would ensure they remained subservient.[19]

The practice of removing Aboriginal children from their families undermined the traditional role of the extended family and kinship networks in many Aboriginal communities. Fournier and Crey argue that it also served to eliminate traditional cultural sanctions against physical and sexual abuse. They write:

> Sexual abuse was not unknown historically in [A]boriginal societies. But the consensus among First Nations in BC, as reported by an [A]boriginal panel that travelled around the province in 1992 reviewing social legislation, is that traditional sanctions, laws and the clanship system among disparate First Nations did much to eliminate or control it. Because the laws "were motivated by internalized acceptance rather than external coercion", authors Evan Jacob of the Kwakiutl Nation and Haida [E]lder Lavina Lightbown conclude in the panel's report, "they were much more binding on each individual" (Fournier and Crey, 1997:117).

Conclusion

The first-hand accounts by former students about their experiences at residential schools are, on the one hand, heart-wrenching because they are accounts about children being subjected to severe acts of violence against their Aboriginal identity and against their physical, psychological, emotional and spiritual well-being.

---

[19]   An example of this is given by the practice of placing female graduates of the schools in the homes of non- Aboriginal families to act as trained housekeepers.

Chapter 5

On the other hand, they are accounts that bring forth both disbelief and disgust, as they tell of such a severe degree of systemic violence meted against innocent children, their families and communities by government authorities and the churches they commissioned, to care and keep safe the children who attended the schools. A review of the historical literature clearly indicates that Aboriginal people suffered greatly because of the residential school system. Widespread abuse at the schools, in its various forms, took an individual and collective toll on the health and well-being of large numbers of Aboriginal people. It should be noted that the resilience of former students and their communities has been quite remarkable in light of this experience and despite the toll it took.

In relationship to the intergenerational links to substance abuse and pregnancy, and fetal alcohol syndrome and other alcohol-related birth defects, it is clear that the residential school system contributed to the central risk factor involved, substance abuse, but also to factors shown to be linked to alcohol abuse, such as child and adult physical, emotional and sexual abuse, mental health problems and family dysfunction. The impact of residential schools can also be linked to risk factors for poor pregnancy outcomes among women who abuse alcohol, such as poor overall health, poor education, and chronic poverty. These issues will be discussed in more detail in the following chapter dealing with the contemporary health and social issues linked to the residential school system.

Chapter 6

Contemporary Health and Social Issues Linked to the Residential School System

Introduction

A central goal of this report is to examine whether links exist between the experience of Aboriginal people who attended residential schools and current rates of fetal alcohol syndrome (FAS) and alcohol related birth effects (ARBEs) found among Aboriginal people in Canada. This exercise is embedded in what Constance Deiter calls an 'intergenerational experience.' Deiter argues that, for the majority of First Nations people living in Canada, the residential school experience extends through four or five generations:

> Because so many generations attended residential schools they have affected all First Nations individuals. For example, even though I was raised in the city, all my family members, including my parents, my grandparents, uncles, and aunts on both sides of the family attended these schools. Most of my friends also attended the schools, including my husband and cousins. As well, all of the people whom my parents associated with during my formative years were residential school [S]urvivors. To say that the school experience did not directly affect my life would be a denial (1999:23).

To understand how the experience of Aboriginal people who attended residential schools is linked to FAS/ARBEs in subsequent generations, requires not only an examination of the experience of individuals, but also an examination of what Joseph Couture (1994) calls the 'communal self'. As a psychologist and an Aboriginal person, Couture has been concerned with the impact of collective traumatic events and experiences on whole communities, and in their response as a community, both negative and positive, to those events. He writes: "Because of acculturation pressures, Aboriginal communities present, in many cases, a damaged collective self, reverberating through community and its component families" (Couture, 1994:15). Similarly, Waldram argues that "many Aboriginal people and societies have experienced a kind of trauma, in some cases for generations, which has had profound consequences for both individual and collective behaviors. This is a trauma that flows from colonialism and oppression" (1997:97).

Despite extensive and systematic assaults by colonialist forces on the identity and cultures of Aboriginal people, many individuals found ways in which to survive and resist against these assaults. For example, in a qualitative study involving twelve women who were former students of residential schools, Noël and Tassé (2001) found common themes of resilience and survival that wove their way through the women's accounts of their experience. Resilience, Noël and Tassé write, is a person's capacity to resist the violent, destabilizing or annihilating effects of a traumatic experience. This, they argue, is acquired in childhood; survival strategies are all the means used to survive and resist the destructive effects of institutional violence on one's personal and cultural integrity. Noël and Tassé write:

> In the face of the violence that was directed towards them, we find small girls who were terrorized and women who suffered. The residential school was a prison whose walls closed in on their Aboriginal identity. The residential school was the monster who deprived them of affection, who wounded them, crushed them and punished them for being who they were. They thought and behaved as a result of the emotional and cultural [experiences] that they inherited from the most significant people in their early

childhood [prior to entering the schools]. This ... was like "the house", the tent, cabin or shelter that they carried inside of them and that many of them drew or built during play in order to remember loved ones, places where they belonged and places where they were safe. Much later, in the hopes of reconstructing their identities, they would reclaim those elements that had been banned, forgotten or erased from Aboriginal culture and history with conviction. Spiritually for one, legends for another, the language and creation stories (Noël and Tassé, 2001:6).

For these twelve women, as for many former students, "liberating their present and their children's future from the legacy of the institutional violence remains an on-going daily struggle" (Noël and Tassé, 2001:5).

The following chapter will review some of the current literature that discusses the health and social impacts of residential schooling on former students and subsequent generations of Aboriginal people in Canada. As with the earlier discussion on alcohol use (see Chapter Three), this chapter will be framed within a broader context that situates intergenerational impacts of residential schools alongside other factors influencing current health and social issues affecting Aboriginal people. Several key areas will be covered, including the general health of Aboriginal people, mental health problems, violence, education, family dysfunction and crime and incarceration.

This will set the stage for a discussion of fetal alcohol syndrome (FAS) and other alcohol-related birth effects (ARBEs) later in the report, including a discussion of the links between FAS/ARBEs and residential schools. The key areas that will be discussed have all been identified as important health and social issues relating to pregnant women who abuse substances, and/or related to persons with FAS/ARBEs, particularly the occurrence of *secondary disabilities* that are the outcome of interplay between *primary disabilities* (functional deficits that reflect central nervous dysfunction inherent in FAS/ARBEs) with environmental *risk factors* (Streissguth et al., 1997).

General Poor Health

Aboriginal people have long been considered to be the most disadvantaged group in Canada and, as a result, they share an increased burden of physical disease (Waldram, Herring and Kue Young, 1995). MacMillan and colleagues point out that an increased burden of physical disease is linked to unfavourable economic and social conditions that are inextricably linked to Aboriginal people's history of oppression (MacMillan, MacMillan et al., 1996; Waldram, Herring and Kue Young, 1995).

Kelm (1998) attributes the residential school system with being partially responsible for the general poor health among Aboriginal people today. She writes:

> The bodies of Aboriginal children were indeed transformed by the residential school experience. But the residential schools did not produce robust workers, as they had promised, but rather weakened children and adolescents. Waves of communicable

disease and endemic tuberculosis found easy prey among the overworked, underfed, and abused students. 'Graduates' frequently convocated not to the waiting world of agricultural labour, but to the sanatorium, the hospital, and the grave.

Those who survived the experience did so embodying competing and contradictory notions of their physical selves. For some, reintegration into their home communities allowed former students to find strength and achieve wellness once again; others, however, would be deeply scarred. The physical impact of residential schooling, the high morbidity and mortality rates of the schools, has never been a secret but remained obscured even in our most recent discussions of residential schooling (1998:80).

As the physical health of many residential school students became compromised while attending the schools, so too was the health of many Aboriginal people living in home communities. The Royal Commission on Aboriginal Peoples (1996b) points out that the low point for Aboriginal health and social conditions in Canada came in the early years of the twentieth century when many First Nations, Inuit and Métis communities were plagued with continuing epidemics. This heavy disease load was accompanied by widespread poverty, including a lack of food; inadequate and inappropriate medical services; and the marginalization and devaluation by mainstream western medicine of Aboriginal healing skills and knowledge of herbal medicines and other traditional treatments. Even though improvements in the health of Aboriginal people has occurred since the early part of the twentieth century, life expectancy rates for Aboriginal men and women remain significantly lower than for their non-Aboriginal counterparts. The Royal Commission on Aboriginal Peoples concluded that "despite the extension of medical and social services (in some form) to every Aboriginal community, and despite the large sums spent by Canadian governments to provide these services, Aboriginal people still suffer from unacceptable rates of illness and distress. The term 'crisis' is not an exaggeration here"[20] (1996b:119).

In a review of Aboriginal health literature, MacMillan and colleagues (1996) confirmed that Aboriginal people were generally at greater risk of physical disease. For example, infant mortality rates were still approximately twice as high (13.8-16.3/1000) as they were for Canadians (7.3/1000). Most of the difference in the infant mortality rate on First Nations communities were due to post-neonatal causes of death, including infectious diseases, respiratory illness, sudden infant death syndrome (SIDS) and injuries (MacMillan, MacMillan et al., 1996; Waldram, Herring and Kue Young, 1995). Aboriginal children also had higher rates of death from injuries than all children in Canada (MacMillan, MacMillan et al., 1996). The mortality rate among Aboriginal adults was higher than among the general population, with an increased risk of death among both men and women from alcoholism (including cirrhosis of the liver), homicide, suicide and pneumonia. The leading cause of death between 1986 and 1988 was injury and poisoning, which accounted for 31.2% of deaths in the Aboriginal population and only 7.5% of deaths among all Canadians (MacMillan, MacMillan et al., 1996). These figures have remained relatively unchanged, specifically among certain sub-groups.

---

[20]   It should be noted that different Aboriginal groups have different relationships with the federal and provincial governments in relation to health care services; for example non-status vs. status Indians, urban vs. reserve communities. While these specific details are important, it is beyond the scope of this report to go into specific detail here. For a more indepth discussion and analysis see Waldram, Herring and Kue Young, 1995 and Royal Commission on Aboriginal Peoples, 1996b, for example.

Chapter 6

Infectious diseases, such as tuberculosis, continue to be a serious health problem among some Aboriginal groups. Hepatitis A and B, gastroenteritis, meningitis and gonorrhea are reported as being above general averages in specific sub-groups (MacMillan, MacMillan et al., 1996). HIV/AIDS has also been identified as a growing concern (Waldram, Herring and Kue Young, 1995; Royal Commission on Aboriginal Peoples, 1996b). Aboriginal children and adults also suffer an increased frequency of acute respiratory infections compared to their non-Aboriginal counterparts (MacMillan, MacMillan et al., 1996).

The Aboriginal Peoples Survey found that thirty-one per cent of the Aboriginal population, fifteen years of age and older, had been informed by health care professionals that they had a chronic health problem (1991 in MacMillan, MacMillan et al., 1996). Illnesses, such as diabetes, end-stage renal disease, cardiovascular disease and specific cancers, occur at higher rates among Aboriginal people generally; however, the information is limited in terms of specific populations and regions that may be at higher risk (MacMillan, MacMillan et al., 1996).

Obesity has become a major problem among some Aboriginal groups. For example, in a study that surveyed 704 Cree and Ojibwa adults in northwestern Ontario and Northern Manitoba, almost ninety per cent of the women between 45 and 54 years of age had a body mass index in the overweight or obese range (Young and Sevenhuysen, 1989 in MacMillan, MacMillan et al., 1996). Rates of disabilities are also more than twice the national average and, among young adults, is almost three times as high (Royal Commission on Aboriginal Peoples, 1996b).

Some of the risk factors for disease and disability include: nutritional problems, specifically iron deficiency and low intake of vitamin D among pregnant Aboriginal women and infants; genetic factors; poverty and over-crowding; and environmental pollutants, such as tobacco smoke and wood smoke. Decreased access to health care services due to geographical isolation and a shortage of personnel trained to meet the needs of local Aboriginal groups also increase mortality and morbidity risks (MacMillan, MacMillan et al., 1996). MacMillan and colleagues also point out that almost thirty to fifty per cent of Aboriginal communities are in remote regions, many accessible only by air. This contributes to gaps in, and barriers to, services for these populations.

Poverty is a serious risk factor, including: poor housing; inadequate clean water supplies and waste disposal; and shortage of food (MacMillan, MacMillan et al., 1996; Royal Commission on Aboriginal Peoples, 1996b; Waldram, Herring and Kue Young, 1995). Environmental contaminants, particularly exposure to heavy metals (such as mercury) and to organic chemicals (such as polychlorinated biphenyls (PCBs)), are of particular threat to those who follow a traditional lifestyle (MacMillan, MacMillan et al., 1996).

Chapter 6

Mental Health Problems[21]

> In retrospect, the legacy of the residential schools can be seen on every street corner in Canada. There are thousands of once-proud native people who have been reduced to drunken shells by their experiences in those institutions. Too many, including my friends, have suffered an ignominious death because of it. My own dad and brother were sexually abused in residential school, and they both suffer incredible humiliation over it. Our parents suffered violent abuse from the priests and nuns who were entrusted with young bodies and souls and they in turn passed on this learned behaviour to us. It is not natural for native people to abuse their children. All of may Dad's friends are dead, mostly from alcohol-related disease. Those with whom I went to boarding school who are still living are almost all alcoholics, to mask their shame. My best friend, Ernie was shot to death by a drunken native for whom he was babysitting. My aunt who administered the vicious whipping to me is still alive, but mean as ever, and a typical dysfunctional Indian (Dickson, 1993 as cited in Miller, 1996:439).

Epidemiological studies suggest that high levels of mental health problems exist in many Aboriginal communities in Canada (Kirmayer, Brass and Tait, 2000; Waldram, Herring and Kue Young, 1995; Kirmayer, 1994; Kirmayer, Gill, Fletcher, Ternar, Boothroyd et al., 1993; Royal Commission on Aboriginal Peoples, 1995). Kirmayer and colleagues state: "The high rates of suicide, alcoholism, and violence, and the pervasive demoralization seen in Aboriginal communities, can be readily understood as the direct consequences of a history of dislocations and the disruption of traditional subsistence patterns and connection to the land" (2000:609). They suggest that mental health problems found among Aboriginal groups are best understood within a framework that examines the social origins of disease. This would include the acknowledgement of the rapid social and cultural changes that occurred, which have "challenged Aboriginal identity and resulted in dramatic generation gaps between youth, adults, and elders" (Kirmayer, Brass and Tait, 2000:613).

An important variable in the examination of mental health and wellness is the residential school system. Attempts to assimilate Aboriginal people through this system led to many disruptive and traumatic experiences, including the abrupt separation of children from their families, multiple losses, deprivation, brutality and a break in the transmission of Aboriginal traditions and identity (Kirmayer, Brass and Tait, 2000). For example, Milloy (1999) contends that the strict regimentation that characterized residential school education produced many individuals who were incapable of leading an independent life within their own communities or in the dominant society.

Participants in a study by Feehan (1995) attributed their inability to express emotions back to their days as residential school students where, as a form of resistance, they refused to show emotion. Similar accounts were given to Haig-Brown (1988) in her work with former students of the Kamloops Indian

---

[21]   The concept of mental health, in many instances, is foreign to Aboriginal understandings of health. Many Aboriginal people believe that physical, emotional, spiritual and environmental health are all essential aspects of well-being. When they are in balance, health and wellness prevail (Royal Commission on Aboriginal Peoples, 1996b). The term 'mental health' is used here mainly for organizational reasons and, as is shown in the discussion, is inter-connected to all aspects of well-being identified in Aboriginal understandings.

Chapter 6

Residential School in British Columbia. Personal testimonies given by former students at the Mohawk Institute and Mount Elgin School in Ontario express how former students felt they have been left culturally and emotionally impoverished because of their experience (Graham, 1997). Many former students have reported feeling unable to express positive emotions and, as a result, have been unable to have functional adult relationships with companions or family members (Royal Commission on Aboriginal Peoples, 1996b).

An American study suggests variance in responses of former students may be attributed partially to the age at which children were apprehended. For example, the separation of a child from his or her parents can cause damage, depending on the child's age and the length of time of separation. Serious effects involving children ranging in age from five to eight can include emotional symptoms that may or may not be irreversible. For adolescents, on the other hand, there appears to be no serious irreversible damage as the result of their being separated from their parents (Colmant, 2000).

In 1991, shortly after the First Conference on Native Residential Schools, the term *Residential School Syndrome* (RSS), appeared as a potential diagnostic category and implied that former students shared a cluster of symptoms uniquely recognizable as a syndrome. RSS never gained much prominence and the suggestion that such a syndrome existed resulted in fierce criticism from Aboriginal and non-Aboriginal scholars, particularly Roland Chrisjohn (Chrisjohn and Young, 1997). A report produced by the Cariboo Tribal Council (CTC) (1991), also questioned the reasoning behind and implications of reifying the experience of former students. Both the CTC and Chrisjohn condemned the diagnosis, arguing that, by making a group's suffering a pathology, serves to deflect attention from the genocidal nature of residential schooling, the immorality of forced religious indoctrination and the paternalism that informed the system (Cariboo Tribal Council, 1991; Chrisjohn and Young, 1997). Chrisjohn and Young (1997) argue that the experience of students were varied and, even if physically and philosophically they were coherent, there is no basis to expect uniformity in their response to this experience.

A number of inter-relating risk factors for mental distress and mental health problems currently found among some Aboriginal groups, such as high incidences of physical and sexual abuse, suicide, psychiatric problems, family breakdown and alcoholism, have been linked to the experience of former residential school students (Haig-Brown, 1988; Bull, 1991; Knockwood and Thomas, 1992; Feehan, 1996; Grant, 1996; Fournier and Crey, 1997; Colmant, 2000). Studies among former American Indian boarding school students have made similar links (Colmant, 2000). For example, Inventory and colleagues reported that the poor quality of boarding schools, including their impersonality and sterility, lack of qualified staff, cultural discontinuities and attacks on American Indian identity, contributed to personality disorders in former students (1966 in Colmant, 2000). Berlin found that the poor conditions at boarding schools contributed to alarmingly high suicide and school drop-out rates among the children (1987 in Colmant, 2000). It was also reported that separation of children from families in kinship dominated American Indian cultures contributed to high incidences of psychosomatic symptoms among students (Colmant, 2000).

Chapter 6

Few epidemiological studies exist that examined the prevalence of psychiatric disorders among Aboriginal people in Canada. The studies that do exist are usually based on service utilization records; however, Kirmayer and colleagues (2000) point out that relying on service utilization records may under-represent true prevalence of distress in a community as many Aboriginal people never access mental health services for treatment. Studies that do exist suggest rates of psychiatric disorders vary, with some levels comparable to those found in the general population and other levels possibly as high as twice those of neighbouring non-Aboriginal communities (Kirmayer, Brass and Tait, 2000).

Mental disorders, such as depression, anxiety and post-traumatic stress disorder (PTSD), are the most common mental disorders found in Aboriginal communities and, in some communities, are endemic (Kirmayer, Brass and Tait, 2000). While psychotic disorders are less common, these disorders make distinct demands on small, remote communities. However, small communities may be "more tolerant and less stigmatizing of some forms of unusual behaviour in individuals who are well known and intimately related to many members of the community" (Kirmayer, Brass and Tait, 2000:611). Few studies exist on the mental health of Aboriginal children; however, there is clear evidence of high rates of problems, including suicide and substance abuse, among adolescents in many communities (Kirmayer, Brass and Tait, 2000; Gotowiec and Beiser, 1994; Beiser and Attneave, 1982). To date, there is no comprehensive study directly linking the residential school experience to high rates of suicide in some Aboriginal communities. However, authors such as Haig-Brown (1988), Furniss (1992), Fournier and Crey (1997), Milloy (1999), Johansen (2000) and Piatote (2000) have all suggested the existence of a relationship.

Alcohol abuse, as discussed earlier in this report, remains a serious health and social problem for some Aboriginal groups. Urban Aboriginal people may be at particular risk, as growing numbers of Aboriginal people migrate to urban centres. For example, a study by Jacobs and Gill (2002) among an urban Aboriginal population in Montreal, the majority of whom were single young Inuit women, found that fully one-third of the sample reported having a current drug or alcohol problem, and a large proportion (85%) experienced medical problems in the year proceeding the interview. Interestingly, those who abused substances were found to be less likely than non-abusers to have the proper identification needed to access medical and social services. Jacobs and Gill write:

> Comparisons between substance abusers and non-abusers revealed that abusers were more likely to live with someone who had a drug or alcohol problems. More substance abusers also reported having had problems getting along with their friends and non-abusers. There were very high levels of parental problems with drugs and alcohol within the sample. The rate of maternal history of drug and alcohol problems among substance abusers was significantly higher (73.7%) than non-abusers (36.7%). No data were collected in the present study to address the issue of whether subjects had been exposed to alcohol in-utero, potentially resulting in FAS (fetal alcohol syndrome) or FAE (fetal alcohol effects). The history of maternal substance use may be related to the

low rate of close relationships with mothers reported by substance abusers. In general, substance abusers rated counselling for their family and social problems as extremely important (2002:11).

Jacobs and Gill add that inner-city urban Native substance abuse can be seen as a 'career or lifestyle,' as dependence rapidly becomes a "lifestyle and social networks of substance abusers become part of a survival strategy for navigating life in the city" (2002:11). The strengths of these social relationships may result in some individuals being resistant to even culturally-relevant treatment programs. Jacobs and Gill point out that data on the prevalence of substance abuse among urban Aboriginal people, as compared to those on reserves or to the general urban population, are not available and, therefore, further research is needed to fully understand risk and protective factors for Aboriginal people living in urban settings.

Former residential school students have been identified as a sub-group that have experienced high rates of alcohol abuse as adults, although no national statistics exist. However, as with other health and social problems, significant improvements have been made, particularly where Aboriginal people have had the opportunity to design and control addiction services targeted for their people (Royal Commission on Aboriginal Peoples, 1996b). Holistic approaches to alcohol and drug treatment used in Aboriginal addiction services highlight the importance of addressing a person's addiction within a broader *wellness* framework, rather than focusing solely on the addiction. Despite the success of many Aboriginal treatment programs, substance abuse remains a central health and wellness issue, particularly among the youth population and is linked to other psycho-social problems, such as suicide, child abuse and family dysfunction. Fournier and Crey (1997) argue that, for most Aboriginal communities, alcoholism is the first hurtle to overcome before other reforms can be accomplished. However, testimony given by Aboriginal addiction workers and others to the Royal Commission on Aboriginal Peoples suggest that "the establishment of comprehensive mental health services encompassing a full range of psycho-social distress presented by the clients of addictions services, with flexible funding to match" (Royal Commission on Aboriginal Peoples, 1996b:162) is what communities need to fully address their mental illness, including addiction needs.

A growing body of research literature suggests that the level of mental health problems, as well as other factors such as levels of family dysfunction, violence and crime are directly linked to social factors. For example, rates of alcohol and drug abuse have been directly related to factors, such as low income, rate of employment, northern isolation, amount of tourism, size of households and level of industrial activity (MacMillan, MacMillan et al., 1996; Adrian, Layne and Williams, 1990). Adrian and colleagues (1990) suggest that improvements in economic circumstances have shown to reduce alcohol consumption Others, such as Chandler and Lalonde (1998), have identified clear links between high levels of community control or autonomy and lower suicide rates in Aboriginal communities in British Columbia. Kirmayer and colleagues (2000) argue that community development and local control of health care systems are important factors in the improvement of mental health. This, they suggest, is important "not only to make services responsive to local needs but also to promote the sense of individual and collective efficacy and pride that contribute to positive mental health. Ultimately, political efforts to restore Aboriginal rights, settle land claims and redistribute power through various forms of self-government hold the keys to healthy communities" (Kirmayer, Brass and Tait, 2000:614; Warry, 1998).

Chapter 6

Child Welfare, Parenting and Family Dysfunction

The most terrible result of my residential school experience was they took away my ability to hold my children. They took that from me, the ability to hold my children (cited in Deiter, 1999:11).

Most of our clients-probably 90 per cent of them-are, in fact, victims themselves of the child welfare system. Most of our clients are young, sole support mothers who very often were removed as children themselves. So we are dealing with perhaps the end product of the child welfare system that was apparent in the sixties scoop. Actually the sixties scoop lasted well into the '70s and we are seeing the reality of that on our case loads ... We take the approach in our agency that it is time to break that cycle. The other interesting note is that while the mother may have been in foster care the grandmother- I think we all know where she was. She was in residential school. So we are into a third generation (cited in Royal Commission on Aboriginal Peoples, 1996b:34-35). [22]

Since early contact with Europeans, Aboriginal families in Canada have:

... been at the centre of a historical struggle between colonial governments on [the] one hand, which set out deliberately to eradicate the culture, language and world view of the First Nations, Métis and Inuit children over whom they assumed control, and Aboriginal parents on the other hand, who believe wholeheartedly that they have a sacred responsibility to maintain balance in the world for their children and others not yet born (Royal Commission on Aboriginal Peoples, 1996b:22).

The residential school system was a central tool of the colonialist government to achieve their goals, however, their assault did not end with the closure of the last school. Removal of Aboriginal children from their parents has continued to present day, with Aboriginal children being over-represented throughout Canada in child welfare systems (Tait, 2003). At the centre of this issue are Aboriginal parents, particularly mothers, who are deemed by welfare agencies to be unable to 'adequately,' care for their children.

Authors, such as Fournier and Crey (1997), suggest that links exist between the negative impact of residential schools and the inability of some Aboriginal parents to adequately care for their children. Events occurring in Canada between child welfare services and Aboriginal communities during the 1960s and 1970s strongly support this argument (Tait, 2003). During the 1960s and 1970s, in what has become known as the 'sixties scoop,' large numbers of Aboriginal children were removed from their homes and placed in non-Aboriginal foster care homes or adopted out to non-Aboriginal families. While this represents a complex series of events, it also represents a change in the way the government justified removing Aboriginal children from the care of their parents or traditional guardians. During the period of the residential school system, assimilation of Aboriginal people was the motivation behind the removal

---

[22]   Testimony given by Executive Director, Native Child and Family Services of Toronto.

Chapter 6

of Aboriginal children and education was the official reason given by government authorities. Aboriginal women, during this period, were not seen as 'unacceptable' mothers, only as incapable of 'educating' and passing on 'proper' European values to their children. During the 'sixties scoop,' Aboriginal mothers (including grandmothers and aunts who were looking after children) were now judged by the 'factual' criteria laid out by provincial child welfare services (Tait, 2003), which drastically changed the way Aboriginal women were evaluated as 'acceptable' mothers (Fournier and Crey, 1997).

As early as 1947, the Canadian Welfare Council and the Canadian Association of Social Workers argued that Indian children who were 'neglected' by their parents lacked the protection afforded to non- Aboriginal children under social legislation (Fournier and Crey, 1997). They condemned both the internment of any Aboriginal child, neglected or not, in residential schools, as well as traditional foster and adoption practices that existed in Aboriginal communities. In 1951, an amendment was made to the *Indian Act,* which stipulated that all laws of general application in force in a province should also apply on reserves unless they conflicted with treaties or federal laws (Fournier and Crey, 1997). Furthermore, the government effectively handed over the responsibility of Aboriginal health, welfare and educational services to the provinces, although it remained financially responsible for status Indians. In this agreement, the provinces were guaranteed payment by Ottawa for each Indian child they made a legal ward of the state. Statistics show that, in 1959, only one per cent of the children who were legal wards of the state were Aboriginal children, a figure that jumped to somewhere between thirty to forty per cent by the end of the 1960s (Fournier and Crey, 1997; MacDonald, 1995).

During the 1960s, child and welfare services focused, in general, on the prevention of 'child neglect,' which placed emphasis on the moral attributes of individual parents, especially mothers, and on enforcing and improving care of children *within* the family (Swift, 1991). However, 'neglect,' in the case of Aboriginal families, was mainly linked to issues of poverty and other social problems that were dealt with under what social workers referred to as 'the need for adequate care.' Improving care within the family was not prioritized and provincial child welfare policies did not include preventive family counselling services, as in the case of non-Indian families. In many situations, lack of resources, such as flush toilets, running water or a refrigerator, were grounds to make an Aboriginal child a ward of the state (Fournier and Crey, 1997). Also, so was the absence of the biological mother and the placement of her children by way of traditional fostering and adoption. The typical pattern of intervention was for non-Aboriginal social workers to apprehend children in 'severe crisis situations' and seek court-ordered committals to care, followed by placement in substitute homes off the reserve (MacDonald, 1995). Furthermore, since there were no services to facilitate family re-unification on reserves, social workers usually chose adoption or long-term foster care for Aboriginal children separated from their parents. The result was that Aboriginal children experienced much longer periods of foster care than their non-Aboriginal counterparts (MacDonald, 1995).

In retrospect, this period is viewed very differently by Aboriginal people, as compared to non-Aboriginal social workers, foster and adoptive parents, and governments. Evidence suggest that this period was not simply about concern for Aboriginal children being 'neglected' as suggested in social work literature, but rather it was a type of cultural genocide that picked up from where residential schools left off, further facilitating the systematic breakdown of Aboriginal families and social structures (Fournier and Crey, 1997). Widespread apprehension of children, besides causing a great amount of trauma and suffering to

Chapter 6

the families concerned, also posed a potential threat to the survival of First Nations communities, from which large numbers of children were removed, never to return (MacDonald, 1995). Due to critiques by Aboriginal leaders and activists, some legislative changes aimed at protecting the rights of Aboriginal families and children have occurred (Swift, 1991; MacDonald, 1995), as well as steps toward educating more Aboriginal people in social service fields.

During this same period, the image of Aboriginal women as 'bad' mothers who were deviant, neglectful and abusive, fully emerged within the child welfare service discourse. Swift (1995) writes that client files from the 1950s and 1960s show that social workers explicitly identified and spoke about Aboriginal families as being distinct. Many written comments, she states, were questionable, insinuating that people with 'decidedly Native features' were somehow *naturally* connected to histories of alcoholism and violence. This was certainly the case concerning transactions around the foster and adoption of Aboriginal children and is reflected in the statistics for this period. By the later 1970s, one in four status Indian children were separated from their parents for all or part of their childhood. When non-status Indian and Métis children are included, it can be estimated that one in three or, in some provinces every other Aboriginal child, spent part of their childhood as a ward of the state. Still, to this day in British Columbia, for example, one of every three legal wards of the state is a First Nations child (Fournier and Crey, 1997; MacDonald, 1995).

The Royal Commission on Aboriginal Peoples (1996b) points out that welfare agencies have typically spent the lion's share of their budgets on placements for Aboriginal children in foster homes, and a much smaller portion of their budgets are allocated to working with these families to prevent apprehension and improving the conditions that lead to neglect, so that children can return home. In many ways, these agencies have contributed directly or indirectly to family dysfunction among Aboriginal groups. However, beginning in 1991, the Department of Indian and Northern Affairs entered into tripartite child welfare agreements with provincial governments and tribal councils or regional groups representing First Nations (Royal Commission on Aboriginal Peoples, 1996b). It is anticipated that these agreements, which place more power in the hands of local communities and councils, will result in families being able to work with social workers and front-line support services to keep their families together.

Family dysfunction is influenced by several factors, including on-going colonialist oppression in the form of chronic poverty and unemployment, inadequate education, poor housing, over-crowding, substance abuse and violence. The Royal Commission on Aboriginal Peoples writes that "family dysfunction today is a legacy of disrupted relationships in the past, but the effects are broader and more diffuse than can be traced in a direct cause-and-effect relationship. There are entire communities whose members are imbued with a sense of violation and powerlessness, the effect of multiple violations having reverberated throughout kin networks" (1996b:36). Loss of parenting skills are an example of the disruption. Martens and colleagues write that the practice of separating children "from their parents and their way of life has had a drastic impact on almost all Indian families. The structure, cohesion and quality of life suffered. Parenting skills diminished as succeeding generations became more and more institutionalized and experienced little nurturing. Low self-esteem and self-concept problems arose as children were taught that their own culture was uncivilized" (Martens, Daily and Hodgson, 1988 in Ing, 1991:71). In light of this, many healing initiatives have begun in Aboriginal communities and in rural and urban settings. However, for many families who are experiencing problems, larger issues, such as chronic poverty and unemployment, hinder their efforts to improve the situation of their family members. Until these issues can fully be addressed in concert with healing initiatives, those communities with the greatest problems will continue to face almost insurmountable challenges to address the needs of their members.

Violence

> While family violence experienced by Aboriginal people shares many features with violence in mainstream society, it also has a distinctive face that is important to recognize as we search for understanding of causes and identify solutions. First, Aboriginal family violence is distinct in that it has invaded whole communities and cannot be considered a problem of a particular couple or an individual household. Second, the failure in family functioning can be traced in many cases to interventions of the state deliberately introduced to disrupt or displace the Aboriginal family. Third, violence within Aboriginal communities is fostered and sustained by a racist social environment that promulgates demeaning stereotypes of Aboriginal women and men and seeks to diminish their value as human beings and their right to be treated with dignity (Royal Commission on Aboriginal Peoples, 1996b:56).

Acts of violence have been identified as a serious concern for Aboriginal people. These acts can be self-inflicted or directed toward others and, in some cases, result in fatal outcomes of suicide or homicide. Rates of occurrence and the types of violent acts are intimately related to the mental health of individuals and the social health of the community (Waldram, Herring and Kue Young, 1995). Family violence, including child abuse and neglect, has received a great deal of attention in the past two decades. However, there are few national statistics demonstrating the incidence of violence or whether there has been a decrease in family violence with increased public awareness and programming to address the problem (Royal Commission on Aboriginal Peoples, 1996b). Some Aboriginal leaders have suggested that the physical, sexual and psychological abuse of children in residential schools may have produced a generation of adults who, in turn, inflict violence on their own children (Waldram, Herring and Kue Young, 1995). The residential school system has also been singled out by some authors as the origin of contemporary violence, particularly sexual abuse, in Aboriginal communities (Milloy, 1999; Fournier and Crey, 1997). However, caution needs to be taken when interpreting this type of statement, as many former students of residential schools have never inflicted violence upon their children or families. What appears to be important are a number of inter-relating factors, particularly chronic substance abuse and poverty (Waldram, Herring and Kue Young, 1995).

While there are no national statistics on the prevalence of violent acts, such as childhood sexual abuse among Aboriginal people, research has shown high rates existing in some communities. For example, a 1989 study sponsored by the Native Women's Association of the Northwest Territories found that eight out of ten girls under the age of eight were victims of sexual abuse and fifty per cent of boys the same age had been sexually molested[23] (Milloy, 1999). A study by the Ontario Native Women's Association found that eight out of ten Aboriginal women had experienced violence. Of these women,

---

[23]   The report is found in INAC Files E6575-18, Vol. 10 entitled *Communications Strategy, Child Sexual Abuse in Residential Schools,* n.d. (Milloy, 1999:298, ftn 14).

eighty-seven per cent had been injured physically and fifty-seven per cent had been sexually abused. A study among Oneida women living in the London, Ontario region, found that seventy-one per cent of the urban sample and forty-eight of the reserve sample had been assaulted by a current or former partner. Although there have been fewer studies involving Métis and Inuit women, levels of violence are believed to be high in certain sub-populations among these groups. This is supported by data from Statistics Canada's 1991 Aboriginal Peoples Survey, in which 36 to 44 per cent of Aboriginal people identified family violence as a problem and 22 to 35 per cent saw sexual abuse as a problem in their community (Royal Commission on Aboriginal Peoples, 1996b).

Importantly, the Royal Commission on Aboriginal Peoples points out that not all Aboriginal communities experience endemic violence nor are all Aboriginal people, whose lives have been touched by violence, necessarily at risk all the time. The Commission writes:

> It can be said, however, that the people who find themselves in high-risk situations are, with shocking frequency, Aboriginal people: pregnant women; children in their formative years; teenaged girls; wives who feel they have no exit from a violent home; and seniors who lack the protection of a functional family. Poverty and all its ills also have an insidious, demoralizing impact on the lives of too many Aboriginal people (1996b:64).

Aboriginal women who experience family violence may be reluctant to seek medical attention for their injuries, as they may fear negative repercussions from partners, family or members in the community (LaRocque, 1993; Jacobs and Gill, 2002). While Aboriginal women are collectively coming together at local, regional and national levels to raise awareness of family violence and violence against women, many women remain silenced by their abusers and the lack of support from those around them to come forward to report their abuse (Royal Commission on Aboriginal Peoples, 1996b).

Crime and Incarceration

In Canada, Aboriginal people appear to be disproportionately involved in crime, either as perpetrators or as victims. Crime rates, however, are not uniform across Aboriginal communities, but vary. Waldram points out that crime is a product of many factors other than simply the commission of a criminal act (1997). Within Canada, Aboriginal inmates are over-represented in the general prison population in both federal prisons and provincial jails. While Aboriginal people make up roughly three per cent of the Canadian population, they represent approximately 17.5% of all federal and provincial inmates. Furthermore, the over-representation of Aboriginal people who are incarcerated seems to be on the rise. Regional differences exist across Canada with Aboriginal inmates representing about 4% in the Quebec region to just over 44% in the Prairie region (Boe, 2000).

Studies have shown that Aboriginal inmates report a number of negative childhood experiences. For example, a study by Johnston (1996) found early drug use (60%) and alcohol abuse (58%) were reported by Aboriginal male inmates as common characteristics, as were childhood behavioural problems (57%). Other childhood experiences included: physical (45%) and sexual (21%) abuse, severe poverty (35%), parental absence (41%) and suicide attempts (21%) (Johnston, 1996 in Boe, 2000). Motiuk and Nafekh (2000) found that both Aboriginal male and female offenders, upon admission into prison, were likely to need treatment for substance abuse and for personal/emotional problems. Métis offenders in federal prisons were more likely to have previous offences, community supervision, open and secure custody as young offenders than their First Nation and Inuit/Innu counterparts. Motiuk and Nafekh add that, as a group, Aboriginal offenders are more likely to have been convicted of a serious offence, to have had extensive involvement with the criminal justice system as a youth or adult and possess some unique criminogenic needs at admission and on conditional release.

In a study of Aboriginal male inmates, Waldram (1997) found that, of 249 men, 66% reported physical violence in their families when they were growing up and 80% suggested that at least one parent (or foster/adoptive parent) had a problem with alcohol or drugs. He goes on to write:

> Familial disruption was also very common. Some 35% of the men interviewed had spent some time in foster homes, 30% in residential schools, and 5% had been adopted. Many had also spent considerable time in various group homes and youth correctional facilities. These experiences, occurring frequently or repeatedly, are significant enough in some instances to lead to a form of complex post-traumatic stress disorder ... PTSD needs to be understood as not simply traumatic memory, but also as lived experience. The DSM-IV fails to comprehend the manner in which long-term exposure to traumatic events shapes personalities, attitudes, values, and behaviors. It would seem that an individual who is exposed to prolonged terror ... is likely to develop into an anti-social being. A whole community or society which is victimized by trauma is likely to develop aberrant moral reference points for its citizens, leading to the intergenerational transmission of pathological behaviors. The experience of trauma then becomes the lived experience of a whole culture (1997:46).

Recently, fetal alcohol syndrome (FAS) and alcohol-related birth effects (ARBEs) have been identified as possible health problems occurring at high rates among prison populations in Canada (Boland, Burrill et al., 1998; 2000; Fast, Schaefer and Gilbert, 1999; Conry and Fast, 2000). Interestingly, persons with FAS/ARBEs referred to in these discussions share certain similarities in terms of behavioural problems with other Aboriginal inmates; for example, those with post-traumatic stress disorder referred to above. Because behavioural problems, particularly 'secondary disabilities' (e.g., substance abuse problems, disrupted school experience, trouble with the law, inappropriate sexual behaviour and mental health problems) associated with FAS/ARBEs are behavioural issues that are also strongly linked to other problems, such as mental distress in adults caused by past child sexual abuse, caution needs to be taken when interpreting the strength of the methodology and conclusions drawn by these recent reports. This point will be further detailed in the discussion of FAS/ARBEs and secondary disabilities in chapter ten.

Education

The majority of First Nations, Métis and Inuit children living outside Nunavut and the Northwest Territories attend provincial schools. In general, education levels of Aboriginal people have been lower than their non- Aboriginal counterparts. For example, in 1981, 63 per cent of Aboriginal people fifteen years or older who were no longer attending school had completed only primary school and only 29 per cent had completed high school. In 1991, the figures were a little better with 76 per cent of Aboriginal people over 15 years of age having completed primary school and 43 per cent having completed high school (Royal Commission on Aboriginal Peoples, 1996b). However, the differences in Aboriginal and non-Aboriginal drop-out rates have narrowed only slightly in the past two decades.

For many former students of the residential school system and their families, education has been mainly associated with government strategies to assimilate Aboriginal children. However, Abele, Dittburner and Graham (2000) write that the period between 1967 and 1982 saw a change in the way Aboriginal people viewed education.[24] In this period, there was a move from thinking about education as a means of assimilation to thinking of it as a means for the revitalization of Aboriginal cultures and economies. Over the past thirty-five years, Aboriginal leaders have made policy recommendations to governments for improved education in their communities and governments have conducted internal studies on Aboriginal education, but change has been slow and has generally fallen short of the goals (Royal Commission on Aboriginal Peoples, 1996b). This, according to the Royal Commission on Aboriginal Peoples, shows an unwillingness on the part of Canadian society to accomplish the necessary power sharing to enable Aboriginal people to control their own education, which has resulted in barriers continuing to exist that prevent significant changes in the education of Aboriginal people.

For Aboriginal children, the educational experience varies. The Royal Commission on Aboriginal Peoples writes:

> Provincial schools have varied in their receptivity to Aboriginal children. In some locations where there are many Aboriginal children, schools have opened their doors to Aboriginal parents and developed vibrant community/school programs. In Toronto, Saskatoon and Winnipeg, school boards have negotiated to establish Aboriginal schools. These are the exception. Most Aboriginal students attend schools where there is no special effort to make them or their families feel part of the life of the school. Aboriginal parents say they are excluded from their children's education. There is a gap between the culture of the home and that of the school (1996b:438).

For some Aboriginal families, helping their children stay in school is an insurmountable task given the multiple family problems they face. Problems, such as chronic unemployment, poor housing and over-crowding, physical and mental health problems, substance abuse, and lack of strong and healthy support networks, can prevent parents from supporting and advocating education for their children. Family dysfunction can also contribute to academic and behavioural problems that a child has in school and, along with school environments that fail to help the child deal with these issues, can contribute to the child dropping out or being dismissed from school by the time they reach adolescence. Multiple foster placements are common among a sub-group of Aboriginal children and may contribute to academic and behavioural problems at school. This maybe particularly true, for children with special needs, such as those with alcohol-related birth effects. The inverse may also be true, whereby alcohol-related birth effects are seen as the cause of academic and behavioural problems in school, rather than the disruption to the lives of children caused by multiple foster placements (Tait, 2003).

---

[24]   Education will be dealt with only briefly here. However, for further reading on Aboriginal education, see the edited volume by Brant-Castellano and colleagues (2000).

Chapter 6

Conclusion

Several contemporary health and social issues that are linked to the residential school system are associated with the issue of pregnancy and substance abuse and/or FAS/ARBEs. A review of the literature suggests that some Aboriginal groups face a barrage of health and social issues that impact negatively upon their communities, including substance abuse by women of childbearing ages. However, a growing body of literature argues that the level of variables, such as physical and mental health problems, family dysfunction, violence, poor education and crime, are directly linked to social factors. These studies have found that community control and autonomy (Chandler and Lalonde, 1998), high level of social integration (May, 1991), community development, local control of health care systems, the settlement of land claims and moves toward self-government (Kirmayer, Brass and Tait, 2000) may be important protective factors in preventing ill health and negative social outcomes among Aboriginal groups.

Chapter 7

Fetal Alcohol Syndrome and Alcohol-Related Birth Effects: Review of the Epidemiology Literature

Introduction

Epidemiological studies are central to understanding how health-related conditions, such as fetal alcohol syndrome (FAS), are distributed in human populations and to identifying factors that influence the occurrence of those distributions. The epidemiological literature, which examines rates of FAS, can be divided roughly into two types of studies: those studies that look at the epidemiology of alcohol use and pregnancy, and those that examine the frequency of occurrence of FAS and other ARBEs. Within epidemiological studies, the frequency of occurrence of a condition is described in terms of incidence and prevalence rates (Abel, 1998a). Abel explains:

> *Incidence* refers to the number of new cases of an anomaly entering a population at a particular time; *prevalence* refers to either the frequency of a condition among identified cases regardless of when they entered, or the frequency of a condition in a population at a particular time.

> For example, if 10 cases of FAS are born for every 10,000 births, the incidence would be 1 per 1,000; if 20, the incidence would be 2 per 1,000. This increase, however, would not affect the prevalence of any FAS-related disorder. If the prevalence rate of cleft palate in FAS is 10%, it doesn't matter if 10 or 20 cases of FAS are born. A 10% rate means there will only be one case of cleft palate for every 10 FAS cases, no matter how many total cases of FAS there are.

> For structural birth defects like an atrial septal defect, prevalence rates are lower in older children than at birth or inutero for a number of reasons: the child may have died in early infancy; surgery may have been performed to correct the problem; or the defect may have healed on its own. The prevalence of congenital functional anomalies, such as hearing impairment or cognitive disturbances, on the other hand, is generally higher for older versus younger children because the disorder is not life threatening and usually not recognized until several years after birth (1998a:139).

Abel (1998a) points out those retrospective studies, population-based prevalence studies, passive surveillance programs and prospective/active surveillance studies are the main epidemiological procedures used to estimate the frequency of occurrence for FAS. Because each of these procedures has its own intrinsic bias, Abel suggests that consistency between studies is precluded. This means that, "depending on the methods of epidemiological use, they will arrive at a relatively high or low estimate of the frequency of occurrence of a disorder like FAS in any population" (Abel, 1998a:140).

Chapter 7

The following review is an examination of epidemiological and related[25] literature on alcohol use by pregnant women, and FAS and related disorders. Special attention has been given to studies that focus on pregnancy and alcohol abuse, and FAS among Aboriginal people in North America. Where possible, 'gray' literature has been reviewed if it provides information to better inform the discussion. This review is meant not only to provide findings from the various studies reviewed, but also to provide a critique of the scientific literature on FAS with regard to research methods and the claims made as a result of findings brought about by those methods. For example, a review of the literature on alcohol-related birth effects (ARBEs) suggests many studies do not control for confounding variables when assessing the risks associated with alcohol abuse during pregnancy.

Variables, such as levels of smoking, the use of prescription and non-prescription drugs, the overall health status of women, nutritional intake, level of caffeine consumption, age, marital status, social class and ethnic identity, are believed by some researchers to be important considerations in predicting alcohol drinking patterns among women (Day, Cottreau et al., 1993) and assist in determining pregnancies that are more likely to be at risk for ARBEs. The correlation between confounding variables and alcohol use is important in the research design of any study that looks at risk factors for ARBEs, as it is only through making these connections that risk and risk behaviour can be better understood.

Canada

In Canada, research that examines alcohol consumption by pregnant women has focused largely on Aboriginal women and their children, or on geographical areas with large numbers of Aboriginal people (Tait, 2003; for example, see Godel, Pabst et al., 1992; Robinson, Conry et al., 1987). Research on FAS and ARBEs supports a commonly held belief in Canada that substance abuse during pregnancy occurs much more often among Aboriginal women than their non-Aboriginal counterparts (Asante and Robinson, 1990; Habbick, Nanson et al., 1996; Smith, Sandor et al., 1981). Some researchers suggest rates of FAS/FAE found in specific communities are alarmingly high and, in some cases, constitute full-blown epidemics (see Moffatt quoted in Square, 1997:59).

The 'high risk' communities identified in research studies have all been First Nation communities or urban or rural settings with large concentrations of Aboriginal people (Asante and Nelms-Matzke, 1985; Robinson, Conry et al., 1987; Square, 1997; Williams and Gloster, 1999). Similarly, American Indians have been over-represented in studies completed in the United States, many of which identify Alaska or the southwestern United States as 'high risk' geographical locations for FAS because of their large American Indian population (Bowerman, 1997; CDC, 1994; Egeland, Perham-Hester et al., 1998).

A 1981 study by Asante (1981) was one of the earliest research studies that examined FAS in Canada. This study reported on children who underwent clinical assessment and follow-up for specific pediatric medical or developmental problems between 1972 and 1980 in northwest British Columbia and the

---

[25]   A number of practice-based studies that use experimental and quasi-experimental methods of research exist within the FAS literature and will be reviewed here and elsewhere in the report. Literature concerning the underlying mechanisms by which alcohol and other substances affect the developing fetus, including animal and human studies, is beyond the scope of this project.

Yukon. Of sixty-two mothers of children diagnosed with FAS, fifty-nine (95%) were Aboriginal. Although this is a striking percentage, the significance of this number is unclear as the percentage of Aboriginal children within the entire population referred for clinical assessment is not given by the author. While the author could not estimate the prevalence rate of FAS based on the data collected for the study, he concludes that "FAS is a frequent and significant cause of physical malformations, growth failure, developmental delay and mental retardation" among Aboriginal people (1981:335). He adds that "the incidence of FAS would appear to be a much larger problem in this area, and probably in other areas of Canada" with large concentrations of Aboriginal people (1981:335).

Asante gives several possible reasons for the large number of Aboriginal mothers and children in his study. He lists higher alcohol consumption and more frequent 'binge-drinking' among Aboriginal women as two possibilities. Although, he does not make reference to studies that support his assumptions. Asante also suggests that the surveillance of Aboriginal women and children (e.g., by social services, outreach agencies), as opposed to Caucasian women living in the region, may also account for some of the discrepancy and the possibility that Caucasian women "drink more discreetly at home" (1981:335).

Lastly, he cites social, economic and psychological factors, along with the 'northern lifestyle,' as contributors to high incidence of FAS in this Aboriginal population. However, he does not go into detail as to the relationship between these factors and negative birth outcomes. The article ends with recommendations for further epidemiological research and "a greater need to educate women in the childbearing years, especially native women, in the serious effects of alcohol on the unborn child" (Asante, 1981:335).

In a second study in the Yukon and northwestern British Columbia, Asante and Nelms-Matzke (1985) found that, out of 586 Aboriginal and non-Aboriginal children referred to them for assessment of handicaps, 82 were diagnosed with FAS and 94 with fetal alcohol effects (FAE). A prevalence rate of FAS among Aboriginal children, based on the study's findings and the total population of children in the catchment area, was estimated to be 46 per 1,000 compared to 0.4 per 1,000 for non-Aboriginal children. FAE prevalence rates for Aboriginal children were 26/1,000. In a critique of Asante and Nelms-Matzke's study, Bray and Anderson write:

> Subjects were selected for study by various agencies who identified children in their community as "chronically handicapped". From this subpopulation, Asante et al. estimated the prevalence of FAS and/or FAE in the total population. The authors are aware that this is less than an ideal way to estimate prevalence. The sample was based on children identified by the health care system and social services as being handicapped, and this in itself may lead to a biased estimate of prevalence (1989:43).

Bray and Anderson (1989) go on to state that Asante and Nelms-Matzke offer no documentation regarding diagnostic assessment and findings, thereby leaving it uncertain if the criteria for FAS was applied equally to both Aboriginal and non-Aboriginal children (1989). As well, developmental assessment in evaluating central nervous system dysfunction (CNS) was not systematic and it was found, during the Asante and Nelms-Matzke study, that the Denver Development Screening Test was biased toward rural children and, therefore, was not given to all of the children in the study.

Chapter 7

In 1981, Smith, Sanders and others (1981) described 76 diagnosed cases of FAS in British Columbia and the Yukon. The participants were seen at hospitals in Vancouver and diagnosis was based on a confirmed history of heavy maternal alcohol consumption during pregnancy and clinical findings of characteristic facial appearance, alteration of brain function and growth retardation in the child. Seven of the patients were of Caucasian descent, with the remainder of the children being born to Aboriginal mothers and whose fathers were of either Aboriginal or Caucasian ancestry. No other racial groups were represented in the study. While Smith and colleagues acknowledge that rates of FAS/FAE are undetermined, they estimate rates to be between 1-5/1,000 live births. They go on to state:

> With only 2½% of the population in British Columbia being native Indian, our statistics reveal a 10.9 to 1 ratio of native Indian children to Caucasian from our population with FAS. This raises the significance of racial susceptibility to the teratogenic effects of alcohol, a very difficult point to satisfactorily answer (1981:151).

Although Smith and colleagues suggest 'racial susceptibility' as a possible factor influencing rates of FAS/FAE among Aboriginal people, they do not define how race and increased susceptibility are linked, apart from observing a large number of Aboriginal children in their diagnosed cohort. As discussed earlier in this report, categories based on biological race are problematic and scientific research to date has not been able to link alcohol metabolism and population genetics to a mother's use of alcohol and negative birth outcomes. Studies looking at the link between alcohol metabolism and fetal damage that would take biological race as a research variable because racial groups are so difficult to define is highly unlikely (Tait, 2003). By considering other factors, such as the socio-economic status of the mothers, Smith and colleagues may have found that these factors were as important, or more important, than 'race' (Tait, 2003; Abel, 1997). Bray and Anderson (1989) also found that they could not repeat the calculation done by Smith and colleagues, which resulted in a 10.9 to 1 ratio; instead, they found a 9.9 to 1 ratio based on 69 Indian and 7 Caucasian children (1989:43).

Smith and colleagues (1981) state that because their patient population is derived from two Vancouver hospitals, which may see only the more serious FAS cases, their study could actually distort the view of affected children (1981). They also fail to report on whether Aboriginal clients are excessively referred to these particular tertiary care units in Vancouver, which may skew the ethnic makeup of their sample population (Bray and Anderson, 1989). The study by Smith and colleagues also fails to provide information about whether the children and/or their mothers come from specific Aboriginal communities with high rates of alcohol abuse or whether any correlation can be made between community of birth and birth outcomes (Tait, 2003).

This information would allow targeted intervention and prevention programs to be developed if certain communities or areas were identified as high risk for alcohol abuse. Instead, the authors suggest that this is a widespread problem for Aboriginal people, in general, in British Columbia and the Yukon. While their findings are significant, the large number of Aboriginal patients may also reflect a willingness of Aboriginal families and/or social service agencies, who have Aboriginal children in their care, to explore the possibility of a FAS diagnosis. Non-Aboriginal children may be under-represented because families and/or health care providers are interpreting physical and mental problems of these children as something other than FAS/ARBEs (Tait, 2003).

Chapter 7

A 1984 survey conducted in an isolated First Nations community in British Columbia reported on the prevalence of FAS and FAE (Robinson, Conry et al., 1987). The community had 350 registered members, including 155 children aged 18 years or less, of whom 123 were living in the community. One- hundred and sixteen of the children participated in the study, with fourteen being diagnosed with FAS (a prevalence of 121 per 1,000) and eight with FAE (a prevalence of 69 per 1,000). The FAS/FAE prevalence rate for the children in the community was 190/1,000, one of the highest rates reported to date (Robinson, Conry et al., 1987). Researchers found that fourteen women out of forty-five had given birth to one or more of the twenty-two children diagnosed. Five of these women accounted for twelve (54%) of the diagnosed children. This finding suggests that the majority of diagnosed cases were born to a small number of women. Abel (1998a) points out that population-based studies often count each sibling as a single case, thereby failing to give proper weight to what may be a serious problem among a relatively small proportion of the mothers. Researchers generally determine prevalence rates based on a mother-child ratio of one-to-one when, in fact, a single mother may give birth to a number of affected children.

Bray and Anderson (1989) argue that the presence of epicanthic folds and other anatomical features of some Aboriginal children makes the measurements of facial characteristics difficult and may have contributed to the high rates of FAS/FAE found in studies, such as that by Robinson and colleagues. They critique the claim by Robinson and colleagues that FAS is a particular problem for Aboriginal people based on the high prevalence rates found in the Robinson study patient population. Bray and Anderson state:

> ... given the high prevalence rate of 190 births per 1000. This statistic would be more convincing if the authors had conducted a prevalence study of FAS in a non-Native comparison group using the same FAS criteria and method. Instead, the authors refer to other research which reports the prevalence of FAS/FAE to be 19.5, 2.7 and 2.5 per 1000 births for three Indian tribes of the Southwest United States. Rather than strengthening Robinson's position, these data indicate significant variation in the prevalence rate across cultural groups with the statistics from two tribes comparable to FAS prevalence rates for the general American population. None of the statistics compare with the rate of 190 births per 1000 (1989:43).

Forty-five mothers participated in the study by Robinson and colleagues. Of the 116 children collectively belonging to them, in-utero alcohol exposure was reported in fifty-four pregnancies. Of the fifty-four offspring where in-utero alcohol exposure occurred, thirty-two were unaffected, according to study findings. The authors of the study found that confirmation of alcohol use was easily determined through interviews with the mothers; however, the women generally could not remember the amounts of alcohol they consumed (Robinson, Conry et al., 1987). Problems with recall were most likely because the births of the children who were examined occurred over an eighteen year period, making it difficult for many women to recall their exact drinking levels. Women who reported to have drank alcohol while pregnant were also not asked about their patterns of alcohol use and subsequent birth outcomes. For example, whether a pattern of binge-drinking or heavy alcohol use was linked more often to negative or more severe birth outcomes is unknown, as is the number of women who stopped drinking during all, or part, of their pregnancy (Tait, 2003).

Chapter 7

The research methodology used by Robinson and colleagues makes it difficult to successfully evaluate variables such as alcohol use patterns (May, 1991) and compounding variables, such as the woman's nutritional intake, smoking status and other drug use (Tait, 2003). Bray and Anderson state that the problem "is to distinguish in utero alcohol exposure from the myriad other experiences of the prenatally exposed child, which is especially the case for the child who is diagnosed as mentally retarded. A more sophisticated analysis would have collected confounding variables in the same way as information on alcohol and then performed multiple logistic regression or a stratified analysis" (1989:43). Furthermore, diagnostic criteria, such as growth retardation, is a criterion for FAS; however, it is also associated with maternal smoking. Bray and Anderson state:

> A careful maternal history is needed to differentiate effects of alcohol from those due to anticonvulsant medication because of similarities in dysmorphology. CNS dysfunction may be associated with other known teratogenic drugs and chemicals, infections during pregnancy and perhaps a host of unidentified teratogens (1989:43).

Over much of the eighteen-year period when the pregnancies discussed in the study by Robinson and colleagues occurred, the dangers of alcohol use during pregnancy were either unknown or only coming to light through medical research and public health education. This can also be said for the two studies completed by Asante that were discussed earlier in this chapter. Therefore, it is important to note that the women in the communities studied, as many women in Canada during this time, did not necessarily make a link between negative birth outcomes and their alcohol use while pregnant. As well, it is very likely that the perception of the risk of damage to the developing fetus held by women in these communities, as well as other communities, was and continues to be greatly influenced by the experiences of other women around them (Tait, 2000a; 2003).

Although Robinson and colleagues were unable to explore the perceptions women had of their children, it is possible that some of the women, along with their family and community members, did not see the children as having a disability prior to the assessment for the study. Therefore, women in the community, even after they may have known more about the dangers of alcohol abuse during pregnancy, might have felt they had given birth to unaffected children, despite their alcohol use. This belief may have a direct impact on their decision about drinking during subsequent pregnancies, as well as influencing the perceptions of younger women around them who were becoming pregnant for the first time. Many of the early FAS/FAE studies provided very limited information about the mothers of the children assessed, including the women's perceptions of alcohol use and pregnancy. Unfortunately, when the researchers did choose to collect information about the mothers, they focused mainly on racial classification (Tait, 2003). Other important factors, such as the drinking patterns of the mothers or socio-demographic information, apart from race, were minimized (Abel, 1998b).

In 1989, Bray and Anderson conducted an appraisal of the epidemiology of FAS among Aboriginal people in Canada. They began by asking two questions: "Is it merely coincidental that Indians are represented in various case studies or is there reason to believe Native children suffer an increased prevalence of FAS? *Is there epidemiological evidence that suggests FAS occurs more frequently in Native populations?*" (Bray and Anderson, 1989:42). The above discussion has included some of the concerns expressed by Bray and

Chapter 7

Anderson with regard to the epidemiology data collected before 1989. A key concern also expressed by Bray and Anderson was the difficulty in FAS/FAE studies of applying a standard diagnostic criteria for FAS across cultures. They state:

> Since anthropomorphic features of Indian children generally differ from Caucasian children, the use of facial characteristics as a diagnostic criterion is questionable. Educational assessment across cultures, especially the use of IQ tests in the evaluation of CNS dysfunction as a criterion, requires special attention (1989:44).

In their appraisal, Bray and Anderson (1989) cite the lack of published research in Canada on the prevalence of FAS in non-Native populations, which, because of its absence, is difficult, if not impossible, to make valid comparisons of the prevalence rates for Native and non-Natives and to draw inferences regarding high prevalence rates. This problem appears to have continued in Canada to the present day, with FAS/FAE epidemiological studies during the past decade focusing mainly on Aboriginal groups or geographical areas with large concentrations of Aboriginal people (Tait, 2003).

At the time of Bray and Anderson's article, only two epidemiological studies on FAS among Aboriginal people had been conducted in Canada; therefore, making any argument concerning prevalence rates inconclusive. Bray and Anderson point out that the two studies were conducted among sub-populations of Aboriginal people living in the west coast region of Canada. They go on to state:

> The investigations themselves may lack methodological sophistication and therefore warrant scientific conservatism in accepting the prevalence rates prima facie ... Native peoples should not be stigmatized by a condition such as FAS which is difficult to prove as factual and which may have negative impact within the Native community. *Caution is warranted before we conclude that FAS is more prevalent in any Native peoples* (1989:44, emphasis added).

However, Bray and Anderson add that methodological problems may only account for some of an inflated prevalence rate and that the studies may be signaling a problem in certain Aboriginal populations. If the studies are signaling increased risk, then they suggest a new question needs to be asked: "*What are the factors that could put Canadian Native women at risk for producing children with FAS?*" (Bray and Anderson, 1989:44).

The question of risk, in relation to prevention of FAS, usually begins with an assessment of alcohol abuse by pregnant women. Bray and Anderson (1989) caution against assumptions that Aboriginal women are more likely than non-Aboriginal women to be alcohol abusers. They point out that no objective data regarding typical and excessive alcohol consumption patterns and drinking styles of Aboriginal women in Canada of child-bearing age exists. This claim, made in 1989, appears to hold true today. Epidemiological studies are inconclusive as to the level of risk Aboriginal women face in relation to alcohol abuse and adverse pregnancy outcomes. Bray and Anderson point out that Aboriginal people in Canada are collectively very diverse in culture, language, geographical location and alcohol consumption.

They recommend that community-specific information regarding alcohol consumption patterns of Aboriginal women be undertaken. This, they state, would "contribute to a solid data base to assess whether a targeted alcohol abuse prevention program is needed and whether an investigation into the prevalence of FAS is worthwhile" (Bray and Anderson, 1989:44). Central to this research should be an analysis of how socio-economic status relates to risk for Aboriginal women and their offspring in relation to adverse pregnancy outcomes and FAS (Tait, 2003). In conclusion, Bray and Anderson write:

> If the prevalence rates of FAS for Canadian Indians were accepted without scrutiny, FAS might be seen as a public health problem of massive proportion. If this were so, subsequent policy and allocation of resources might be misdirected to programs aimed at widespread efforts of preventing FAS. Given the weakness in the data from which these prevalence rates were calculated, this could represent a waste of both human and financial resources (1989:44-45).

In 1991, Philip May published a review article on FAS among North American Indians. May began his article by discussing the myths that surround 'Indian drinking.' He states that, in the United States, American Indians have been wrongly stereotyped in literature, popular and professional, as having greater problems with alcohol, particularly alcoholism, despite the scientific evidence being inconclusive. May (1991) also writes that American Indian women show higher rates of abstention than U.S. norms in most age groups; and several different drinking patterns exist among Indian groups, some of which are not typically abusive. However, May adds that sporadic alcohol abuse (heavy binge drinking) is more common among American Indians and causes a number of negative outcomes, including greater frequency of mortality than does chronic abuse. American Indians are also more likely to drink in ways that produce very high blood alcohol levels. This type of drinking behaviour, combined with the high-risk environments in which many Indian people drink (rural, border town settings), produce very high levels of intoxication, arrest, morbidity, trauma and mortality. This, May suggests, has helped to shape lay and professional opinions of the 'drunken Indian' stereotype.

May (1991) reviews the FAS/FAE literature that estimates prevalence and incidence rates among Aboriginal people in North America. He cautions against direct comparison of prevalence rates of Aboriginal and non-Aboriginal studies as, methodologically, they suggest very different problems. For example, studies that have produced European and North American prevalence estimates have been clinic-based, urban-area studies with little or no outreach. Under-surveillance is, therefore, likely (May, 1991; Little, Snell et al., 1990). On the other hand, May writes:

> ... the studies of Canadian Indians have focused mainly on small communities in high risk (heavy drinking) areas. In such settings, surveillance is quite complete, and the prevalence is expected to be high (Bray and Anderson 1989). Therefore, differential screening is a major issue of comparison (1991:241).

May also refers to a study by Chavez and colleagues (1988), who conducted a national survey of all major physical anomalies in the United States by examining birth certificates. The researchers found that, "in some instances, physicians may tend to look for a particular malformation more in certain racial [and] ethnic groups than they would in others. [This is] detection bias" (Chavez, Cordero and Becerrant, 1988 in May, 1991:241). This point was also raised in a subsequent review article by Burd and Moffatt (1994). To date, only one study (Nanson, Bolaria et al., 1995) has been completed in Canada concerning physician bias and diagnosis with regard to FAS/FAE; however, this concern has been raised by various health and social service professionals (Tait, 2003). For example, Jo Nanson, an FAS researcher and clinician in Saskatchewan, reported that, with regard to Aboriginal children, it is not uncommon if a child who has an unusual appearance and has a mother who drank at all during her pregnancy, then he/she may receive a diagnosis of FAS by a primary care physician (Nanson personal communication, 1995 in Abel, 1998b). Abel (1998a) writes that the result of this 'glib diagnosis' is that these children could easily end up being misdiagnosed and receiving inappropriate treatment.

A third article by Burd and Moffatt (1994) reviewed the epidemiological data of FAS in American Indian, Alaskan Native and Aboriginal people in Canada. Their review included six published papers and four unpublished reports. Canadian studies reviewed by Burd and Moffatt included the study by Robinson and colleagues (1987), Asante and Nelms-Matzke (1985) and an unpublished study by Wong (1983). Wong's study used the British Columbia Birth Defects Registry to review all reported cases of FAS in the province. The incidence rates were determined to be 6.6 per 1,000. Burd and Moffatt (1994) suggest that several methodological problems exist in each of the studies they reviewed and concur with Bray and Anderson's (1989) conclusion that caution should be used before concluding that the Aboriginal population of Canada has elevated rates of FAS. They add that this caution should be extended to American studies reviewed in their article. Burd and Moffatt (1994) suggest that high prevalence rates are most likely caused by the communities being chosen for research because FAS is thought to be a major public health problem. Comparable studies of Aboriginal communities selected because rates of FAS are presumed to be low have not yet been completed. Burd and Moffatt also suggest that physician bias may contribute to high rates, as clinicians may be more likely to diagnose FAS in the newborn period in Aboriginal infants than in other ethnic groups.

Burd and Moffatt (1994) identify several avenues for research that may determine sensitivity and specificity of clinical diagnosis by experts of FAS. They suggest studies, which seek to examine patients at birth, at 4 or 5 years of age and in adulthood, to determine the confidence one can place in current diagnostic criteria. Longitudinal information on diagnostic consistency, they argue, is very important as the developmental course of FAS results in less distinctive clinical features as individuals grow into adults. A major obstacle to diagnostic consistency is the lack of 'gold standard' diagnostic measurements to compare with clinicians' diagnoses. Burd and Moffatt also suggest that, given the potential for misdiagnosis of FAS and the very adverse social ramifications for the parent, family and child, considerably more research is needed. They go on to state that:

> Future studies should include four features: (a) the cohorts should include people with both FAS and developmental disorders other than FAS, (b) the cohorts should be stratified by ethnic status, c) the blinding of diagnosticians to the history of maternal alcohol use during pregnancy, and (d) the expansion of study designs to allow for identification of sensitivity and specificity of both screening methods and diagnostic criteria (Burd and Moffatt, 1994:692).

Added to Burd and Moffatt's list of features should be study designs that examine the socio-economic status of women and their offspring, including information concerning whether the child is being raised by a biological parent(s) and/or the child's foster and adoption history. Comparative data, which cross-references these factors with ethnic status, would help to determine the role of socio-economic status, multiple foster placements and ethnicity (Tait, 2003). Burd and Moffatt suggest that physician bias could be examined by a surveillance system that would determine the frequency with which physicians make a diagnosis of FAS. They argue that it is important to determine "if a minority of ... physicians account for the majority of cases of FAS" (Burd and Moffatt, 1994:622). Other related findings, which need to be examined further, are why so few adult females, as opposed to males, are diagnosed with FAS (Burd and Moffatt, 1994; Tait, 2003).

In a survey of 273 pediatricians and general practitioners in Saskatchewan in December 1990 and January 1991, Nanson and colleagues (1995) found that physician detection bias may have played a role in the high prevalence rates of FAS among Aboriginal groups. They found that 27.5% (75/273) of the physicians in their study responded that they thought FAS occurred primarily in ethnic minority families. This, Nanson and colleagues (1995) suggest, may simply reflect the realities of the particular client base of these physicians, rather than detection bias. Burd and Moffatt's suggestion of studies that look at physician bias and seek to determine the frequency with which each physician makes a diagnosis of FAS, may have given some insight into this particular finding by Nanson and colleagues. For example, Nanson and colleagues found that 48% of the physicians they surveyed reported having diagnosed at least one case of FAS, which suggests there may be under-diagnosis in certain areas or pockets of the province, which may be divided along ethnic and, possibly, socio-economic lines.

In 1992, Godel and colleagues (1992) published a study on the prevalence of reported smoking and caffeine and alcohol consumption during pregnancy for 162 women who presented for prenatal care in any one of 10 communities in the western region of the Northwest Territories, or who gave birth in Inuvik between September 1987 and January 1990. The study's goal was to look at the relationship between prevalence of smoking, caffeine and alcohol consumption by pregnant women, and infant birth weight, length and head circumference. The ethnic breakdown of the women was as follows: 56 (35%) of the women were Inuit, 38 (24%) Indian, 37 (23%) white and 31 (19%) mixed race. In relation to alcohol, the study wanted to specifically look at differences between drinkers and nondrinkers, and effects of binge drinking from those of moderate or frequent drinking.

Godel and colleagues (1992) found that the prevalence of smoking and the reported caffeine intake were significantly lower for white women than the three other groups. No statistical difference was found between the groups in relation to the proportion of women who drank alcohol; however, Inuit and Indian mothers were more likely than the others to be binge drinkers. Ninety-five (66%) of the 145 women who completed the questionnaire on alcohol intake abstained from alcohol use during pregnancy, 22 (15%) were moderate drinkers, 10 (7%) were frequent drinkers, and 18 (12%) were binge drinkers. Authors of the study point out that under-reporting of smoking and alcohol intake may suggest possible errors in the survey's findings. They also state that the small size of the four ethnic groups reduces the precision in estimating differences. Adjustment for one or more confounding variables, such as maternal age, smoking, drinking and race, were also considered to have potentially skewed results.

Godel and colleagues (1992) found that the prevalence rate of smoking during pregnancy was very high (64%), especially among Native women and those of mixed race (more than 70%), and among women aged 14 to 18 years of age (80%). Moderate alcohol intake during pregnancy did not appear to have a detrimental effect on fetal growth. While decreases in all three fetal measurements (birth weight, length and head circumference) was observed, in babies of heavier drinkers, a significant decrease in head circumference only was observed, especially in infants of binge drinkers. A high correlation was found between smoking and drinking. However, to differentiate between the effects of alcohol and smoking on fetal growth was impossible. Godel and colleagues concluded that, while the study documented high incidence rates of smoking, caffeine intake and drinking in a northern population, the most 'disturbing' finding was "the high rate of smoking, especially among native mothers, and the high incidence of binge drinking" (1992:186).

Godel and colleagues (1992) recommend that planned prevention programs specifically aimed at children and young adults should be implemented. As well, they suggest that confounding variables, such as poverty, unemployment and 'helplessness,' need to be better understood in relation to alcohol consumption patterns. Unfortunately, the authors of the study did not collect information about levels of poverty, unemployment and 'helplessness;' however, their findings suggest that variables such as these may play a significant role in women's consumption patterns. For example, only 11 of the 49 Inuit women in the study drank when pregnant, as did 12 of the 35 Indian women, rates that are lower than both white and mixed race women. Yet, the Inuit and Indian women were reported to engage in binge-drinking more often. It could be speculated that socio-economic and employment status may be indicators of binge-drinking abuse patterns and, if these variables are correlated in reference to all the women in the study, this could point to a vulnerability among a certain sub-group that cross-cuts ethnic lines (Tait, 2003). Other factors, such as acceptable and common drinking patterns among certain ethnic and socio-economic sub-populations, could also be explored.

In efforts to report incidence rates of FAS for an entire province in Canada, Habbick and colleagues (1996) conducted a study in two major Saskatchewan centres where almost all of the province's cases of FAS are treated. In the period prior to and including 1993, 207 cases were identified and 178 (86%) were Aboriginal. From 1973 onwards, incidence rates of FAS in Saskatchewan have been fairly steady, with an average of 0.585 per 1,000 live births. In all diagnosed cases of FAS where patients were born prior to 1993, history of excessive maternal alcohol intake during pregnancy was confirmed and standard diagnostic criteria for the syndrome was met. Habbick and colleagues (1996) cite several reasons for the high rates among Aboriginal people, including 'cultural influences' (although not defined or explained), patterns of alcohol consumption and abuse, child-bearing at a later maternal age when alcohol abuse is apt to be greatest, and possible dietary and metabolic influences. However, Nanson points out that the high rates found among Aboriginal people in Saskatchewan may actually represent a combination of socio-economic and ethnic factors:

> The women described by Habbick and associates were mostly of [A]boriginal descent. Again, information about education, socioeconomic status and employment history was lacking ... By various measures, [A]boriginal people have a lower health status than other Canadians, and poverty and substance abuse are covariates in many of the health problems that they experience. Thus the prevention of fetal alcohol syndrome must be seen in the context of improving the overall health of impoverished [A]boriginal—and non-[A]boriginal—families in Canada (1997:807).

In a subsequent study, Habbick and colleagues (1999) reported on the mortality rate among the cohort from their 1993 study (Habbick, Nanson et al., 1997). Among the cohort of 207 identified cases, 12 deaths were reported, which yielded a mortality rate of 5.8%, almost 3.5 times what would be expected in the general population. All twelve deaths (58% males) were Aboriginal, with ages ranging from 13 days to 30 years. Most of the patients described had several surgical procedures and very complicated medical and social histories. Death was primarily due to congenital anomalies (seven due to congenital heart disease). No deaths were reported because of suicide.

Williams and Gloster (1999) conducted a study to estimate the incidence of FAS in northeastern Manitoba. Hospital records for all live births occurring in the hospital in Thompson, a northern city that serves around 50,000 people, were reviewed. Researchers found that, in 1994, of the 745 live births at the hospital, 90 cases remained for further assessment of FAS after infants were excluded who did not have low birth weights, small head circumferences, developmental delays or who had some of these characteristics but lost them by the two-year follow-up. Forty-one of the ninety remaining infants were examined by a physician; the other forty-nine cases were not examined because of the difficulties in undertaking the follow-up examination due to the remoteness of the home community of some of the children (n=16), because some children could not be located by the research team (n=8) or because the home community of some of the children did not grant permission for the pediatricians to visit (n=25). The authors of the study note that:

> … although community consent was not sought, there was one community that became aware of our work and expressly asked the pediatricians not to conduct FAS assessments on the reserve, despite reassurances that the community of origin for FAS cases would not be identified (Williams and Gloster, 1999:193).

While the authors did not state the reasons behind community leaders not wanting their members to participate in the study, the reluctance may have been caused by several mitigating factors. For example, within the province of Manitoba, the Assembly of Manitoba Chiefs has created a research protocol concerning health research conducted on reserves in the province. While communities remain autonomous in their decision to participate in research, as do individuals, Aboriginal leaders have been concerned that 'informed consent' is not often explained properly or understood fully by participants or communities. While in the past many Aboriginal communities and individuals felt they were required to participate in research studies, Aboriginal leaders and their constituents have become much more critical of the research process, requesting information derived from research in their communities be given back to their people.

In some instances, Aboriginal communities have demanded that research follow, what has become known as, the guidelines of O.C.A.P. (Access, Ownership, Control and Possession of the research processes and findings by the Aboriginal community). Some Aboriginal communities are also questioning the value of research if it does not result in concrete interventions to better improve the health and well-being of their communities (Tait, 2003). While it is unclear if these factors contributed to the community's refusal to participate in the Williams and Gloster study, it should be noted that, unlike mainstream Canadian society where individuals are basically autonomous actors when choosing to participate in health research, informed consent for research with Aboriginal people, particularly those living on reserve, is often an issue of both individual and community consent (Tait, 2003).

Chapter 7

A further concern of the community who refused to participate in the Williams and Gloster study may have been the link between a diagnosis of FAS and child apprehension. Williams and Gloster (1999) note that, of the five cases of FAS found in their study, three of the children had been apprehended by Manitoba Family Services (two prior to the study and one during). Identification of a child with FAS or related ARBEs may bring fear to community leaders and their constituents that these children will be taken out of the community and placed into foster care (Tait, 2003). Local communities may fear that social service agencies would demand that a child identified as having FAS/ARBEs be removed permanently from the community to live in a larger center, such as Thompson, in order to receive medical and educational services that cannot be obtained in a remote community. Fear of apprehension may also have played a role in the researchers being unable to locate eight of the children who were originally screened for the study and who qualified for follow-up assessment.

In their study, Williams and Gloster (1999) found that five of the forty-one children examined at the time of follow-up met the diagnostic criteria for FAS, which gave an incidence rate of 7.2 cases per 1,000 live births. Since only 41 of the 90 cases identified were examined, the authors suggest that the actual incidence rate could be much higher if the unexamined group were to be included. Williams and Gloster suggest that if the rate is the same in the unexamined group, then the actual incidence would be 14.8 cases per 1,000. The majority of the babies born in the Thompson hospital are of Aboriginal descent and all cases diagnosed with FAS were either Aboriginal (First Nations) or Métis.[26] The authors conclude by stating:

> It seems clear that the incidence of FAS and FAE in northern Manitoba is quite high and of concern. If nothing else, the frequency of new mothers reporting consumption of alcohol during pregnancy (26%) is disturbing. This, too, is likely an underestimate, as a recent study found that 51% of Aboriginal women in northern Manitoba retrospectively reported consuming alcohol during one or more of their pregnancies (Williams and Gloster, 1999:194).

A rate of 26% of pregnant women drinking does raise concern in relation to birth outcomes; however, it should be pointed out that this rate is significantly lower than prevalence rates found among the general population in Canada and the United States. The prevalence rates of drinking prior to or during pregnancy are estimated to be 68% and 49% respectively (Abel, 1998a, see below for further discussion). Therefore, the contention by Williams and Gloster that the incidence rates of new mothers consuming alcohol during pregnancy is 'disturbing' as well as 'suggestive' of high incidence rates of FAS/FAE in northern Manitoba does not coincide with larger epidemiological findings.

In a second study conducted among Aboriginal people in northern Manitoba, Williams and Gloster (1999) reported that 51% of the women interviewed (sample size=242) reported drinking alcohol during one or more of their pregnancies. They also reported that 39% used other drugs, 10% sniffed solvents and 61% smoked tobacco during one or more of their pregnancies. Based on these findings, the authors conclude that rates of drug and alcohol use during pregnancy among Native women in

---

[26]   The term "Aboriginal" in the study by Williams and Gloster refers to First Nations only, and the category of Métis does not fall under this umbrella, but is used as a separate category.

northern Manitoba is 'quite high.' However, the study does not have a sample group of either non-Native women or Native women from a different region of Canada to use for comparison purposes as part of the research design.

Therefore, when the researchers claim drug and alcohol use during pregnancy is high, we are not told what it is high in relation to (Tait, 2003). Williams and Gloster (1999) acknowledge the lack of a comparison sample and try to compensate for this methodological weakness by comparing their findings to an American study that examined pregnancy and alcohol use. In the American study (CDC, 1997), only 16% of the pregnant women surveyed reported consuming alcohol during their pregnancy. This, Williams and Gloster suggest, can reasonably be compared to the 51% of Native women in their study who drank during pregnancy.

While the comparison may, at first, appear to be straight forward, several problems with this type of cross-study comparison exist, suggesting that, rather than being a valid comparison, this is simply a rhetorical use of statistical data by the authors to make a particular point: rates of drug and alcohol use during pregnancy among Native women in northern Manitoba is 'quite high' (Tait, 2003).

The use of statistical data for rhetorical purposes is not new in areas of medical research, where researchers present data that is inconclusive and only suggestive of possible directions for interventions, such as community programs and services (Tait, 2003). This is particularly the case with 'preventable' illnesses, such as FAS/ARBEs, where researchers see the presentation of their findings as opportunities to influence policy makers, funding bodies, health and social service professionals, and local communities in areas of prevention and intervention. However, what is troublesome about a study such as the one by Williams and Gloster is that the design of their studies precludes them from being equipped with sufficient data to support many of the claims they make in their discussion section (Tait, 2003).

The Williams and Gloster study is based on information gained from 5-10 minute interviews (in some cases, with the need for a Cree translator) with Aboriginal people. In this short period, demographic information, information on drug and alcohol use during pregnancy, and participant knowledge about the dangers of alcohol use during pregnancy are covered. Apart from the rushed nature of administering the questionnaires, which suggests obvious problems such as participants having difficulty recalling past alcohol use during a pregnancy that happened twenty years ago, there are several other problems with this type of interview style. For example, of the 51% of the women who reported drinking during one or more of their pregnancies, the number of women that consumed alcohol before knowing they were pregnant and then ceased drinking alcohol once they knew they were pregnant, is unexamined. This is a key issue in understanding alcohol use during pregnancy, not only among Aboriginal women, but women in general (Tait, 2003).

Second, since these were retrospective accounts of drinking during pregnancy, a percentage of the women in the Williams and Gloster study were reporting about pregnancies that occurred during a time when the dangers of alcohol use during pregnancy were unknown or only coming to light in medical research. This is evident in the information collected from female and male respondents in the study who reported on their use, or their spouse's use, of alcohol during pregnancy.

Of the retrospective accounts of pregnancies by women who, at the time of the study, were over the age of 40 (n=126), 82% of the women reported drinking some alcohol during one or more of their pregnancies, as opposed to 42% of the women in the age cohorts under 40 years of age. This is very different from the American CDC study referred to by Williams and Gloster for comparison purposes. The CDC study (1997) looked at alcohol consumption by pregnant women during the period of 1991 to 1995, a time when the dangers of alcohol use during pregnancy was highly publicized in the United States. The CDC study was also not a retrospective study, but occurred while the women in the study were pregnant, therefore, making it more likely that the participants under-reported their alcohol use (see, for example, Jacobson, Jacobson, Sokol, Martier, Ager et al., 1991).

In their analysis, Williams and Gloster fail to acknowledge that Aboriginal women in Canada may be more likely to give an accurate account of their alcohol use, even during pregnancy, due to an acknowledgment more general among Aboriginal than non-Aboriginal people, that alcohol abuse/use is a health and social problem among their people. Because of collective recognition that a problem exists, it has become more acceptable, in some contexts, for Aboriginal women with substance abuse problems to talk openly about their substance use/abuse (Tait, 2003).[27] In fact, many Aboriginal people believe that talking publicly in a safe, therapeutic setting about one's alcohol abuse problems can be very beneficial to the recovery process. This is different from the general Canadian population, where individuals, particularly women, are more likely to feel stigmatized if they admit, in any context, to abusing alcohol. Highly publicized public health campaigns, which give a message that any amount of alcohol is dangerous to the developing fetus, have significantly added to stigma associated with alcohol abuse by women and, most probably, influence under-reporting of use by many women (Tait, 2003).

In a review of the research literature that examines the prevalence of drinking prior to or during pregnancy, Abel (1998a) found that European/Australian and American/Canadian women were almost identical in their rates of drinking. In the American and Canadian studies, the prevalence rates of drinking prior to or during pregnancy were 68% and 49%, respectively. This is very close to the 51% found in Williams and Gloster's study (1999), which would indicate that alcohol consumption during pregnancy among the Aboriginal women they studied was in line with North American rates, as well as with international findings. The question remains as to why Williams and Gloster chose to compare their study to one that would indicate Aboriginal women in northern Manitoba were almost four times more likely to consume alcohol when pregnant than the general population?

Many studies, such as Williams and Gloster's (1999), which look at the prevalence of drinking during pregnancy do not report on pregnancy outcomes, including rates of FAS/ARBEs among the children from the pregnancies considered. Therefore, findings that indicate 51% of women in a study sample drank during pregnancy should not automatically be read as evidence of high rates of FAS or ARBEs. Nor should a lack of knowledge on the part of participants about the relationship between alcohol use

---

[27]   This is not to suggest that all Aboriginal women feel they can speak openly and freely about a substance abuse problem. Many Aboriginal women who have substance abuse problems still feel very stigmatized by family and community members, as well as by the general public, and are, therefore, reluctant to discuss their use. However, over the past two decades, because of increased awareness and sensitivity generated from Aboriginal addiction programs and community willingness to address addiction, many Aboriginal women with substance abuse problems do feel safe in acknowledging, talking about and addressing their substance abuse problems.

during pregnancy and birth outcomes be seen as an automatic indication of 'high risk' behaviour by participants. In the study by Williams and Gloster, they suggest that answering 'yes' to the statement "a safe amount of alcohol can be consumed when pregnant" and/or "a father's drinking can biologically affect an unborn baby" is an indication that participants and/or their spouses are ignorant or ill-informed about the dangers of alcohol use during pregnancy (1999:836).

Williams and Gloster clearly state that, within the framework of their study, an answer of 'yes' to either of these statements suggests participants may engage in risk behaviour due to their misperceptions. However, medical researchers generally agree that safe levels of alcohol can be consumed during pregnancy, but these levels may vary depending on several factors, including genetic factors related to both the woman and the fetus, the woman's overall health status, her age at the time of pregnancy and her patterns of substance use. The Institute of Medicine (IOM) in the United States recently made the following statement about alcohol as a teratogen:

> While alcohol is the necessary teratogen, it alone may not be sufficient to produce FAS in humans or birth defects in animals. As with most teratogens, not every fetus exposed to significant amounts of alcohol is affected. The outcomes might be modulated by numerous biologic and environmental factors (Stratton, Howe et al., 1996:20).

Ernest Abel (1998a), a researcher in the field of FAS who has written extensively on the subject, is a vocal advocate for a clear distinction as to what the diagnostic label FAS implies. Abel argues that the term FAS is misleading because it implies that any amount of alcohol consumption during pregnancy is toxic. However, hundreds of case reports and clinical studies have found that alcoholic women are the women who give birth to affected children. In none of the case reports or clinical studies reviewed by Abel found that an effected child was born to a mother who drank a single drink of alcohol each day of her pregnancy. It is clear, however, that Williams and Gloster, despite medical research suggesting the contrary, believe that there are *no* safe levels of alcohol consumption during pregnancy. It appears that it is they, rather than their study participants, who are ill-informed or ignorant of the current medical findings. It could also be suggested that this is a clear example of moral value being disguised as objective medical knowledge in order to manipulate the behaviour of certain groups of people, in this case, Aboriginal women (Tait, 2003).

Currently in Canada, public health information is not clear and is, at times, even contradictory, on whether there are safe levels of alcohol that can be consumed by pregnant women. What many public health campaigns have chosen to do is err on the side of caution. Some public health messages state that safe levels of alcohol use by pregnant women have yet to be determined, while others clearly state that all alcohol use while pregnant is dangerous. These messages are directly intended to impress upon pregnant woman that they should refrain from any alcohol use as *all* alcohol is *potentially* dangerous to the fetus. However, pregnant women in Canada regularly receive differing advice on alcohol use and pregnancy from several sources; for example, health care providers, friends and family members, medical literature, internet sources, or self-help literature (Tait, 2000a; 2003).

The purpose in critiquing Williams and Gloster and the general public health message in Canada is not to suggest pregnant women should drink alcohol without concern about how it will effect their health, their pregnancy and their offspring. Rather, women, including Aboriginal women, as health care consumers should be given the most up-to-date and accurate medical information by those in the position to do so. Medical knowledge, whether provided through research, clinical services, public health education or prevention programs, should be very clear as to what the current medical research states and health and social service providers should refrain from giving misinformation or exaggerating medical findings in the belief that this will dissuade consumers of the knowledge from engaging in risk behaviour. There are dangers inherent in the dissemination of misinformation: for example, misinformation of the known risks associated with alcohol use and pregnancy may lead to the termination of wanted pregnancies by women who believe they have caused serious developmental damage to their fetus by consuming even small amounts of alcohol (Tait, 2003).

In the study by Williams and Gloster, the women who answered that a safe level of alcohol can be consumed during pregnancy (57%) are not wrong or misinformed in their answer. Studies such as this only contribute to the confusion among health care providers and consumers and result in groups, such as Aboriginal women, being labelled as misinformed and, therefore, 'high risk' populations. What looms large in a publication, such as the Williams and Gloster study, is a research bias that suggests more of a moral comment on alcohol use by Aboriginal people than a true understanding of either the knowledge Aboriginal people in northern Manitoba have about substance abuse and pregnancy or about rates of alcohol consumption by pregnant Aboriginal women in this geographical region (Tait, 2003).

Studies Among American Indians

Within the United States several studies have been conducted that focus specifically on rates of FAS in American Indian communities. From 1979 to 1983, the Indian Health Service and a tribal organization, All Indian Pueblo Council, undertook a pilot project to determine prevalence rates of FAS for the three major Indian cultural groups[28] in New Mexico, northeastern Arizona and southern Colorado (May and Hymbaugh, 1983). The pilot project was also designed to meet the FAS treatment needs of the American Indian population in this region and to provide training for local treatment staff such as clinicians, outreach workers and community groups. The specific research goals of the project were "to establish incidence and prevalence figures for the entire population and for individual tribes, to understand the etiological factors involved in the development of fetal alcohol syndrome, and to use this knowledge to devise prevention strategies" (May and Hymbaugh, 1983:8).

May and Hymbaugh's assessment of the pilot project is one of only a few studies or articles that describe an existing program of prevention. Initial findings from the project suggest incidence rates of FAS vary among the reservations:

---

[28]   American Indian cultural groups in the southwestern United States are divided into three cultural groups, 'Navajo, ''Pueblo ' and 'Southwestern Plains.' These groups are then divided into different tribes. A number of Navajo groups live on one large reservation in New Mexico, Arizona and Utah. There are also three small reservations in New Mexico. Nineteen Pueblo tribes live in New Mexico (Zuni, Acoma, Laguna, Santo Domingo and Taos Indians) and one group lives in Arizona (the Hopi). Southwestern Plains is a cultural type that generally describes a variety of groups of Apaches living on four different reservations in Arizona and New Mexico, and Utes living on three reservations in Utah and Colorado (May, 1991).

> On some [reservations], no fetal alcohol children have been found, while on others there are children with severe problems ... Tribes with a loose, band-level social organization tend to have a higher incidence of alcohol-related problems than do those with a strict, highly structured tribal organization. In general, FAS distribution follows this pattern, with the more highly structured tribes having the fewest drinking mothers and lowest incidence of fetal alcohol damage (May, in press). The incidence of FAS among southwestern Indians may be higher than that reported in the United States generally ... Some of the reservations in the project have a significantly higher incidence of FAS than the general United States population, which cancels out the effect of lower incidence reservations and, therefore, makes the overall incidence slightly higher (May and Hymbaugh, 1983:8).

A significant finding of the pilot project was the prevalence of woman giving birth to more than one FAS or FAE child. May and Hymbaugh (1983) found that, among all the mothers in their study who had given birth to a child with FAS/FAE, 22.6 per cent had given birth to more than one affected child (average 2.36 children per multiple producing mother). May and Hymbaugh suggest the importance of the incidence of FAS be calculated in two ways: the proportion of damaged offspring produced per all births; and the proportion of all mothers producing alcohol-damaged babies. This research, they argue, will provide more specific indicators of risk and better insight for prevention. Research findings from the pilot project suggest the ostracism of drinking mothers may play a role in the production of multiple FAS offspring. May and Hymbaugh write:

> In many southwestern tribes, few women drink. Alcoholic women therefore are not tolerated and are frequently left out of regular social interaction. The consequence is almost total lack of social control over their behaviour. These women generally migrate to bordertowns where their only friends and associates are other alcoholics - a setting where there is little stigma attached to the production of multiple FAS children (1983:8).

May and Hymbaugh go on to state that the project's data suggest a high percentage of the children diagnosed with FAS were in foster placements, a high percentage of the mothers of affected children were deceased (21 per cent) and most mothers of affected children had extensive clinical records for alcohol-related problems, such as accidents, trauma and alcohol withdrawal.

The findings given by May and Hymbaugh suggest several avenues of investigation for research in Canada among Aboriginal people. For example: research that examines the correlation between social integration and levels of alcohol abuse or rates of FAS/ARBEs; examination of the treatment by community members of drinking women in various Aboriginal populations with differing levels of alcohol abuse among the general population; examination of whether out-migration of women who abuse alcohol occurs and, if so, when and for what reasons do women migrate; and profiling of women who have given birth to a child with FAS/FAE, in relation to previous and subsequent birth outcomes, maternal health status, percentage of deceased mothers and their cause of death and the percentage of women who are parenting their affected children. Since little is known about women in Canada who give birth to FAS/FAE children, investigation into the life circumstances of these women is an important area of investigation (Tait, 2000a; 2003).

Chapter 7

In a review of the research literature looking at ARBEs among North American Indians, May (1991) suggests that the amount of attention paid to high rates of FAS in a few American Indian communities may have resulted in a distorted view of other American Indian communities and the prevalence of FAS/FAE in the overall American Indian population. May writes:

> Given the popular, negative association between Indians and alcohol, Indians have received a substantial amount of negative attention regarding FAS and FAE (Kolata, 1989). Furthermore, because the main subjects of the book *The Broken Cord* (Dorris, 1989)[29] are Indians, many people have arrived at a narrow and erroneous interpretation of Indians from the text. These influences may have brought many to the conclusion that FAS and FAE are mainly or exclusively Indian problems (May, 1991:240).

May suggests that one of the shortcomings of FAS studies among Aboriginal people in North America is that they tend to focus on communities where high rates of FAS/FAE are expected. Bray and Anderson (1989) point out that, despite this tendency, these studies still fail to specify which sub-populations within the study population are at highest risk for alcohol problems and FAS/FAE. May (1991) adds that the inverse is also true, whereby researchers are generally not concerned with identifying the Aboriginal women and children at low-risk; however, some studies in the southwestern United States have begun to address these questions.

May and Smith (1988) found that, among southwest American Indians, only a minority of women consumed alcohol. For example, among the Navajo, 52 per cent of women aged 20 to 29 and 37 per cent aged 30 to 39 were alcohol users. May and colleagues (1983) found that a much smaller number of women gave birth to a FAS or FAE child: 6.1 per 1,000 women of childbearing age gave birth to an affected child, with the range between cultural groups being 4.6 to 30.5 per 1,000 women aged 15 to 44 years of age (May, Hymbaugh, Aase and Samet, 1983). May (1991) points out that this finding suggests the target of tertiary prevention is actually quite limited, even in higher prevalence communities, as only a sub-group of pregnant women who drink alcohol are giving birth to affected children.

Older women were found to be more often the mothers of FAS/FAE children, with a mean age of mothers at the birth of a child with FAS or FAE being 29.7 years. The mean age of mothers who had children without FAS or FAE screened in the project by May and colleagues was 26.7 years and the mean age for all women in these groups who had children was somewhere around 24.8 years (May, Hymbaugh, Aase and Samet, 1983). According to May (1991), the relationship between maternal age to fetal alcohol damage may be influenced by the following factors: drinking style, drinking severity and progression of consumption to chronic levels; physiologic, metabolic and enzymatic factors; and individual genetic predisposition to alcohol problems. May goes on to state:

---

[29]   *The Broken Cord*, by Michael Dorris (1989), is the true story of an American Indian Anthropology professor and his adopted son, Adam, a Sioux child who had severe FAS. Dorris documents the difficulties Adam faced as a child and adolescent, and the problems he had as a parent learning about his son's illness. May suggests that even though the problematic traits that Adam manifests are typical of most children with FAS regardless of ethnic identity, many people have associated these traits with other events that are typically Indian and described in the book. The confusion, May adds, of Indian cultural characteristics with the characteristics of FAS has been a problem for some readers (May, 1991:240 n2).

Chapter 7

Regardless of the specific etiology, no woman in this study who had one child with FAS or FAE ever had a less affected child in a subsequent pregnancy unless she became a total abstainer. The relationship between maternal age and FAS needs to be examined further, for it was a very definite and highly complicated variable of risk (1991:243).

May further explains the complexity of the lives of mothers who gave birth to affected children:

> The social situation of all southwestern Indian mothers who had children with FAS or FAE was found to be very disrupted and highly lethal; their medical situations also were highly lethal. Twenty-three percent of these mothers were dead at the time the damage was diagnosed in their children (May, Hymbaugh, Aase and Samet, 1983). This is similar to that reported by others in subsequent studies (Asante and Nelms-Matzke, 1985; Streissguth et al., 1985). In the studies of southwestern Indians, all mothers of children with FAS or FAE died of alcohol-related causes, from cirrhosis to trauma. Few living mothers who were drinking led a life in the mainstream of the culture, community, or family; most were involved with highly alcoholic peer groups, having been downwardly mobile and ostracized by non-drinking friends or relatives. Because of this, 73 percent of the children with FAS and FAE had been adopted or were in foster homes by the time of diagnosis in the study. This trend is also being reported in studies of other populations (Streissguth et al., 1985; 1988; Streissguth, Aase et al., 1991). The lives of alcoholic women who give birth to children with FAS and FAE are very chaotic, placing a tremendous burden on others in the rest of society (1991:243).

In concluding his review, May (1991) suggests that balancing societal and individual interests are essential in addressing prevention and intervention of FAS/FAE. Of central concern, he argues, are the needs, problems, and rights of the mothers, as well as their children, and the need to consider the long-term effects of alcohol-related birth effects on the larger community or society.

A pilot FAS surveillance project was carried out in four American Indian communities in the Northern Plains to determine the incidence of FAS during the period of 1987 to 1990 (Duimstra, Johnson et al., 1993). Four of the 1,022 children included in the project were found to have FAS, a rate of 3.9 per 1,000 live births. The authors suggest the rate is an under-estimate because 39 per cent of the infants were not screened and 25 per cent of the suspected infants were not evaluated. As a result, they proposed a much higher rate of 8.5 cases of FAS per 1,000 live births, which they believe is still an under-estimate of the actual number of cases.

In 1991 and 1993, a Centers for Disease Control (CDC) (1994) survey was conducted to determine the prevalence of alcohol consumption by women of child-bearing age in Alaska. Based on 511 respondents, an estimated 45 per cent were categorized as non-drinkers, 38 per cent as light drinkers and 17 per cent as heavy drinkers. Non-American Indian/Alaskan Native (AI/AN) women reported light drinking (41%) more often than AI/AN women (17%). The prevalence of heavy drinking among non-AI/AN women (15%) was half the rate found in AI/AN women (32%).

Chapter 7

Egeland and colleagues (1998) attempted to determine the prevalence and characteristics of FAS in Alaska, the American state with the highest rate of alcohol-related hospitalizations and the highest per capita alcohol consumption levels. Alaska is among the top five American states in terms of prevalence of binge drinking. Identification of potential FAS cases was determined through review of medical charts from the private medical sector, the state of Alaska, the Indian Health Service and regional Native health corporations.

The number of live births in Alaska from 1977 to 1982, the period in which the majority of identified FAS patients were born, provided the denominator. A total of 630 potential FAS cases from all of the available data sources were identified. Almost 23 per cent (n=145) met the five diagnostic criteria for FAS, had medical charts available for review, confirmed prenatal alcohol exposure or a maternal history of alcohol abuse and had a physician notation of diagnosed or suspected FAS. Of the patients diagnosed with FAS and whose custody status was known (n=127), 67 per cent were either adopted or in foster care (Egeland, Perham-Hester et al., 1998).

The prevalence of FAS in Alaska was found to be 0.8 per 1,000 live births during 1977 to 1992. Among Alaska Natives, the prevalence of the condition ranged from as low as 1.4 per 1,000 live births from 1977 to 1980, to a high of 4.1 per 1,000 live births from 1985 to 1988. Among non-Alaska Natives, the prevalence ranged from a low of 0.1 between 1977 and 1984, to a high of 0.3 in 1989 through 1992 (Egeland, Perham-Hester et al., 1998).

Sixty-five per cent of all case patients were uniquely identified by active screening and referral programs for diagnostic clinics, whereas birth certificates and hospital discharge summaries of live births did not yield sufficient numbers of cases to be considered important data sources. The greater FAS rates observed among Alaska Natives relative to non-Alaska Natives may be attributed, in part, to the extensive case finding activities of the Indian Health Service and to the under-diagnoses of FAS in the non-Alaskan Native group (Egeland, Perham-Hester et al., 1998).

As with earlier studies, Egeland and colleagues (1998) found that a limited number of women gave birth to multiple affected children. In their study, fourteen women gave birth to thirty-two children who were case patients (22 per cent of all affected children in the study). In one example, a woman gave birth to four affected children and to three other children who had a physician mention FAS in their medical chart. Egeland and colleagues write:

> Birth certificates obtained for 102 case patients (70%) showed that 63% of mothers were not married at delivery and that 41% had not completed high school. (In contrast, for the general population, only 18% of Alaska mothers delivering between 1989 and 1993 had no or late prenatal care, and only 15% did not finish high school). The average number of living children born prior to the child with fetal alcohol syndrome was 2.4 (SD=2.0). Sixty-nine percent of mothers either had no prenatal care (33%) or began prenatal care after the first trimester (36%). Medical charts and birth certificates documented an average maternal age at the time of delivery of 29 years (SD=5.0, range = 15 to 45) and documented prenatal tobacco use for 39% of the case mothers. Medical charts mentioned cocaine use for 8% and marijuana use for 8% of the case mothers (1998:784).

Chapter 7

In conclusion, Egeland and colleagues (1998) caution that the report's reliance on medical chart notations has, most likely, resulted in an under-representation of the actual rate of FAS. Other factors, such as the exclusion of some pediatric practices and hospitals, and the risk that a portion of the individuals in their patient population meeting the five case definition criteria for FAS may not have FAS, are also limitations of the study's methodology.

The United States

Along with research studies in American Indian communities, several other studies have been conducted in the United States. In a medical-record based prospective cohort study conducted in a hospital in Cleveland, Ohio, Sokol and colleagues (1980) found that 5 of 12,243 infants born over a 52-month period were diagnosed with FAS, giving a prevalence of 0.41 per 1,000. However, no specific diagnostic criteria for FAS was given by the study's authors and the study lacked detailed information on levels of alcohol exposure. In this type of study, risk information is collected prospectively for a total patient population sample and outcomes are evaluated. The advantage of such a study is that it allows for direct comparison of pregnancy risk factors associated and not associated with alcohol abuse and of relative risks for exposed and unexposed infants. Sokol and colleagues (1980) found that alcohol-abusing patients were, on average, more than two years older than the control patients in the study and were more likely to have been married in the past, but less likely to be married during the index pregnancy than the control group. Racial distribution and maternal or paternal educational levels were not found to be significantly different among the alcohol group as compared to the rest of the pregnant patients, but pregnant women in the alcohol group were more likely to have had a previous pregnancy and one or more previous viable infants and/or abortions. Cigarette smoking was a major confounding variable and was significantly associated with alcohol abusers. Sokol and colleagues write:

> ... the alcohol-abusing patients were nearly three times more likely to have had previous psychiatric or social service contact, there were few other important differences in the medical histories of the two groups. However, initial comparison revealed that the previous obstetric histories of the alcohol abusers were considerably worse than those of the comparison group. Because the alcohol group had more previous pregnancies, these comparisons were limited to ... patients who had a previous pregnancy history. Controlling for gravidity in this way, the alcohol group was found to be more than twice as likely to have a history of habitual abortion (three or more consecutive, spontaneous). History of induced abortion and other previous low-birth-weight infants was found to be increased 1.5-fold, and the frequency of previous fetal anomaly to be increased over fourfold in the alcohol group (1980:138).

In conclusion, Sokol and colleagues (1980) caution that prospective cohort studies that adjust for confounding variables, such as their study, are never complete and, therefore, inferences concerning etiology should be interpreted with great caution and considered to be speculative. However, they add that, despite methodological weaknesses, the study strongly suggests that the prevalence rates of FAS produced by this study are most likely the "tip of the iceberg."

The Centers for Disease Control (1993) (CDC) Birth Defects Monitoring Program (BDMP), which uses hospital discharge data on newborns (both live and stillborn), has collected data on the incidence of FAS among newborn infants since 1979. From 1979 through 1992, a total of 1,782 FAS cases were reported among 9,057,624 births, a rate of 0.2 per 1,000. The incidence rates increased from 0.1 per 1,000 in 1979 to approximately 0.4 per 1,000 in 1991, which could reflect either an increase in the recognition and reporting by physicians and/or a true increase in incidence. In another CDC report published in 1993, FAS was reported in 126 of 188,905 newborns, a rate of 0.67 per 1,000. Overall, during 1979 to 1993, FAS was reported in 2,032 of 9,434,560 newborns, a rate of 0.22 per 1,000 (Centers for Disease Control, 1995). Nevertheless, neither the sensitivity nor the specificity of the BDMP data is known and, therefore, it is difficult to interpret the increase in the incidence of FAS.

In attempts to develop a more accurate estimate of the prevalence of FAS in a defined population, the CDC linked data from the Metropolitan Atlanta Congenital Defects Program (MACDP) and the Metropolitan Atlanta Developmental Disabilities Surveillance Program (MADDSP) for children born in Atlanta during 1981 to 1989 (Centers for Disease Control, 1997). During the study period, the two systems combined identified 92 children with possible FAS; the observed prevalence of full-blown FAS was 10 cases per 1,000 live births.

From data collected through the 1990 National Institute on Drug Abuse (NIDA) House-hold Survey, researchers estimated that, of the approximately 60 million women of child-bearing age (15 to 44 years) assessed in the United States, 50.8 per cent used alcohol, 29 per cent smoked cigarettes, 6.5 per cent used marijuana, 0.9 per cent used cocaine and 8.0 per cent used some type of illicit drug during the month prior to the study interview (National Institute on Drug Abuse, 1991).

Some studies attempt to assess changes in alcohol consumption during pregnancy. Serdula and colleagues (1991) analysed data on 38,244 women (aged 18 to 45) who were randomly selected from twenty-one American states over a 4-year period beginning in 1985. Overall, 429 (25%) of 1,712 pregnant women and 19,903 (55%) of 36,057 non-pregnant women reported using alcohol in the previous month. Although the prevalence of alcohol consumption among pregnant women declined steadily, from 32 per cent in 1985 to 20 per cent in 1988, the median number of drinks per month for pregnant women who drank did not change. In another American study (Day, Richardson et al., 1990) of pregnant women, 44 per cent of whom were considered heavy drinkers before becoming pregnant, researchers found that drinking decreased markedly during pregnancy, but after delivery, returned to equivalent pre-pregnancy rates.

Other Countries

A number of FAS/ARBE epidemiology studies have occurred outside of North American. In a study aimed at assisting in the development of a standardized instrument to evaluate the symptoms associated with FAS, the offsprings of all women who had been registered since 1970 for treatment of alcoholism in Budapest, Hungary, and who gave birth after January 1, 1964 were studied. Out of the 301 children in the study, 25 met typical FAS diagnostic criteria (an incidence of 83 per 1,000) and all were confirmed to be born to mothers who consumed alcohol during their pregnancies (Vitez, Koranyi et al., 1984). The sample studied was not representative of the general population since participants were all women who were registered for alcoholism treatment.

Chapter 7

In a letter published in 1985, Palmer reported the incidence of FAS in a hospital in Cape Town, South Africa. During the 12-month period from July 1984 to the end of June 1985, 14 infants were diagnosed with FAS, giving an incidence of 1 in 281 newborns (3.6 per 1,000). The incidence for *Coloured* infants was 1 in 196 (5.1 per 1,000) and 1 in 395 (2.5 per 1,000) among *Blacks; Whites* were not seen at this hospital. The majority of women were from low socio-economic backgrounds and the study took place during apartheid in South Africa. In all cases, heavy alcohol abuse by the mother during pregnancy was confirmed and many women reported being largely unaware of the potential dangers of drinking alcohol during pregnancy. No further information on the characteristics of the women studied, nor of their children, were reported by the researcher (Palmer, 1985).

The prevalence of FAS in a community in Western Cape Province of the Republic of South Africa was estimated through active case ascertainment (May, Brooke et al., 2000). Twelve out of the thirteen elementary schools in the community studied (n=992 children aged 5 to 9 years) were assessed. The one school that refused to participate was an all-White school with 80 children. Age-specific rates of FAS (ages 6 to 7) were 39.2 to 42.9 per 1,000 children. May and colleagues (2000) suggest that the high rates found may be due to most people of the Western Cape being involved in growing grapes and producing wine, which influences regional drinking patterns. Wine is also distributed among and consumed daily by workers as partial payment for labour, and increased availability of inexpensive commercial wine, beer and liquor has also contributed to heavy drinking in the region. Weekend binge drinking is a major form of recreation among sub-segments of the population. Several mothers of the children diagnosed with FAS during the study were either deceased or could not be located, as in American and Canadian studies discussed earlier. Researchers suggest this is indicative of the chaotic and often dangerous lives some alcoholic women lead (May, Brooke et al., 2000).

The community studied by May and colleagues (2000) is an established community with a low-wage economy that is under-going only moderate rates of modernization, which raises the question of the effects of socio-economic status and ethnicity on the estimates given. The children who were diagnosed were primarily from the *Coloured* or mixed ancestry group; fewer than 5 per cent were exclusively Black African and fewer than 6 per cent were White. Mothers of children diagnosed with FAS characterized their pregnancy as a time in their lives when they had many life problems and drank more heavily. In conclusion, May and colleagues write: "The early stages of economic development, low education attainment, low SES [socio-economic status], increased access to alcohol, and loss of folk and traditional culture may cause extreme alcohol misuse, which elevates the risk of fetal alcohol syndrome" (2000:1911).

Studies have also tried to estimate the rate of alcohol consumption by pregnant women. One study (Gibson, Baghurst et al., 1983) looked at women who gave birth at an Australian hospital between 1975 and 1981, in order to report on maternal alcohol consumption. Among the 7,301 births reported for that period, 25.5 per cent of the mothers had abstained altogether from drinking alcohol during their pregnancy, 67.9 per cent reported drinking one drink or less on average per day (less than 10g per day) and 1.5 per cent reported being heavy drinkers (more than 30g per day).

Two studies estimating the incidence or prevalence of FAS were conducted in France. The first study included pregnant women presenting at a public maternity hospital between 1985 and 1986. Two children were diagnosed as having FAS (one born to a woman who was alcoholic and the other born to a woman who was a light drinker) from the 202 infants assessed (a prevalence of 9.8 per 1,000). It is believed that this was an over-estimation because the hospital from which participants were recruited was located in an area of higher than average alcohol consumption (12 per cent were alcoholics, 13 per cent were heavy drinkers, 28 per cent were moderate drinkers and 47 per cent were light drinkers) (Rostand, Kaminski et al., 1990). The second study was conducted by Maillard and colleagues (1999) in Réunion Island, an overseas French county situated in the Indian Ocean. During the entire year of 1996, 2,778 newborns were delivered in an obstetric unit and were included in the study. The incidence of full-blown FAS was found to be 1.8 per 1,000 births, whereas the incidence of both full and partial FAS was found to be 4.3 per 1,000 births (Maillard, Lamblin et al., 1999).

Olegard and colleagues (1979) reported on a prospective study of approximately 7,600 deliveries in the city of Göteborg, Sweden, between May 1977 to November 1978. The study suggested a minimum incidence rate of 1/300 for FAS/FAE and 1/600 for FAS alone. In a subsequent study, Olegard (1992) reported that the incidence of FAS in Sweden in 1983 was 0.42 per 1,000 (1 in 2,400). He suggested that a decrease in the incidence rate of FAS may have been linked to increased public health information, support given by prenatal clinics and to the attention by the mass media to FAS issues since the late 1970s.

A self-completed survey was sent in 1993 to all New Zealand pediatricians registered in the country, in order to estimate the prevalence of FAS (Leversha and Marks, 1995). The pediatricians were asked to state the number of children less than 10 years of age with FAS under their care at the time of the survey. Eighty-four per cent of surveys sent were used in the analysis through which 63 cases of FAS (cared for by 36 pediatricians) were identified. Prevalence rates were not determined by the study due to methodological problems; however, the researchers felt that under-diagnosis was the norm in most clinical practices. Leversha and colleagues (1995) found that the majority of pediatricians caring for children diagnosed as FAS or ARBE were more likely to consider the diagnosis when assessing children with certain clinical features, the most frequent being children of high risk mothers and children with dysmorphic features. Nowhere in their report did they include information on ethnic or socio-economic status or how they defined 'high risk mothers.' Rather, the definition of 'high risk mothers' was based on each physician's personal definition of high risk (Leversha and Marks, 1995). Glasgow (1996) points out that the indirect retrospective study by Leversha and colleagues does not provide justification for their claim that the incidence of FAS is somewhere between 0.33 to 5.9 per 1,000 live births. Rather, Glasgow suggests that, based on international findings, New Zealand is more likely to have rates in the average range, closer to 0.33 per 1,000, making this figure an average rather than minimum estimate.

Some studies have chosen to address the association between alcohol consumption during pregnancy and fetal outcomes that is *suggestive* of FAS/FAE, rather than base a determined diagnosis. In a study, which was conducted between 1982 and 1984 to investigate the effect of low or moderate alcohol consumption before pregnancy upon birth outcomes, 605 consecutive pregnant women attending a public maternity hospital in Western Australia were selected, based on their alcohol intake prior to pregnancy, to represent a wide spectrum of drinkers (Walpole, Zubrick et al., 1990). The participants filled out extensive questionnaires that covered information on demographic characteristics and lifestyle during pregnancy (including alcohol and cigarette consumption). Infant birth weight, birth length, head circumference, as well as other morphological data were not found to be significantly associated with pre-pregnancy absolute alcohol consumption. The authors concluded that newborns of mothers who drank light or moderate amounts of alcohol showed no detrimental effects that could be attributed to such exposure; rather, such an effect might follow a dose-response relation, with a yet undetermined heavier dose level leading to a response in fetal development (Walpole, Zubrick et al., 1990).

International Review Articles

Abel and Sokol (1991) estimated the incidence of FAS in the Western world based on 15 prospective studies of general obstetric populations appearing for prenatal care. The incidence of FAS was determined to be 0.33 cases per 1,000. The estimate among Whites was 0.29 per 1,000, compared with 0.48 per 1,000 for Blacks. No estimate for Aboriginal people was calculated because of the absence of prospectively gathered data on FAS for this group.

Abel and colleagues conducted two reviews of the epidemiological literature in which they reported on the worldwide incidence of FAS (Abel and Sokol, 1986; Abel, 1995). The first review was completed in 1986 and reviewed 19 different epidemiological studies in which 164 FAS cases were reported from populations totalling 88,236 live births. Collectively, these studies gave a frequency of 1.9 per 1,000 live births (Abel and Sokol, 1986). Three points should be raised about this estimate, which was based on different published studies before 1985: first, most of the published articles were case reports rather than analytical epidemiological studies and were based on a small number of cases; second, these case reports included specific populations who were not representative of the general population; and third, most of the case reports reviewed did not provide an estimate of the number of live births.

The second report, published in 1995, reviewed 29 prospective studies (Abel, 1995). Abel estimated the worldwide incidence rate of FAS to be 0.97 cases per 1,000 live births (95 cases out of 97,576). However, an estimated incidence was found to be lower than 0.50 per 1,000 when, instead of determining the overall rate per 1,000 (adding all cases of FAS and dividing by the number of total live births), Abel averaged the incidence rate from each study. Following this analysis, Abel found the median rate per study was zero cases of FAS per 1,000, which was also the mode. He points out that this discrepancy between the mean and the median indicates that FAS has not been uniformly encountered in these studies and, thus, FAS appears to occur considerably more often (or less often) at some sites than others. Rates of FAS among heavy drinkers was calculated to be 43.1 per 1,000. Abel concluded that the most critical determinant for the presence of FAS is the country in which the study is conducted. In Abel's study, the rate of FAS in the United States was found to be 1.95 per 1,000 (91 out of 46,497 cases) compared to 0.08 per 1,000 (4 out of 51,079 cases) for other countries.

The 'American Paradox,' Abel (1998b) states, refers to the high rate of FAS in the United States on the one hand; and, on the other hand, the relatively low rate of per capita alcohol consumption. Abel found that this phenomenon is similar to the association between spontaneous abortion and alcohol consumption. Epidemiological studies that reported an increase in spontaneous abortion rates, with very low levels of drinking during pregnancy, were conducted almost entirely in the United States or Canada. Those studies, which did not find a significant link between the two variables, were studies conducted in Europe or Australia. Abel summarized the per capita alcohol consumption for 13 different countries, along with incidence data for FAS obtained from prospective epidemiological studies (to minimize selection bias that could affect estimates). The United States had the world's highest incidence of FAS (1.95/1,000), but had a relatively low per capita rate of alcohol consumption (7.31 of absolute alcohol). The United Kingdom, which had an annual per capita consumption very similar to the United States, had 0 cases of FAS per 1,000 births. France, which had the highest per capita consumption (13.0 of absolute alcohol), had an estimated incidence of 1.3 per 1,000 births. These differences were not explained by any difference in the percentages of women of reproductive age who were drinking prior to, or during, pregnancy in each of the countries. In other words, the incidence of FAS was not higher in the United States because more American women drink during pregnancy compared to elsewhere.

Disparity between countries in the reported incidence of FAS may lie in either the physicians who are making the diagnosis (e.g., bias, knowledge of diagnostic criteria, skills) or the populations being diagnosed. For example, incidence rates may be higher in the United States because American clinicians are more inclined than physicians elsewhere to characterize anomalies as FAS (Abel, 1998b). Facial features associated with FAS may also be a normal variant among some Native American and African-American populations. Since these populations are overly represented in epidemiological studies of FAS in the United States, their presence contributes greatly to the incidence of FAS. Finally, in the United States, incidence rates for FAS vary widely, depending on the study site and are almost entirely a function of socio-economic status (SES). In studies where the population examined was primarily of middle SES and Caucasian, the incidence rate was found to be 0.26 per 1,000, which is very close to the incidence rate in Europe. By comparison, the incidence rate at sites where the patient population was primarily of low SES and was African-American, the rate was 10 times higher, 2.29 per 1,000. Abel (1998b) concludes that the most likely alternative is that FAS arises out of a combination of alcohol abuse and poverty.

Conclusion

The studies reviewed in this chapter suggest that rates of FAS/ARBEs, especially among Aboriginal people in North America, may be increasing. However, this claim, along with suggestions that FAS/ARBEs are more prevalent among Aboriginal groups than non-Aboriginal groups is questionable, based on the available research data. For example, researchers selected some of the Aboriginal communities surveyed because FAS/ARBEs were thought to be a major public health problem. Furthermore, while there are few epidemiological studies on FAS/ARBEs among Aboriginal people in Canada, there is even less research on the prevalence of FAS/ARBEs in non-Aboriginal populations. This makes it difficult, if not impossible, to make a valid comparison of the prevalence rates for Aboriginal and non-Aboriginal people in Canada.

Before it can be concluded that Aboriginal children are at an increased risk of being born with FAS/ARBEs, important questions should be addressed. Research examining how demographic, socio-economic and socio-cultural factors may be related to an increased risk of FAS/ARBEs for some Aboriginal groups needs to be conducted (Bray and Anderson, 1989). Furthermore, obtaining an accurate measurement of the prevalence of FAS/ARBEs in a given region involves the study of every family and child, or at least selecting a representative sample from the region in which to carry out screening. Abel (1998a) argues that studies that rely on referral only for their sample population may not account for environmental and cultural factors, especially where minorities are concerned. Furthermore, these studies may end up with an over-representation of affected individuals and, thus, higher prevalence rates because of the use of referral as a way to identify study participants, rather than the use of representative sampling. While FAS/ARBEs are a serious health problem, Aboriginal people should be critical of claims that suggest Aboriginal people are at greater risk and should be cautious in applying prevalence rates found in particular high risk communities to all Aboriginal groups.

Chapter 8

Risk and Protective Factors for Women

Introduction

> It is simplistic to assume that women at risk for AARBEs [alcohol abuse-related birth effects], i.e. pregnant women who abuse alcohol, will reduce their drinking simply because they are told that to do so will reduce the risk of birth defects. If helping someone to stop or reduce his or her drinking were that simple, the tremendous individual and social costs associated with alcohol abuse (Rice, Kelman, Miller and Dussmeyer, 1990) would vanish overnight (Abel, 1998c:418).

> In many settings, women who abuse alcohol have been considered social "throw aways," have been ostracized, or have been otherwise stigmatized and left to produce one, two, or more FAS or FAE children before their own alcohol-related death ...Thus FAS prevention efforts hold the additional promise of reducing premature mortality among high risk mothers (Masis and May, 1991:488).

A general consensus exists among scientific researchers, medical and social service professionals, para-professionals and lay persons that fetal alcohol syndrome (FAS) and alcohol-related birth effects (ARBEs) are one-hundred per cent preventable (Tait, 2003). This consensus is based on a simple premise: 'if pregnant women refrain from drinking alcohol, babies with FAS/ARBEs will not be born.' While this premise may appear straightforward, creating and implementing effective programs and services to assist pregnant women to avoid engaging in substance abuse have been difficult. Most programs currently in place in North America have had limited success in achieving mass prevention[30] among women believed to be at highest risk for producing affected offspring.

Before discussing 'best practices' in relation to the programs and services created to prevent ARBEs, it is important to review the literature on risk and protective factors for pregnant women and for women of child-bearing age, more generally, who struggle with alcohol abuse. This review is required in order to understand the myriad of challenges faced by women with substance abuse problems, as well as those faced by service providers, researchers, local communities and governments in providing successful prevention, identification and intervention services and programs.

---

[30]   A very limited amount of literature exists that evaluates prevention programs and services or 'best practices' for the prevention of ARBEs. Within the past five years, several outreach programs in Canada have been developed for 'high risk' women, particularly in the western provinces and in some First Nations and Inuit communities; however, there is only limited information available as to the success of these programs (see Leslie and Roberts, 2001). Information that is available will be discussed in detail in Chapter Nine.

Chapter 8

The Controversy Over Defining 'Risk' and 'Risk Behaviour'

> ... one to three drinks per day in the first two months of pregnancy can cause brain damage in the developing fetus ... Maybe pregnant women should learn that "life is not a beer commercial." Their lament need no longer be, "if only we had known". Fetal alcohol syndrome is a 100-percent preventable tragedy (Waldman, 1989:437).

> The simple fact is that the term fetal alcohol syndrome has created such a false impression that large numbers of clinicians now believe even minimal amounts of alcohol consumption during pregnancy can produce the syndrome. Because no cases of this syndrome have ever been found outside the context of alcohol abuse, renaming it fetal alcohol abuse syndrome ... should also keep many children from being misdiagnosed and receiving treatment, if any, for a condition they do not have. The mistaken impression that minimal amounts of alcohol can cause individual anomalies is also rampant. Individual anomalies resulting from alcohol toxicity in utero were initially called "possible fetal alcohol effects". The 'possible" was subsequently dropped and, like fetal alcohol syndrome, the term *fetal alcohol effects'* (FAE) took on a life of its own (Abel, 1998a:8).

> She explained that she had gone out with friends after work and had had "more than you would normally have." She said, "Well, then I found out that I was pregnant and I was hysterical." At that time of the interview she reported that she felt better but that she remained concerned. She said, "Last weekend we went out to dinner and I asked for a cranberry spritzer and I went to take a drink of it and it had wine in it. I took a strawful ... I started crying ... I just don't want any alcohol" (Barbour, 1990:82).[31]

Alcohol is a known teratogen that, if consumed by pregnant women, can potentially cause harm to the developing fetus. However, the amount of alcohol, which is safe for a pregnant woman to consume, is, as yet, undetermined and may, in fact, vary to some extent from woman to woman (Abel, 1998a). Potential harm to the fetus may also depend on genetic characteristics of the fetus; however, this has yet to be determined. In a context where no safe amount of alcohol is known, the public health message in North America tends to err on the conservative side, suggesting women who may become pregnant or who are already pregnant should not consume alcohol (Warren and Bast, 1988). It also suggests that any decrease in use will be of benefit to the developing fetus as organ development occurs throughout the pregnancy. There is only limited discussion of risk as it relates to the health of pregnant women who abuse alcohol, and a clear distinction has been made between the health of the pregnant woman and the health of the developing fetus (Tait, 2003). 'Risk,' in most studies, is defined as risk to the fetus and pregnant women engage in 'risk behaviour' that has the potential to harm the developing fetus. While some have suggested the diagnosis 'FAS' implies that there are two patients (Clarren, 1998), the bulk of the literature reviewed for this report clearly indicates the focus is squarely situated on the health of the fetus and not that of the woman (Tait, 2000a; 2003).

---

[31]   Discussion of an interview with a pregnant study participant.

Chapter 8

Assessing Risk

> A great deal of time and money is currently spent interviewing light drinkers and abstainers, while those who drink enough to be of interest are lumped together in a vast heterogeneous category of "heavier" drinkers. A more detailed study of heavier drinkers would enable us, for one thing, to arrive at a better idea of what we are talking about when we speak of "problem drinkers" (Knupfer, 1987 in Abel, 1998:2).

> Because no level of alcohol consumption is free of risk to the fetus, health care professionals should assess the alcohol use of women who are pregnant and those who are considering pregnancy and should counsel these women to abstain from drinking any alcohol (Serdula, Williamson et al., 1991:879).

In FAS/ARBE research, establishing the relationship between the drinking patterns of pregnant women and subsequent birth outcomes is a key area of investigation. In the first study, which introduced FAS as a diagnosis, the infants described were all offspring of *alcoholic* mothers (Jones and Smith, 1973). As Abel (1998a) points out, it was not the alcohol per se, but the abuse of alcohol that was seen to have led to the pattern of anomalies. While a discussion of how alcohol works as a teratogen (Schenker, Becker et al., 1990) is beyond the scope of this report, it is important to discuss some of the basic principles of threshold levels, as well as some of the methodological challenges, such as self-reporting of alcohol use and the use of 'averaging' in alcohol research.

Threshold Levels

> The myth that small amounts of alcohol are not dangerous to the unborn child is common. Many pregnant women want proof that having a drink actually does damage their baby ... The burden of proof is coming up with the numbers that show X-amount of alcohol causes X-amount of damage ... There is no known safe amount of alcohol consumption during pregnancy (Remkes, 1993:1).

> Although the data strongly support a relationship of chronic high levels of maternal alcohol intake to the full FAS, what remains unclear is whether there is a continuum of dose-response effects ranging from anatomic and behavioural changes at low to moderate maternal doses to full-blown FAS at high maternal doses, or if there are two or more thresholds resulting in degrees of impairment in function and structural malformation. As yet undefined is whether there is a LOEL [lowest observable effect level] distinct from the LOAEL [lowest observable adverse effect level] for alcohol exposure in the fetus (Stratton, Howe et al., 1996:42).

At the center of discussions of 'risk,' in relation to ARBEs, is the question of 'safe' levels of alcohol and whether such a level exists. In a review of the literature on dose-effects, Abel (1998a) argues that there has been a tendency in the research literature towards arguments that suggest relatively low levels of alcohol consumption can cause teratological effects. For example, in an article published in February

Chapter 8

2001, Barr and Streissguth wrote that "there is no known low dose that appears to be safe for every pregnancy" (2001:283). However, several problems arise from this type of argument. Determining threshold levels is one such problem. Abel writes:

> Low dose-effects would be possible if teratological effects were conceived in terms of a monotonic dose-response relationship with the etiological agent. But there are no monotonic dose-response relationships in teratology or pharmacology. Instead, every substance has a "threshold" or *no observable effect level (NOEL)* for every response (Hutchings, 1985). In teratology, dose-response relationships are generally "S" shaped- at relatively low doses, there is no observable effect. If the dose is increased, a threshold is exceeded and an effect is triggered. Relatively small increments above that threshold trigger larger effects, until every response capable of being affected is affected and the organism is either severely disturbed or killed (1998a:9, emphasis in text).

What Abel suggests is that, even if alcohol is present in the pregnant woman's system, this does not necessarily mean it will have an effect on the fetus. This is further complicated by the fact that, although alcohol abuse during pregnancy is the 'necessary' cause of ARBEs, it alone is not sufficient to cause these effects. Abel argues that individuals differ in their responses to alcohol implying that there are inherent physiological susceptibilities to its effects (1998a; Stratton, Howe et al., 1996; Streissguth, 1997). The influence of biological, genetic and environmental factors may cause the threshold dose to vary with each patient (Wheeler, 1993). This is reflected, for example, in the fact that some alcohol-abusing women have children with FAS, others have children with FAE and still others have apparently normal children (Abel, 1998a; 1995; Streissguth and Martin, 1983). This finding also indicates that differences in times and frequency of exposure are important variables, even when heavy drinking occurs (Abel, 1998a; Streissguth, 1997). Several researchers suggest that a decrease in alcohol consumption at any time during a pregnancy has significant potential benefit for the developing fetus (Wheeler, 1993; Streissguth, 1997; Abel, 1998a; Stratton, Howe et al., 1996).

Averaging

The easiest way for researchers to determine how much alcohol individual people drink is to ask them how much they drink during a typical week or month and divide this amount by the appropriate number of days, which then gives an average number of drinks per day. Typically, a single drink contains about 0.5 ounces of alcohol, which is expressed as average ounces or absolute alcohol (AA) per day, or AA/day. In most studies, which look at alcohol consumption levels, a woman who consumes seven glasses of wine once a week, for example, is treated the same way as a woman who drinks an average of one glass of wine per day, even though their drinking patterns are very different (Abel, 1998a). Abel suggests that, because averaging of alcohol consumption has been used in FAS/ ARBE research, some study findings suggest a low threshold level at which alcohol use by a pregnant woman can have deleterious effects on the developing fetus. He writes:

> Although there are several research reports stating that drinking an average of two drinks a day can cause 'significant' effects on offspring, that average of two drinks often turns out to be the result of seven or more drinks on 1 day and the balance spread out over others. It is hardly ever two drinks a day, each day (1998a:10).

Chapter 8

Unless someone was to take the time to examine closely the clinical literature, they may not realize that a measurement of 'average' drinks per day could include women with very different consumption patterns. Abel (1998a) argues for a unifying principle to operationally define the terms used to characterize the low levels of consumption believed by some researchers to cause FAS/ARBEs.

In a review of the literature, Abel also points out the discrepancies that exist around terms such as *moderate* and *heavy* drinking (1998a; Wheeler, 1993). He writes:

> Some, for instance, defined *moderate* as an average daily consumption ranging upward from one and one-half drinks a day (Little, Asker, Sampson and Renwick, 1986) to an average of three drinks a day (Kaminski, Franc, Lebovier, Du Mazubrun and Rumeau-Roquette, 1981). A *drink* is defined as 12 ounces of beer, 5 ounces of wine, or 1.5 ounces of 80-proof distilled spirits. Although heavy drinking implies greater consumption than moderate drinking (Abel and Kruger, 1995), in many cases the operational definition of *heavy* is less than what others call moderate. For example, the threshold for heavy drinking has been defined in some studies as an average of 0.89 drinks a day (Day et al. 1989), 1 drink a day (Shiono, Klebanoff and Rhoads, 1986), or 2 drinks a day (Virji, 1991) ... Emphasizing that ARBEs are due to alcohol abuse not only clarifies our understanding of the amounts of alcohol involved, it also allows us to examine previously reported studies with a more critical eye (1998a:13-14).

Most researchers believe that binge drinking—drinking large quantities of alcohol in short spans of time, particularly chronic binge drinking— is more dangerous for the developing fetus than consumption of the same amount of alcohol over an extended period of time (Abel, 1998a:160; Stratton, Howe et al., 1996). Chronic binge drinking extends the period of alcohol toxicity over a longer duration of pregnancy and, as a result, exposure is more likely to occur during critical periods of development (Abel, 1998a). Abel suggests that since the potential for damage is related to binge drinking, there is little point in describing drinking in terms of 'average drinks per day' because that statistic yields virtually no information about binge-like patterns of consumption and, therefore, little about risk. Abel goes on to argue that, to be biologically relevant, "researchers would be well advised to abandon the average-drinks-per-day measure in favour of one that reflects maximal drinking per occasion and its frequency" (1998a:161).

Self-Reporting

Self-reporting of alcohol use by women is the methodology used by researchers to determine levels of alcohol consumption and patterns of alcohol use by pregnant women. The accuracy of self-reports of alcohol is a concern in the design, conduct and interpretation of studies of ARBEs (Ernhart, Morrow-Tlucak et al., 1988; Robles and Day, 1990). Ernhart and colleagues suggest that under-reporting appears to be more common than over-reporting and that this is a general concern for alcohol studies that rely on self-reporting (1988). Rosett and Weiner suggest that women may report their use of alcohol more accurately while pregnant than afterwards because of concern for the well-being of the fetus (1984; Hingson, Alpert, Day, Dooling, Kayne et al., 1982). Others have suggested a greater social stigma regarding alcohol use during pregnancy might lead to an under-estimation of reported drinking patterns by women (Celentano and McQueen, 1984; Ernhart, Morrow-Tlucak et al., 1988; Duimstra et al., 1993). Self-reporting of alcohol intake, variability of drinking patterns and beverages of differing strength complicate alcohol quantification (Walpole, Zubrick et al., 1990; Ernhart, Morrow-Tlucak et al., 1988). Self-reports may also be jeopardized by the length of time from the birth of the child to the collection of a woman's drinking history while pregnant (Robles and Day, 1990; Tait, 2003). In some instances, this has been as long as eighteen (Robinson, Conry et al., 1987) to twenty (Williams and Gloster, 1999) years. Ernhart and colleagues (1988) argue that role expectations are a central concern for women when giving self-reports. They state:

> Role expectations for pregnant women are probably more stringent than for nonpregnant women. The onus of drinking in pregnancy may thus be sufficiently great so that tendencies toward denial and under-reporting are particularly strong. When a woman has had a reasonably healthy child and when sufficient time has passed for her to distance herself from the behaviour, the need to protect herself through underreporting is reduced and a more valid report may be obtained (1988:506).

Ernhart and colleagues (1988) suggest that under-reporting has a significant impact on the creation of public policies regarding education about the effects of drinking during pregnancy (1988). They argue that the use of under-reported information in setting threshold figures also confounds the task of physicians advising patients about 'safe' levels of drinking during pregnancy. At the extreme, Ernhart and colleagues add: "the uncertainty regarding a threshold for alcohol-related birth defects [which] may affect decisions regarding therapeutic abortions for alcoholic women" (1988:510). Ernhart and colleagues discuss several methodological tools to limit under-reporting; however, they caution that, methodologically, this is a very difficult problem for researchers to fully address.

Timing of Alcohol Consumption and Fetal Development

Assessing risk in relation to alcohol consumption and the timing of various fetal developments has presented several difficulties for researchers and, for the most part, animal studies have been used to try to pinpoint risk periods (Streissguth, 1997; Schenker, Becker et al., 1990). Only a handful of studies have attempted to calculate the risk involved with women who abused alcohol during different trimesters of pregnancy and then gave birth to an affected child. One study was conducted on a random sample of women attending an out-patient clinic in the United States in 1986 (Day, Richardson et al., 1990). Information on alcohol use, as well as medical problems, was collected at different points in times (at each trimester of the pregnancy and when the offspring was 8 months of age) from the study sample, which included 461 mother-infant pairs. Although no infants were diagnosed with FAS at birth, some were diagnosed with FAE (prevalence was not calculated). Two outcomes were considered at the age of 8 months: minor physical anomalies (two or more physical anomalies vs. none) and FAE (two or more characteristics vs. none).

The relative risks for minor physical anomalies were found to be 1.42, 1.41 and 2.21 in the first, second and third trimester; whereas, those for FAE were 1.22, 1.67 and 2.82, all were significant at the 0.05 level of significance. Nevertheless, no information on the exposure categories in the logistic analysis were provided by the researchers, which makes it difficult to place these risks into context. Another factor that might have affected the validity of the estimates is the fact that most of the women in the sample were of low socio-economic status (with the median income between $400 and $499 per month). The same cohort was used in a later analysis to assess the effects of prenatal alcohol use on the growth and morphology of children at three years of age. No diagnosis of FAS/FAE was reported, but traits suggestive of this outcome were considered. Weight and head circumference were found to be significant and inversely associated with alcohol use during the second and third trimester, whereas height was found to be significantly associated with alcohol use during the third trimester only (Day, Richardson et al., 1991).

Rostand and colleagues (1990) examined alcohol use during the first trimester of pregnancy. They found that the proportion of children with features suggestive of FAE was significantly higher among women who reported heavy drinking (three drinks a day or more) early in their pregnancy and among alcoholic women than among light and moderate drinkers. The relative risk was 5-4 for alcoholics compared to light and moderate drinkers (95% confidence interval: 2-5 to 12-0) and 2.9 for heavy drinkers (95% confidence interval: 1-1 to 7-8). However, the relative risk estimation, as it extends to pregnancy outcomes in general, is questionable, since the calculation is based on a small number of infants having features *suggestive* of FAE (7 born to light and moderate drinkers, 19 born to heavy drinkers and 36 born to alcoholics).

Ernhart and colleagues (1989) screened 7,764 women who registered in the antenatal clinics of a Cleveland hospital over a three-year period. Three hundred fifty-nine mother-infant pairs from the larger cohort were recruited into a prospective child development cohort to examine early pregnancy exposure. Three indices, based on self-reporting by women, were used in the study and were correlated with each other to measure alcohol exposure with reasonable accuracy. Ernhart and colleagues arrived at a conservative threshold value of AA/day=1.5 or an average of about three drinks per day during the period prior to knowledge of pregnancy.

However, Ernhart and colleagues (1989) point out that, for a number of heavy-drinking women, the average was derived from weekend drinking and, therefore, many of the fetuses whose mothers averaged three drinks per day were often subject to much heavier drinking. Ernhart and colleagues found that the offspring of women drinking small amounts of alcohol early in pregnancy did not differ from the offspring of abstaining women with respect to FAS-related neonatal anomalies. Their results thus support the inference of a threshold level for significant effects related to heavy drinking.

Perceptions of Risk

Perceptions of risk held by members of certain sub-populations have been the focus of several research studies to better understand why some women abuse alcohol while pregnant. These studies generally focus on lay members of the community, particularly women of child-bearing age. Within this body of research, there are differing views between researchers themselves as to what constitutes 'risk behaviour' in relation to substance abuse and pregnancy. For example, Williams and Gloster (1999), in a study of perceptions of risk associated with alcohol consumption and pregnancy among an Aboriginal group living in northern Manitoba, found that 61% of the women (n=242) and men (n=224) in the study believed that there was a safe amount of alcohol that could be consumed during pregnancy, and 28% believed a father who abused alcohol could biologically affect the unborn baby at the time of conception because of his drinking. Williams and Gloster suggest that answering 'yes' to the statement "a safe amount of alcohol can be consumed when pregnant" and/or "a father's drinking can biologically affect an unborn baby" is an indication that participants and/or their spouses are ignorant or ill-informed about the dangers of alcohol use during pregnancy. The researchers add that, within the framework of their study, an answer of 'yes' to either of these statements suggests participants may engage in risk behaviour.

Koren and colleagues (1996) take a differing stance than that taken by Williams and Gloster. They examined the perceived risk of mild maternal drinking and pregnancy outcome held by thirty non-pregnant adult women between the ages of 19 to 52 years. Women in the study were asked to complete a questionnaire on alcohol consumption during pregnancy to ascertain their perceptions of risk levels. They were then asked to view a one minute public health video released in 1991 by the Manitoba Medical Association.

The video contained the following narrative and was accompanied by a view of a fetus frozen in an ice cube, which was dropped in slow motion into a glass of whisky:

> Your baby ... Drinking alcohol during pregnancy may cause physical, mental and behavioural abnormalities in your baby. There is no known safe amount. Regardless of age or race, any drink containing alcohol puts your baby at risk. What you drink your baby drinks. Is there any choice?

The video ends with a view of a pregnant woman being offered a drink, to which she answers: "No thanks, we are not drinking" (Koren, Koren et al., 1996:157). Prior to screening the video, twenty-one participants responded that one drink per day throughout pregnancy is harmful to the developing fetus, whereas only seven believed that even a single drink during pregnancy could cause fetal damage. Following the video screening, nineteen women believed that even one drink during pregnancy could harm the fetus (P—0.0001). No women changed their view to a less alarming one (Koren, Koren et al., 1996). Koren and colleagues suggest that, by using the statement: "any drink containing alcohol puts your baby at risk" (1996:161), the Manitoba Medical Association was advising women against the body of scientific literature that has determined there was no increased risk of fetal damage from low level exposure.

Koren and colleagues (1996) suggest that, while many services for pregnant women advise abstinence, this is complicated when considering unplanned pregnancies, and such a message is unduly alarming. They argue that, based on the change in perceptions of study participants, women are greatly influenced by public health messages and, in this situation, may result in unnecessary anxiety and termination of wanted pregnancies. They conclude: "While it may be politically incorrect to suggest that an "evil" such as alcohol can be safe at low dose in early pregnancy, scientists and physicians should refrain from political considerations when offering health advice to the public" (Koren, Koren et al., 1996:162).

Tait (2000a) found that perceptions of risk attributed to in-utero alcohol exposure varied among Manitoba women who reported using alcohol during one or more of their pregnancies, and among service providers in the province who provided front-line services to these women, including counselling for pregnancy and substance abuse. Tait attributed these differences to the lack of a standard public health message agreed upon by service providers in the province and to women's experience with pregnancy outcomes not reflecting the public health messages they were receiving (e.g., most women who drank alcohol, including some alcoholic women, did not give birth to affected children). For example, women generally reported that they felt the public health message was mainly about alcohol use rather than abuse and it promoted only an abstinence message. Therefore, whether one drank a little alcohol or a lot did not seem to be that significant. What mattered most was that a pregnant woman should not drink alcohol. While abstinence, according to many of the women, was also the message given to them by most service providers, maintaining abstinence was simply not a viable option for most of the women, given the severity of their addiction problems (Tait, 2000a).

Some studies found that women had received mixed public health messages about the risk of substance use during pregnancy, particularly concerning when the fetus was most susceptible to being affected. Others reported that women switched from drinking 'hard liquor' to wine or beer because they thought this was less harmful to the fetus (Barbour, 1990). Women also reported that they had known family members or friends who drank alcohol throughout their pregnancy and had very normal children (Barbour, 1990; Tait, 2003) or that they had a previous child whose health was normal despite their consumption of alcohol while pregnant. Some women used their own health status as an indication that the risks were minimal, as they knew their mothers had consumed alcohol when they were pregnant with them (Tait, 2000a).

In a comparative study looking at the perceptions of the Norwegian general public and, more specifically, pregnant women, toward alcohol use during pregnancy, Ihlen and colleagues (1993) found that, over a five-year period, attitudes changed significantly in both groups and levels of alcohol consumed by pregnant women decreased by more than fifty per cent. They attribute this outcome to the education of health care personnel about the dangers of substance use during pregnancy, which was subsequently passed on to pregnant women and to mass media campaigns targeting pregnant women (1993). Ihlen and colleagues point out that alcohol consumption among pregnant women who had the highest levels of consumption may, however, not have decreased significantly and, therefore, would require further intervention services for this sub-group (1993; Blume, 1996).

Poole points out that at the forefront of psycho-social influences on women's use and misuse of substances is the stigma arising from societal attitudes toward substance use and women (1997; Finkelstein, Kennedy et al., 1997). Women often internalize this societal stigma, causing them to feel intense guilt and shame as their substance use/misuse continues. Poole adds that guilt and shame can underlie the often well-founded fear of women with substance abuse problems that they will lose custody of their children if their substance use becomes known to those in authority (1997; Tait, 2000a).

Physicians' Perceptions

In a 1996 study of 500 obstetricians, pediatricians and general practitioners in Michigan were asked to respond to a questionnaire about FAS. One-third of the study participants stated that FAS could be the result of the consumption of as little as one drink of alcohol a day (Abel and Kruger, 1998). Abel (1998a) states that this belief is held despite there not being a single instance in hundreds of case reports and clinical studies within the scientific literature, where the mother of a child with FAS was not an alcoholic.

Chapter 8

Abel refers to the work of Dr. Hans-Ludwig Sophr, a well-known FAS researcher:

> Dr. Hans-Ludwig Spohr, whose clinical experience with this disorder spans several decades, commented that whereas clinicians were once skeptical a condition such as fetal alcohol syndrome even existed, this skepticism has given way to glib diagnosis: "When FAS was first detected, pediatricians didn't believe it was a specific syndrome. Now they start to make a diagnosis by association …They see a 'funny-looking' child, they have heard about FAS, and *if somebody says the mother is drinking, they make the diagnosis*" (Spohr, 1984:153; italics added) (Abel, 1998a:7).

Abel (1998a) argues that, because the term fetal alcohol syndrome has created this false impression, large numbers of clinicians now believe that even minimal amounts of alcohol consumption during pregnancy can produce FAS. This is also reflected in scientific writing, particularly in the alcohol and public health literature where many studies clearly state there are no 'known' safe levels of alcohol nor a safe time during pregnancy to consume alcohol (Funkhouser and Denniston, 1985; Serdula, Williamson et al., 1991).

Alcohol use may be seen by pregnant women and by service providers as a less harmful substance for the developing fetus (e.g., because it is legal to use and is used widely by women) than other illicit substances. However, as it has become clearer in medical research and public health messages that alcohol is a particularly harmful substance for the developing fetus, this perception appears to be changing (Tait, 2003).

In a survey of 273 pediatricians and general practitioners in Saskatchewan in December 1990 and January 1991, Nanson and colleagues (1995) found that physician detection bias may have played a role in the high prevalence rates of FAS among Aboriginal groups. They found 27.5% (75/273) of the physicians in their study responded that they thought FAS occurred primarily in ethnic minority families. This, Nanson and colleagues suggest, may simply reflect the realities of the particular client base of these physicians, rather than detection bias. Burd and Moffatt's (1994) suggestion that studies of physician bias should seek to determine the frequency with which each physician makes a diagnosis of FAS may provide some insight into this particular finding by Nanson and colleagues.

For example, Nanson and colleagues (1995) found that 48% of the physicians they surveyed reported having diagnosed at least one case of FAS, which suggests that there may be under-diagnosis in certain areas or pockets of the province that may be divided along ethnic and possibly socio-economic lines.

The Pregnancy Outreach Program (POP) in British Columbia attempts to improve the reproductive health of women at risk of producing an alcohol-effected child by reducing at-risk behaviour and by educating health workers about the relationship between alcohol and drug use and pregnancy. A one-day conference was held in each of the eight communities selected for implementation of a POP. These conferences found that some of the concerns of attending community members and physicians were the reluctance of some physicians to identify maternal drinking and FAS/ FAE, and the limitations of existing intervention resources. The British Columbia Fetal Alcohol Syndrome Resource Group, contracted to provide the alcohol and drug education component of the program, suggested that efforts be focused on training local professionals, particularly on identification of maternal drinking,

Chapter 8

the value of intervention at all stages of pregnancy and the importance of diagnosing FAS/FAE (Asante and Robinson, 1990).

A lack of understanding of class differences by health practitioners could be a barrier to identification and treatment for poor women. Handwerker (1994) found that, although practitioners were generally aware of the importance of class differences, this did not translate into a greater understanding by the practitioners of difficult life circumstances faced by patients in low socio-economic groups. Practitioners in Handwerker's study placed the burden of blame for the outcome of the pregnancy on the pregnant woman and expected her to have control over her life circumstances, regardless of her socio-economic or environmental circumstances. Patients' understanding of risk generally differed from that of medical professionals and was predicated on several factors, including their values, education, class and other markers affecting their location in the social structure. Handwerker concludes that: "reasons why individual women fail to take action to reduce their risk may be, in part, because they are acting on a concept of risk that is qualitatively different from clinical risk as discussed in a prenatal setting" (1994:671). The tension, she adds, that can emerge when medical professionals recommend changes in behaviour that their patients are unwilling or unable to follow may result in fewer poor pregnant women seeking prenatal treatment.

Within the antenatal clinic, staff are seen as a source of information by mothers; however, "the literature is full of complaints about lack of communication between obstetricians and mothers, which are partly due to perceived status differences." (Waterson and Murray-Lyon, 1990:356) For this reason, Waterson and Murray-Lyon suggest that midwives are likely to be seen as more helpful. An increased role in antenatal preparation and imparting health education advice may be a role midwives can adopt. Simple and personalized advice from health professionals is cheap and has been used to good effect in alcoholism treatment (Waterson and Murray-Lyon, 1990). An early American study emphasized the importance of discussion between pregnant women and health care practitioners in fostering a reduction in alcohol consumption. (Minor and Van Dort, 1982; Waterson and Murray-Lyon, 1990).

Characteristics of Women at Risk

An important question in FAS/ARBE research has been the identification of characteristics of women who are at risk of giving birth to an alcohol-affected child. The following discussion, through a review of the research literature, will examine this question first in relation to early alcohol and pregnancy studies and then through a review of more recent studies, as they relate to particular risk and protective factors. Early alcohol and pregnancy studies focused a great deal of attention on levels of alcohol use and were less concerned with the factors contributing to that use. The exceptions were studies among Aboriginal people, where researchers suggested a number of variables, particularly 'cultural' factors, as playing a role in drinking patterns among pregnant women. Along with this, some studies put forth theories that suggested Aboriginal women and their offspring were at greater risk than other groups because of 'racial susceptibility' or 'physiological risk factors,' a claim not being made for any other ethnic groups. These claims suggested that risk was located not only in the patterns and levels of abuse by individual women, but also in the 'biological' make-up of an entire 'racial' group. These claims, while unsubstantiated by the authors, were combined with 'cultural' explanations to support a growing belief that Aboriginal groups were at greater risk for FAS/ARBEs, and they had higher prevalence rates than those found in the general population (Tait, 2003). As will be shown in the discussion of more general studies, 'cultural' and 'biological' explanations were not drawn upon to explain prevalence rates among other ethnic groups, even when the rates may have suggested ethnic identity was an important variable.

Early Alcohol and Pregnancy Studies

In 1973, Jones and Smith (1973) published their seminal article introducing the diagnosis of fetal alcohol syndrome (FAS). In this study, a handful of infants born to women with severe alcohol addiction were discussed. After the publication of the first article on FAS, researchers attempted to further understand the links between alcohol use during pregnancy and ARBEs, of which women were at risk of producing an affected offspring.

In 1978, Clarren and Smith (1978) wrote that nearly all patients recognized as having the full fetal alcohol syndrome phenotype were born to daily heavy alcohol users. They suggested that chronic consumption of 89 ml of absolute alcohol or more per day—the equivalent of about six drinks—constituted a major risk to the fetus. Early on in FAS research, concern about intermittent binge drinking was expressed, as was concern about confounding variables such as tobacco, caffeine, other licit and illicit drug use, and socio-economic and ethnic status (Jones et al., 1973; Clarren and Smith, 1978). However, these were generally not explored to any significant degree in the early studies. Concern was also expressed over the likelihood of increased rates of spontaneous abortion, stillbirth and infant mortality among offspring of alcoholic women (Jones and Smith, 1973; Jones et al., 1974).

Hanson and colleagues (1978) suggested the strongest relationship between maternal alcohol consumption and affected offspring was drinking that occurred in the month preceding recognition of pregnancy. Among the eleven infants diagnosed with FAS in their study (n=163), nine had mothers who consumed ≥1.0 ounce of absolute alcohol per day prior to recognition of pregnancy, whereas the other two affected infants were born to mothers consuming ≤0.1 ounce per day, suggesting a significant relationship. When maternal alcohol intake during the first five months of pregnancy was considered, three of the eleven infants were born to mothers who consumed ≥1.0 ounce of absolute alcohol per day, whereas the numbers were four and four for mothers who consumed between 0.11-0.9 ounces of absolute alcohol per day and ≤0.1 ounce, respectively (the difference was not significant). In conclusion, Hanson and colleagues suggested that moderate levels of alcohol consumption (3-6 drinks per day) during early pregnancy could adversely affect the developing fetus:

> Although the mothers of the two infants who had the most obvious features of FAS both drank heavily preceding and during the early stages of pregnancy, six of nine other women who had children with numerous features consistent with a prenatal effect of alcohol had AA [ounces of absolute alcohol] between 1 and 2 (Hanson, Streissguth et al., 1978:459-460).

This early report identified the timing of drinking, as well as the levels of alcohol consumption as risk factors; however, the study used 'average ounces of absolute alcohol per day' and did not question women on patterns of drinking, such as binge drinking (Tait, 2003).

Chapter 8

Kaminski and colleagues (1978) published a study in which 9,236 pregnant women were interviewed from 1963 to 1969 in twelve maternity hospitals in Paris. Follow-up reports at delivery, of the infant at birth and during the first six days of life were also completed. Kaminski and colleagues found that the heavier drinkers in their study were at greater risk of stillbirth, especially for death from abruptio placentae (premature separation of part of the placenta from its attachment to the uterus), lower mean birth weight and small-for-date infant, and placental weight decrease. In relation to confounding variables, heavier drinkers (more than 40 cl of wine per week)[32] were found to be more often older, single and of high parity; there were fewer professional women among them and they were more often from a lower socio-economic class. Heavier drinkers weighed more and were more likely to be smokers than lighter drinkers. They were also more likely to have complications during pregnancy, such as bleeding early in gestation and a history of low-birth-weight infants in former pregnancies. Birth outcomes for light drinkers (less than 40 cl of wine per week) were essentially the same as they were for abstainers, with risk rising in the group consuming 41-60 cl and continuing to rise with increasing consumption. Kaminski and colleagues also suggest that beer consumption, as opposed to wine, may have played a role in birth outcomes, with heavier drinkers who consume beer being especially at risk for having a stillbirth or for intra-uterine growth retardation. This finding, however, has not been supported in subsequent studies. Other pregnancy outcomes, apart from data collected on rates of stillbirth, birth weight and intra-uterine growth retardation, and placental weight, were not collected for this study.

Between May 1974 and September 1979, 1,700 women who registered for prenatal care at the Boston City Hospital Prenatal Clinic were interviewed regarding their alcohol consumption and their use of cigarettes and other drugs (Rosett and Weiner, 1980). Information on nutritional intake was also collected. Women who were heavier drinkers (five or more drinks on some occasions with at least 45 drinks per month), and who were unable to cut down or stop drinking during their pregnancy were found to be at greatest risk of producing an affected child. Rosett and Weiner (1980) found that the reduction of alcohol consumption by pregnant women was directly related to better birth outcomes for newborns and occurred independently of the mother's smoking patterns. In a follow-up study in Stockholm, Sweden, similar methodology was used to test the findings by Rosett and Weiner (Larsson, 1983; Weiner and Larsson, 1987). Findings from Rosett and Weiner's study were confirmed among a study population of 464 women. The authors of these studies, however, offer no information about rates of smoking and other drug use, nor nutritional intake among the women surveyed. Neither do they provide socio-economic or ethnic breakdowns of the women, nor discuss the reasons women gave for either cutting down their alcohol use while pregnant or for continuing to drink despite being aware of public health warnings about substance use and pregnancy.

In only a few studies, which look at risk and protective factors in relation to pregnant women and substance abuse, is a study control group built into the research design (Tait, 2003). One of the early prospective studies that included a control group was conducted by Sokol and colleagues (1980) in 1980 at a hospital in Cleveland, Ohio. The researchers found that women who abuse alcohol were significantly more than two years older than the controls (23.7 years vs. 21.4 years) and less likely to

---

[32]   The researchers examined the number of litres of wine, beer and cider drunk per week by pregnant women, which is expressed in litres of wine—40 cl of wine is equivalent to about 1.6 ounces of absolute alcohol (at 11% ethanol) per week.

be married (18.6% vs. 35.2%), whereas neither race nor education were significantly different from the controls. Sokol and colleagues also found that women who abused alcohol during their pregnancy were significantly more likely to have had a previous pregnancy (79.1% vs. 62.1%), previous abortion (39.5% vs. 23.1%) and previous low birth weight infant (25.8-8% vs.17.4%), and to have given birth to a baby with a fetal anomaly (5.9% vs. 1.4%), as compared to the controls. They go on to state:

> Although the alcohol-abusing patients were nearly three times more likely to have had previous psychiatric or social service contact, there were few other important differences in the medical histories of the two groups [alcohol group and control]. However, initial comparisons revealed that the previous obstetric histories of the alcohol abusers were considerably worse than those of the comparison group ... the alcohol group was found to be more than twice as likely to have a history of habitual abortion (three or more consecutive, spontaneous). History of induced abortion and other previous pregnancy losses (stillbirth and neonatal death) were not more frequent (Sokol, Miller et al., 1980:137-138).

Alcohol-abusing patients were found to be nearly twice as likely to smoke cigarettes and nearly three times as likely to smoke heavily as were non-alcohol-abusing patients. It was also more likely that they abused other drugs as compared to controls and were recognized clinically as having psycho-social problems (Sokol, Miller et al., 1980).

Sokol and colleagues (1980) estimated the risk for FAS from pregnancies with confirmed alcohol abuse as 2.5 per cent (5 out of 204 infants), as compared to none in the control group. The validity of the estimate is questionable, however, since confounding variables reported to be associated with alcohol abuse were not controlled through proper statistical analyses. The authors also found that infants born to mothers who abused alcohol were of significantly lower birth weight than those in the comparison groups, whereas there was no difference in the weeks of gestation at birth. Those born to alcohol abusing mothers were at higher risk of neonatal deaths and perinatal mortality (relative risk = 1.8 and 1.3 respectively), but this was not statistically significant.

In 1983, Streissguth and colleagues (1983) published findings from a comparative study, which examined drinking and smoking patterns during pregnancy from two cohorts of women accessing prenatal care in Seattle, Washington. The first group was interviewed in the mid-1970s when the dangers of alcohol use during pregnancy were first being discussed in the medical literature. The second cohort was interviewed in 1980/1981, a time when public health messages warning women against the dangers of consuming alcohol during pregnancy were widely disseminated in the United States. All women were interviewed prior to the sixth month of pregnancy. The majority of women in the study were white, married and middle-class, although the demographic characteristics of the groups gave a fairly wide representation. The researchers found that the number of women who reported abstaining from alcohol use during their pregnancy had increased threefold over the six-year period between studies. Fifty-eight per cent of the women reported abstaining by their first prenatal visit. Significantly fewer pregnant women reported heavier drinking (AA≥1) at the time of their first prenatal visit, but no significant change was recorded in the number of women who reported heavier alcohol consumption around the time of conception. Streissguth and colleagues also recorded a decrease in the number of women who reported drinking five or more drinks on a single occasion; however, there was no change in binge drinking reported around the time of conception.

An interesting finding of the Streissguth study was that while women were decreasing their use of wine (40%) and hard liquor (50%) after knowledge of their pregnancy, women were less likely to stop drinking beer (30%). Streissguth and colleagues suggest that this could be a result of some women not considering beer as being an actual alcoholic beverage or that possibly beer drinkers are actually a different population from drinkers of wine and hard liquor. Data from the study suggested that women who drink beer may have lower levels of education and come from disadvantaged socio-economic groups. Older and highly educated women were shown to have had the highest reduction of alcohol use during pregnancy. The proportion of heavy drinkers remained constant in the 1980/81 cohort of women; however, binge drinking during pregnancy decreased significantly in the six-year period, as did the use of hard liquor. The number of heavier drinkers and binge drinkers for the earliest part of pregnancy remained the same during the six-year period. Unfortunately, the authors of this study did not provide further information on links between levels of alcohol abuse during pregnancy and ethnic status, socio-economic status, age, education and marital status, which may have better defined the women who were most at risk.

Several of the early studies on pregnancy and substance addiction found that many women decreased or stopped their use of alcohol and other substances during their pregnancies. A percentage of these women did so without formal intervention programming, either as a result of adverse physiological reactions to alcohol or out of concern for the developing fetus (Smith, Lancaster et al., 1987). In several studies, women who were amongst the heaviest drinkers decreased their use of alcohol without intervention. For example, Little and colleagues (1976) found that forty per cent of the heaviest drinkers ($\geq$.5 ounces of absolute alcohol per day) decreased their alcohol consumption by their eighth month of pregnancy. Little and Streissguth (1978), in a retrospective study, found that fifty-one per cent of alcoholic women (n=41) reduced their alcohol consumption while pregnant. A study by Fried and colleagues (1980) reported decreases in alcohol consumption after the first trimester of pregnancy by light drinkers (30%), moderate drinkers (12%) and heavier drinkers (18%).

In each of these studies, a percentage of the women reported increasing their use of alcohol. For example, in the study by Little and colleagues (1976), 36% of the women reported increased use during their pregnancy. The percentage of women who increased their use in the other studies ranged somewhere between 3% to 7% (Little and Streissguth, 1978; Weiner, Rosett et al., 1983). Vitéz and colleagues (1984) reported that two-thirds of the women in the abstinence group of their study reported becoming alcoholics after pregnancy. These findings, although relatively unexplored in the literature, suggest potential risk factors for increased use, including the possibility that being pregnant or factors related to giving birth and having a child, may be risk factors for increased alcohol abuse by some women (Tait, 2003). Unfortunately, exploration into why women increase their use during pregnancy was not examined in detail in these studies.

Smith and colleagues (1987) interviewed 267 women applying for prenatal care at Grady Memorial Hospital in Atlanta, Georgia between February 1980 and September 1983. The women were divided into two drinking groups, 'stopped drinking' (n=50) and 'continuous drinkers' (n=96), and a matched control of women who reported abstinence from alcohol during pregnancy (n=121). Participants were mainly African-American (94%), of low socio-economic status (mean income $372.47/month) and unmarried (65%) which was representative of the hospital's prenatal population. Women in the two drinking groups did not differ from controls in their use of caffeine-containing beverages, cigarettes and marijuana use during pregnancy. Women who drank were more likely to associate with men who also drank, which was reflected in 93 per cent of the women reporting that the father of their baby also drank. Only 68 per cent of non-drinkers reported paternal alcohol use. Women who drank were also more likely to report illicit drug use by their baby's father. Smith and colleagues write: "The greater likelihood of alcohol use among other family members suggests that the drinking behavior of the continued-drinker group may be heavily influenced by familial attitudes toward alcohol use" (1987:308).

Smith and colleagues reported no difference between women who continued to drink and those who discontinued alcohol use with regard to race, income, age, marital status, parity, consumption of caffeine-containing beverages or use of cigarettes, marijuana or other drugs (1987). Women who continued to drink were more likely to have had a mother who was a heavy drinker and siblings who also drank. Smith and colleagues state:

> One of the most intriguing findings of this study was the higher incidence of maternal heavy drinking reported by subjects who continued to drink during pregnancy. At the present time, little is known about the long-term effects of prenatal alcohol exposure, particularly with regard to the development of chronic alcohol-related problems in adulthood. Although it is impossible to determine how many of these subjects were prenatally exposed to alcohol, this is clearly an area for future research (1987:308).

Smith and colleagues (1987) reported that fourteen per cent of the women who drank alcohol during their pregnancy also had a history of alcohol-related organic illness—one or more of alcoholic gastritis, delirium tremens or hallucinosis, pancreatitis or organic brain syndrome. Prevalence of alcohol related pathology was not significantly different in women who continued to drink and those who discontinued alcohol use. Women in the drinking groups did not differ from each other in the amount of weight gained during their pregnancy; however, a greater percentage of women who continued to drink had a history of previous premature births (8.7% vs. 23.3%) and low-birth weight infants (12.2% vs. 25%). Women who continued to drink reported drinking at younger ages than women who discontinued use; however, the two groups did not differ in the frequency of alcoholic black-outs, social disruptions due to drinking behaviour, number of intoxications during pregnancy or the amount of alcohol being consumed at the time of the initial interview for the study. Women who continued to drink, however, were more likely to meet the criteria established by DSM-III (American Psychiatric Association Task Force on Nomenclature and Statistics, 1980) for alcohol dependence, reporting symptoms of pathological drinking, social dysfunction or physiological signs. This suggests that women with chronic alcohol-related problems may require special programming and services that address the severity of their abuse. Smith and colleagues (1987) caution against a generalization of their findings to all women as the study group was made up predominantly of African-American, low-income women.

Serdula and colleagues (1991) conducted a population-based study of self-reported alcohol use among pregnant and non-pregnant women in twenty-one American states from 1985 to 1988. They found the prevalence of alcohol consumption during pregnancy had declined by thirty-eight per cent among pregnant women. However, use among pregnant women remained highest for two groups, smokers and women who were unmarried. No decline in alcohol consumption was reported during the study among the least educated women and younger women. In general, women who continued to drink during their pregnancy did not decrease the number of drinks they consumed.

Spohr and colleagues (1993) found that the risk of FAS is higher for those who already have a child affected by FAS and the risk is also higher when the mother has a longer history of alcohol misuse. Characteristics in pregnant women that have been found to be associated with alcohol consumption include age, parity, marital status, smoking status, coffee consumption and use of other drugs (Walpole, Zubrick et al., 1990). These factors may act as confounders for the association between alcohol and pregnancy outcome, but in much of the research, they were not controlled.

Wheeler (1993) reported that use of alcohol is an important risk factor for trauma. Anada and colleagues (1988) found that persons who consume five or more drinks per occasion as their usual quantity have twice the injury death rate than persons who usually drink less alcohol. A dose-response relationship between the numbers of drinks consumed per occasion and incidence of fatal injuries has also been reported. In relation to pregnant women, Wheeler writes:

> The implications for alcohol use during pregnancy are obvious because trauma is the most common non-obstetric cause of death in pregnant women, occurring in 6% to 7% of pregnancies. Placental abruption has been described in from 6% to 66% of gravid patients undergoing "major" abdominal trauma, defined as injury resulting from motor vehicle accidents or direct blows to the abdomen (1993:195; Higgins and Garite, 1984; Kattel, Branch and Scott, 1988).

Summary

Early pregnancy and alcohol studies identified heavy maternal alcohol use and a pattern of binge drinking as risk factors for ARBEs; however, controversy around 'light' and 'moderate' drinking remained (Waterson and Murray-Lyon, 1990). Some authors argued that public policy advising mothers that even small quantities of alcohol use during pregnancy could potentially damage the developing fetus were not scientifically verified and most likely counter-productive (Walpole, Zubrick et al., 1990). Others warned that what was known about the prevalence of FAS/ARBEs was only the 'tip of the iceberg' and that public policy should be designed in ways to educate women that abstinence was the only way to ensure the developing fetus was protected from damage. This controversy over what constitutes 'risk' levels of alcohol consumption by pregnant women has continued through to present day within scientific circles; however, overwhelmingly, public health messages in North America have adopted the position that 'no levels of alcohol are safe' for the developing fetus (Tait, 2003).

Several other risk factors relating to pregnant women were identified in this early literature, including previous psychiatric or social service contact, age, tobacco use, poly-drug use, socio-economic status, familial drinking and having given birth previously to an alcohol-affected child. Although these factors were identified, they were relatively unexamined in relation to how they actually contributed to negative birth outcomes. This research question would become of particular importance in later studies in attempts to develop prevention and intervention strategies.

Chapter 8

Early Alcohol and Pregnancy Studies Among Aboriginal Populations in North America

> In the studies of southwestern Indians, all mothers of children with FAS or FAE died of alcohol-related causes, from cirrhosis to trauma. Few living mothers who were drinking led a life in the mainstream of their culture, community, or family; most were involved with highly alcoholic peer groups, having been downwardly mobile and ostracized by nondrinking friends or relatives (May, 1991:243).

Within Canada and North America more generally, a great deal of discussion as to whether Aboriginal women are at greater risk than their non-Aboriginal counterparts for having children with ARBEs has occurred. In a 1989 appraisal of the epidemiology of FAS among Aboriginal people in Canada, Bray and Anderson (1989) wrote that despite Aboriginal women and children being over-represented in epidemiological studies in Canada, the research had not yet established whether any Aboriginal population was a high risk group for FAS. They pointed out that Aboriginal people in Canada represent a very diverse population in both social customs and alcohol consumption patterns and, because of this caution, is warranted in discussions of rates of FAS among the general Aboriginal population. Bray and Anderson write: "Native peoples should not be stigmatized by a condition such as FAS which is difficult to prove as factual and which may have negative impact within the Native community. Caution is warranted before we conclude that FAS is more prevalent in any Native peoples" (1989:44).

Since the publication of Bray and Anderson's article in 1989, no epidemiological studies have been published that have shown FAS is more prevalent among Aboriginal people in Canada than among non-Aboriginal people. However, significantly more attention has been directed toward Aboriginal communities, particularly First Nations communities, with regard to research, prevention, identification and intervention services, which has added to the perception that Aboriginal people generally are at greater risk than other groups (Tait, 2003).

In a study of American Indian women living on reserves in the southwestern United States, Aase (1981) concluded that this group may be at particular risk for producing affected children. She identified four categories of 'risk': cultural factors, drinking patterns, demographic variables and physiological factors. Five cultural factors were identified:

1. generally permissive cultural attitudes toward drinking alcohol;

2. the ostracization of certain individuals who severely abused alcohol, resulting in social isolation of this high risk group and, in turn, possible increases in their alcohol consumption;

3. alcoholic couples supporting each other's drinking and their children exhibiting a greatly increased propensity for alcohol abuse themselves in later life;

4. many alcoholic individuals showing little motivation to achieve sobriety and rehabilitation programs being only marginally successful for this sub-group; and

5. rehabilitation being aimed primarily toward male alcoholics and special provisions for women, such as separate facilities, child care and female counsellors, being rare.

Chapter 8

Family dynamics and identity were also identified by Aase as risk factors:

> Indian families tend to be large and mutually interdependent, and the sense of "being Indian" is often a source of considerable pride and solidarity. Unfortunately, some of these same unifying influences can also produce considerable pressure for conformity, especially among teenagers, where early experimentation with alcohol often proves to be a group activity (1981:154).

Drinking patterns were identified as being somewhat different from those seen elsewhere in the United States due to several factors. First, prohibition on many First Nations communities led to some community members regularly engaging in 'binge drinking' episodes for two or three days in nearby cities or towns, resulting in severe intoxication (Aase, 1981). While Aase (1981) acknowledges research findings that suggest American Indian women have significantly lower rates of alcohol use than other American women, she argues that American Indian women who do drink, often drink to excess. This is indicated, for example, by alcohol-related deaths among some American Indian groups being twenty times higher than in the general American population.

Demographic risk factors identified by Aase (1981) included the American Indian population being younger (median age of about 16.5 years) than the general American population, child-bearing generally beginning at an earlier age and child-bearing extending into later years, resulting in a longer period of child-bearing and in high fertility rates (over twice the national American average). Aase writes:

> The combination of a longer span of childbearing years, greater fertility, a pattern of binge drinking, and possibly a younger age at the outset of alcohol abuse may result in a higher total of pregnancy-years of exposure to alcohol in some American Indian women. This, coupled with what appears to be a very severe degree of alcohol abuse in some women with implications of higher dose levels to the fetus, provides at least a theoretical basis for concern over an increased risk for FAS in American Indian children (1981:154).

Finally, Aase (1981) suggests possible physiological risk factors, including increased rate of alcohol degradation in American Indians, metabolic differences and zinc deficiency in alcoholic women.

In a study of FAS in British Columbia and the Yukon Territory, Smith and colleagues (1981) identified seventy-six cases of FAS, all with a confirmed history of heavy maternal alcohol exposure. Fifty-nine of the patients had mothers who were Aboriginal. Apart from confirmation of heavy maternal alcohol exposure, Smith and colleagues provide no other information about the mothers. In their assessment of the high numbers of Aboriginal children in their study, they suggest that 'racial susceptibility' to the teratogenic effects of alcohol may be at play, or different metabolic pathways of alcohol and possible deleterious effects of acetaldehyde, rather than ethyl alcohol, may be factors impacting upon Aboriginal women and their offspring. However, 'racial susceptibility,' as discussed earlier, is a very difficult concept to apply and measure and, among most scientific researchers, has been discarded as a useful explanation in alcohol research. Factors such as different physiological variables, which can impact pregnancy outcomes, have yet to be confirmed or fully understood by researchers.

Chapter 8

Asante (1981) reported on clinical experience with seventy-four children diagnosed with FAS in northwestern British Columbia and the Yukon. In all cases diagnosed, a history of maternal alcohol exposure was confirmed. Ninety-five per cent of the mothers of diagnosed children were Aboriginal; however, no details are provided about the referral process of children to the study, making it unclear if the population from which the study group was derived was over-represented by Aboriginal children to begin with. For example, seventy-two per cent of the children diagnosed with FAS were either currently or, in the past, involved with social services; however, Asante does not compare this to the percentage of Aboriginal children within the foster care system generally. Although he does not include this type of information, he concludes that Aboriginal women in this region are at highest risk for having alcohol-affected children.

Asante (1981) suggests that the high number of Aboriginal mothers giving birth to affected children may be due to higher alcohol consumption rates, more frequent binge drinking or non-Aboriginal women being more discrete when they drink and, therefore, tending to drink at home (1981). However, Asante did not engage in any systematic collection of levels and patterns of drinking among Aboriginal women nor among their non-Aboriginal counterparts to support these claims. Asante also suggests that life style, social, economic and psychological factors may contribute to Aboriginal women being at greater risk, but he provides no details about the links between these factors and alcohol abuse among pregnant Aboriginal women, nor how these factors may impact differently on other ethnic sub-groups of women that he suggests have lower prevalence rates (e.g., poor Caucasian women) (Tait, 2003).

May and Hymbaugh (1983) found that FAS distribution among American Indian groups in the southwestern United States varied according to tribal organization, with highly structured tribes having the fewest drinking mothers and lowest incidence of fetal alcohol damage (May, 1991). A significant finding of their study was the prevalence of multiple FAS/FAE children being born to certain mothers. Of the mothers in the communities with an affected child, 22.6 per cent had produced more than one damaged child (average 2.36 per multiple producing mother). Ostracism of the drinking mother was given as a potential risk factor for multiple FAS babies. May and Hymbaugh (1983) suggest women who are ostracized by the community often migrate to border towns where their only friends and associates are other alcoholics, and where the social stigma attached to the production of multiple FAS children is limited. They also found that a high percentage of the FAS children in the study group were in foster care (approximately 73%); however, the significance of this is unclear as fifty-seven per cent of the children in the study group without FAS were also in foster placement at the time of the study. A significant percentage of the mothers of affected children were deceased (21%) and most mothers had extensive clinic records for alcohol-related problems such as accidents, trauma and alcohol withdrawal.

Robinson and colleagues (1987) examined the prevalence of FAS in an isolated First Nation community in British Columbia. For 46 per cent of the pregnancies considered, the mothers were abstainers and, of the 54 pregnancies during which the mothers drank, 32 of the 54 children were determined to be unaffected. Twenty-two children had diagnosable fetal alcohol-damage (14 with FAS and 8 with FAE).

Of the forty-five mothers who drank during one or more of their pregnancies, fourteen women had 22 children with FAS/FAE and 5 of these women accounted for 12 (54%) of the affected children (Robinson, Conry et al., 1987). This supports earlier findings by May and Hymbaugh. Robinson and colleagues also reported denial and under-reporting of alcohol use by women in the community as methodological problems.

Masis and May (1991) reported on a cohort of Navajo women living in the Tuba City Service Unit who were considered to be at risk for producing an affected child. Of forty-eight women referred to the FAS program, thirty-nine 'at risk' women were included in the study. Of the thirty-nine women, nine had produced FAS or FAE children, two had possible (awaiting diagnosis) FAS or FAE children, and eight were pregnant. Most mothers of FAS/FAE children had given birth to a number of normal children prior to giving birth to a damaged child. Masis and May point out that, while Navajo women generally drink less alcohol than women in the overall American population, drinking, particularly abusive drinking, is concentrated in a minority of families that suffer from a multitude of other social problems. A number of women at high risk for giving birth to FAS/FAE children came from families, either immediate or extended, where alcohol abuse was common, even normative. The majority of FAS/FAE birth mothers in their study were known to be adult children of alcoholics and also had spouses or in-laws, or both, who were heavy drinkers.

Duimstra and colleagues (1993) reported on a pilot FAS surveillance project by the Aberdeen Area Indian Health Service in four American Indian communities in the Northern Plains. Although only limited information is given about the mothers, placement of a woman's children in foster care and the place where she gave birth (a hospital that could accommodate high-risk pregnancies instead of a low-risk obstetrical facility) were indicators of high risk women. Duimstra and colleagues suggest that an examination of infant mortality may also help to identify women most at risk.

Godel and colleagues (1992) reported on smoking, caffeine and alcohol intake during pregnancy in a northern population. The majority of the women in their study were Aboriginal: 56 Inuit (35%), 38 Indian (24%), 31 mixed race (19%) and 37 white (23%). Inuit and Indian mothers were more likely than the others to be binge drinkers, despite the overall proportion of women who drank alcohol having no statistical difference between racial groups. Indian, Inuit and women of mixed race were more likely to smoke (64%) than white women (32%). Godel and colleagues found that smoking and alcohol intake were under-reported.

Summary

Early FAS/ARBE studies clearly identified Aboriginal groups in North America as being at risk. While the groups studied were generally chosen as research subjects because alcohol abuse was known to be high within these groups, this was not reflected in the understanding of the wider problem (Tait, 2003). For example, in 1992, a government sub-committee reporting to the Minister of Health and Welfare Canada suggested that, while there was no national data on FAS and FAE, the incidence rate of FAS in the general population could be estimated as being between one and two cases per one thousand live births (Godel, Pabst et al., 1992). However, expert witness testimony to the sub-committee stated that "exceptionally high rates of FAS among Aboriginal Canadians" existed (1992:4). Implicated in early research studies were two things: the biological make-up of Aboriginal people and 'cultural factors' that contributed to high levels of alcohol use.

Interestingly, what were referred to as 'cultural factors,' such as 'cultural attitudes toward drinking,' had very little to do with Aboriginal cultures and more to do with historical factors such as colonialist oppression and socio-economic marginalization (Tait, 2003). Furthermore, it is unclear in the studies involving Aboriginal and non-Aboriginal women whether, if socio-economic status had been considered as a variable alongside ethnic identity, the ethnic identity would become far less important a variable in identifying women at risk (Tait, 2003).

Recent Alcohol and Pregnancy Studies

Early alcohol and pregnancy studies identified several 'risk factors' related to pregnancy and substance use that have been expanded upon in studies during the past decade. In a 1990 review of the prevention literature on ARBEs, Waterson and Murray-Lyon (1990) found that research literature reported the most common risk factors for producing an alcohol-affected child to be heavy drinking, lower socio-economic status, being older, smoking and divorce or separation.

In a second review, Barbour (1990) reported that a marked reduction in both frequency and amount of alcohol consumed by pregnant women had been noted by researchers; however, it was found that, because drinking alcohol was a habit established before pregnancy, women who drank before becoming pregnant were still likely to drink some alcohol during their pregnancy. Factors that Barbour found to be associated with alcohol use during pregnancy were use of tobacco, social pressure and professional status, being single, divorced or separated, and having an alcoholic husband and/or father. As stated previously, being Aboriginal was also identified as a risk factor (Asante, 1981; Aase, 1981; Godel, Pabst et al., 1992).

Due to a wide-range of characteristics being attributed to pregnant women at risk of giving birth to a child with FAS/ARBE, researchers at the beginning of the 1990s were unclear as to which factors specifically characterized women who drank alcohol during pregnancy versus those who did not, or which women were at highest risk for giving birth to alcohol-affected children (Barbour, 1990). The following discussion will review the studies of the past decade, looking specifically at how understandings of 'risk behaviour' by pregnant women have evolved during this period.

Permissive and Provocative Factors

Without an explanation as to how permissive factors create a biological environment that increases or decreases the susceptibility to alcohol's effects, identifying such factors would mean little more than acknowledging the fact the alcohol abuser does not live in a vacuum. By characterizing these personal and environmental conditions in terms of their biological consequences, a model such as the one proposed here offers a heuristic explanation as to how these factors produce the sufficient conditions that act in conjunction with alcohol to produce FAS (Abel, 1998a:159).

Chapter 8

Abel (1998a) argues that the relatively low rate of occurrence of FAS among heavy drinkers means alcohol is a necessary, but not sufficient, cause of FAS. To better understand this, he developed a model that identifies predisposing behavioural, social and environmental factors called *permissive conditions* that create the differential reaction to alcohol responsible for the occurrence/non-occurrence of FAS/ ARBEs. Unlike most other researchers, Abel pushes his analysis further in an attempt to understand how permissive conditions produce or 'provoke' the physiological changes needed to increase vulnerability to alcohol's toxic effects. He writes:

> Epidemiological studies typically focus on identifying the *permissive* factors associated with a particular condition. More often than not, however, these "black box" epidemiological studies do not explain how these conditions relate to the problem being examined. Unless these conditions can be associated with a biological milieu that affects the occurrence of that condition, they cannot lead to any meaningful inferences about the conditions itself (1998a:175).

The following discussion, which examines permissive 'risk' factors, will be strengthened by the model developed by Abel and will help to shed light on where attention should be given in relation to prevention and intervention aimed at pregnant women who abuse alcohol and their affected offspring.

Levels and Patterns of Drinking [33]

Levels and patterns of drinking are central in determining risk associated with in-utero alcohol exposure. Studies have found that lifetime alcohol use and treatment histories can point toward women who may be at greater risk of heavily abusing alcohol during pregnancy (Astley et al., 2000b). Astley and colleagues (2000b) found that, of a cohort of birth mothers of FAS children, the average age when the women first started drinking was fifteen years old. Between the ages of twenty-three and twenty-eight, the majority of women were drinking maximally and, around the age of twenty-six, was the period that they first tried to stop drinking. The mothers were, on average, twenty-seven years old when they gave birth to their index FAS child. The women reported drinking, on average, nine fluid ounces (or 266 ml) of alcohol per drinking occasion just before the birth of the index child. Nearly half of the eighty women (47%) reported drinking daily at that time. Astley and colleagues write:

> While 84% reported that they felt that they had a problem with alcohol use, 94% reported they did not want to reduce their use, because it helped them cope, and 72% did not want to reduce, because they were in an abusive relationship; with 79% reporting that they were too depressed to do anything about it. The four most common reasons for not seeking alcohol treatment were that they did not want to give up alcohol (87%), that they were afraid they would lose their children (42%), that there was no one to take care of the children (40%), and that their partner did not want them to go to treatment (39%) (2000b:513).

---

[33]   Alcohol metabolism and risk have been discussed in some detail in chapter three and any further examination is beyond the scope of this report. For further discussion, see Abel, 1998a:166-168.

Chapter 8

Of the eighty women interviewed, forty-one reported that they were abstinent by the time their child was diagnosed with FAS or with static encephalopathy. On average, women reported six concerted attempts to stop drinking. Astley and colleagues (2000b) concluded that thirty-seven (46.2%) were still at risk of producing another child damaged by alcohol exposure at the time of the index child's diagnosis, by virtue of these women still being fertile and actively drinking or at high risk for drinking.

Abel (1999a) argues that we should not confuse the levels of alcohol consumption that cause fetal damage by characterizing the drinking behaviour associated with FAS/ARBEs in terms of 'average drinks' per day or weeks. He writes: "This problem needs to be considered in terms of the broader context of alcoholism: the emphasis should be on the alcoholic who is also pregnant, rather than on the pregnant woman who (never) becomes an alcoholic during pregnancy" (1999a:6).

Patterns of drinking have been identified as an important factor for the health of the mother and the developing fetus. A pattern of binge drinking—the consumption of alcohol equivalent to five or more standard drinks per occasion—has been identified as a major risk factor for negative birth outcomes (Abel, 1998a; Nanson, 1997). Many women who consume alcohol during pregnancy do not drink every day but binge drink on occasion (Nanson, 1997). The more chronic the bingeing, the greater the damage, since chronic bingeing extends the period of alcohol toxicity over a longer duration of the pregnancy.

As a result, exposure is more likely to occur during critical periods of development (Abel, 1998a). Abel argues that this possibly becomes more evident when considering certain sub-populations in relation to larger populations. For example, a pattern of binge drinking is more common in the United States than in countries with higher per capita alcohol consumption. This, he suggests, would be a likely explanation for the higher rates of ARBEs found in the United States. Researchers also suggest that binge drinking may be a more common pattern of drinking among Aboriginal women and may place this group at high risk for producing affected children.

Gladstone and colleagues (1997) reported that 3.1 per cent of the women counselled in a clinic and 0.8 per cent of those counselled over the telephone by the Motherisk Program, a teratogen-information service based in Toronto, reported binge alcohol consumption during pregnancy. The women who reported binge alcohol consumption represented a unique risk group with a clustering of other risk factors. For example, the women were significantly younger, were more likely to be single and had a higher rate of previous elective abortions. A limitation of the study, however, is selection bias, as all the women surveyed were clients of the Motherisk Program and, therefore, not necessarily representative of all pregnant women.

Gladstone and colleagues found that binge drinking was associated with an increase in the frequency of unplanned and unprotected sexual activity, suggesting that women who engage in binge drinking may increase their likelihood of unplanned pregnancy and may subsequently expose the fetus to repeated binges until the pregnancy is discovered. Nanson (1997) suggests that the failure of Gladstone and colleagues to provide information about other factors, such as socio-economic status, employment history and education, means that it is impossible to identify, from the study's findings, women whose children are most likely to be affected by prenatal alcohol exposure.

Chapter 8

Abel (1998a) suggests that the reason binge drinking is a potential hazard for a mother and her unborn child is the accompanying blood alcohol level (BAL), which is more likely to exceed a biological threshold for perturbation of cellular function. He writes:

> All teratogens, including alcohol, produce their effects within a range of alcohol exposures. Below one level, they are harmless; above another level, any of the various anomalies ... occur. At very high levels, a teratogen may be embryo-or fetotoxic, thereby providing an upper limit on the number of potential live births associated with exposure to that teratogen .... [d]rinking patterns such as bingeing are permissive because they produce high peak BALs. High peak BALs are provocative because they exceed toxicity threshold and thereby induce biological changes at the cellular level that result in FAS (1998a:175-76).

Majewski suggests that a mother's health status, with respect to her alcoholism, is a key factor in determining ultimate embryonic toxicity (Majewski, 1993 in Abel, 1998a; Majewski, Fischback, Pfeiffer and Bierich, 1978; Seidenberg and Majewski, 1978). Among women in the initial stages of alcoholism, Majewski found no cases of FAS, a frequency of twenty per cent among those women in the critical stage (psychologically and physically dependent) and forty-three per cent for those in the chronic stages (compulsive drinking).

Clarren (1999) found that, mothers of children diagnosed with FAS and who attended a FAS clinic in Seattle, Washington, began drinking early in their lives and had various influences in their lives that supported heavy alcohol abuse. In general, the women reported having histories of severe unresolved abuse. In addition, they reported suffering from mental health problems (including agoraphobia fear of open and public places), were living with partners who did not support them going to an addictions treatment program, were involved in drinking sub-cultures and feared abandonment by family or friends if they stopped drinking. About twenty per cent of the women also had alcohol-related organic brain dysfunction (Clarren, 1999 in Roberts and Nanson, 2000).

In a study examining the subjective experience of women with substance abuse problems, Tait (2000a) found that eighty per cent of study participants (n=74) reported continued substance use during one or more of their pregnancies after they knew that they were pregnant. Thirty-eight per cent of the women reported they began to use again or had increased their use during their pregnancy after having previously stopped or decreased their use because of being pregnant. Increased use was linked to problems such as a breakdown in a woman's support network, a crisis situation occurring or an inability to cope with daily circumstances without the use of substances. For example, of the women who increased their use of substances after they had cut down or quit using during their pregnancy, 57% stated that one reason they increased their use was due to the difficulty of dealing with feelings of depression, isolation, loneliness, stress and painful memories.

Tait (2000a) found that fifty per cent reported they used substances during their pregnancy because their partner was using. Increased use during a pregnancy was linked to relationship problems and included partners leaving the relationship (sometimes for other women), physical abuse, lack of partner's support during the pregnancy, or a partner not wanting another baby or claiming not to be the father of the baby. Several other reasons for increased use during pregnancy were given. These included:

having other children apprehended by child welfare services; familial relationship problems; a partner going to jail; leaving or finishing an addictions treatment program and having no after care support; and being surrounded by friends who were all using. Thirty-two women (43%) in the study reported regular binge drinking (more than once a week) during one or more of their pregnancies, and 35 women (47%) reported infrequent binge use (roughly once a week to once a month) during one or more of their pregnancies. In relation to binge drinking and risk, Tait writes:

> While approximately 61% of the women reported cutting down their use of substances during one or more of their pregnancies—which they understood as being a way to improve the outcomes of their pregnancies—many women did not make the distinction between the potential risk of minimal substance use as opposed to consuming large amounts of substances at one time (2000a:50).

None of the women in Tait's study reported seeing a public health poster or pamphlet that gave information on binge use and pregnancy. Poly-substance use has been reported as common among women who abuse alcohol during pregnancy (Lex, 1990; Loebstein and Koren, 1997; Tait, 2000a; Loock, Kinnis, Robinson, Segal, Blatherwick et al., 1993). In some instances, this is a combination of alcohol with an illicit substance, such as cocaine or cannabis. However, there has been limited research on the use of licit drugs and alcohol use during pregnancy, so little is known about the frequency of this type of poly-substance use. Lex argues that, because many women with substance abuse problems suffer from high rates of mental distress and are victims of family violence, including sexual abuse and poly-substance abuse, may reflect efforts to self-medicate mental distress and other family dysfunction. He also suggests that, because many women with substance use problems are not screened for their use when accessing mental health services, they may be prescribed psychotropic medications for their mental health problems that, together with untreated alcohol dependence, increases the potential for dual dependency (Lex, 1990 in Roberts and Nanson, 2000).

Genetics

Typically, in FAS research, genetic factors are related to genetic differences between populations based on race. This, Abel (1998a) argues, has diverted attention from socio-economic and environmental contributions to disease in general and, in particular, to poor infant outcomes in the case of FAS. However, this does not mean that individual genetic susceptibilities of the mother and the fetus are not factors contributing to FAS. Support of this observation is found in reports of human twins, where one twin has FAS and the other only partial effects (Streissguth and Dehaene, 1993; Streissguth, 1997). However, research has not yet yielded specific correlates involving genetic susceptibilities and negative birth outcome related to in-utero alcohol exposure (Stratton, Howe et al., 1996).

Tobacco

A large percentage of women who are reported to be at 'high risk' for having a child with an ARBE use other substances during pregnancy, particularly cigarettes (Astley et al., 2000c). Research has shown that smoking tobacco can contribute to adverse pregnancy outcomes, especially decreased birth weight (Abel, 1984). Abel points out that, although the concurrent influences of alcohol and smoking can be examined statistically to assess the independent effects of each alone, statistically significant interactions between the two are very difficult to demonstrate, other than by stratification, because there are usually too few subjects in any study who are heavy drinkers and light smokers, or light drinkers and heavy smokers. In relation to socio-economic status and smoking combined, Abel writes:

> Smoking cigarettes is not only an important permissive factor in FAS, it may be the reason FAS occurs in the rare occasions when it is not associated with poverty. The common link between poverty and smoking is that each provokes a common biological milieu that increases susceptibility to alcohol's teratogenic action (1998a:175).

Abel (1998a) suggests that smoking is a permissive factor because it is highly correlated with poverty (Hogue, Buehler, Straus and Smith, 1987; Nordstrom, Cnattingius and Haglund, 1993; Polednak, 1991) and alcohol consumption. What makes smoking a provocative factor for FAS are the ingredients in tobacco (for example, nicotine and carbon monoxide) that directly reduce blood flow and oxygen content, respectively, which can cause ischemia and fetal hypoxemia, decrease nutrient availability to the fetus (Abel, 1984) and promote teratogenesis through free radical formation (Abel, 1998a). Abel (1998a) adds that smoking can also increase blood lead levels (Ernhart, Wolf, Sokol, Brittenham and Erhard, 1985), thereby increasing risk from that element.

Overall Health Status

Women who give birth to children with FAS have severe alcohol-related pathology (Abel, 1998a; Coles, Smith et al., 1985). Research indicates that three-quarters of these women will die within five years of giving birth to a child with FAS (Clarren, 1981; Olegard and Sabel, 1979; Streissguth et al., 1987). Cirrhosis of the liver is the most common ailment found in this patient population, which has also been linked to increased rates of spontaneous abortion and preterm birth (Abel, 1998a). Detectable levels of acetaldehyde in the blood are also more likely to be produced by alcoholics with cirrhosis than by those with non-alcoholic liver disease.

Abel (1998a) suggests that many of the effects directly attributed to alcohol exposure in-utero may instead be due to combined effects of maternal cirrhosis and alcohol consumption. Apart from cirrhosis, DTs (delirium tremens), psychiatric hospitalizations, anemia and poor nutrition, tremors, gastrointestinal bleeding due to alcohol, and epilepsy and seizure disorders are health problems commonly found in mothers of children with FAS. Sexual dysfunction, infertility, menstrual irregularities, alcohol-related cancer, hypertension, obstructive pulmonary disease, alcohol-related cognitive deficits and HIV (including all the other health consequences associated with injection drug use) have been noted by Poole (1997) as added health problems experienced by women who abuse substances.

Poole (1997) points out that women develop a wider range of adverse health consequences from the use and misuse of alcohol and other drugs over shorter periods of time and with lower consumption levels than do men. Abel (1998a) points out that alcoholic women are typically emaciated, having very low pre-pregnancy weight and pregnancy weight gains. In one study (Abel 1982), four mothers were found to actually loose weight during their pregnancies. Although it has been assumed that all alcoholics are under-nourished, this appears to apply most often to alcoholics in the lower socio-economic groups (Abel, 1998a; Salaspuro, 1993). Abel (1998a) suggests that sub-optimal maternal nutrition is a provocative factor for FAS because, when it occurs, the nutrient pool necessary for supporting fetal growth and maintaining maternal health is reduced. He adds:

> Nutrition is compromised in alcoholism because alcohol has a high energy content and replaces other energy sources in the diet. While nutritional factors alone cannot give rise to FAS, alcohol consumption alone cannot account for its occurrence. The two almost invariably go together (Abel, 1998a:176).

Alcohol, in addition to contributing to a decrease in food consumption, can reduce nutrient absorption; meaning that, even if nutrient intake were not decreased, the concentration of nutrients absorbed in the mother's blood and potentially available to cross the placenta could be reduced (Abel, 1998a).

Lex notes that physical dependence on alcohol has negative effects on female reproductive health, including amenorrhea, anovulation, luteal dysfunction, ovarian atrophy, spontaneous abortion and early menopause (1990 in Roberts and Nanson, 2000). Roberts and Nanson suggest that, because of this, "the most severely alcohol-dependent women may be less likely to conceive and bring an affected fetus to term, whereas women who binge drink (often younger women), but sober between binges, are more likely to produce an affected child" (2000:10; Lex, 1990).

Age, Parity[34] and Family Planning

Abel (1999a) writes that women who have given birth to children with FAS are not merely a variation of the general population of drinkers; they are the group that defines the risk for FAS. Maternal age and parity increase have been identified in case reports and epidemiological studies as risk factors for FAS (Abel, 1998a; 1988; Jacobson, Jacobson and Sokol, 1996; May, 1991; Sokol, Ager, Martier, Debanne, Ernhart et al., 1986; Astley et.al., 2000a; 2000b).

These findings are directly related to findings that suggest women are at greater risk if they have given birth to a previously affected child (Abel, 1998a; Clarren, 1998) and findings that suggest younger siblings are more impaired than their older siblings when the mother continues to use alcohol at elevated rates during pregnancy (Abel, 1998a; 1988; Majewski, 1993; May, 1991; Streissguth, 1997). Abel (1998a) points out that researchers have not been able to determine if the more important risk factor, in this case, is increased maternal age or increased parity. Animal studies, however, suggest maternal age as the greater risk factor (Abel and Dintcheff, 1984; 1985; Vohees, Rauch and Hitzermaun, 1988).

The question of whether pregnant teenagers are less likely to give birth to children with FAS/ARBEs than older women has only recently been explored in the FAS literature (Abel, 1998a).

---

34   Parity refers to 'live births.'

Chapter 8

In a recent study, Barr and Streissguth (2001) examined 1,439 pregnancies and found that thirty-six of the mothers had given birth to a child with fetal alcohol spectrum disorders (FASD).[35] Nine of the thirty-six mothers were teenagers (less than 20 years old) when they gave birth to their child and sixteen of the thirty-six infants were first born children.

Barr and Streissguth (2001) suggest that filtering for older multiparous (multiple births) mothers would, for this sample, not improve the classification of children presumed to be at risk for FASD. However, the study did find that the mothers of FASD children who reported daily drinking with low or zero frequency of binges were also among the oldest mothers of FASD offspring. While the combination of older age plus daily drinking may reflect an age effect, an alternative interpretation may be that the number of drinks per day reported by these women is an under-estimation.

An important added dimension in examining levels of risk for teenage pregnancies may be the number of years individual teenagers have been using alcohol and the severity of their use. For example, in some sub-populations where high rates of alcohol use occurs, some teenagers at age nineteen may have drinking histories as long as five to ten years (Tait, 2003).

Abel argues that, if alcohol ingestion, especially binge drinking, was the only factor in the etiology of FAS, then the number of drinking years should not be an important factor:

> ... as far as the fetus is concerned, it would not matter whether a mother drank for 2 years or 12 years before becoming pregnant-the only important factor would be the amount of alcohol exposure during pregnancy. As of yet, there are no clinical or epidemiological studies addressing this question with respect to teenagers, but as noted earlier, older women are at greater risk for FAS than younger women. Whether this higher risk factor is because of a longer history of drinking, higher blood alcohol levels associated with the same amount of drinking, development of alcohol-related [illness] such as cirrhosis (Majewski, 1981), or other factors has not been determined (Abel, 1998a:166).

Advanced age/high parity can be provocative factors for FAS/ARBEs because of the relationship between age and history of alcoholism (Abel, 1998a). Abel writes:

> The longer a woman drinks heavily, the more severe her potential medical complications (Ashley, et al., 1977). Later born children may thus be more prone to FAS because they are exposed to higher BALs [blood alcohol levels] in utero than their older siblings.

---

[35]   Barr and Streissguth use the term 'fetal alcohol spectrum disorders' (FASD) as an umbrella term for people with the most identifiable forms of alcohol-related birth defects diagnosed as fetal alcohol syndrome (FAS), fetal alcohol effects (FAE), alcohol-related neuro-developmental disorder (ARND) or static encephalopathy-alcohol exposed. These forms of FASD are differentiated primarily by the facial features present or absent, but they have developmental abnormalities in adaptive functioning, attention and memory problems, distractibility, learning problems, poor judgement, and fine and gross motor difficulties (Barr and Streissguth, 2001; Streissguth and O'Malley, 2000).

This higher exposure may, in turn be due to lower body water (Church, et al., 1990), tolerance-related increases in maternal alcohol intake, a greater severity of maternal alcohol-related medical problems, and so on, interacting with continued alcohol exposure (1998a:178).[36]

Increased parity, Abel (1998a) adds, is associated with increased uterine collagen and elastin content, a condition that can potentially decrease blood flow to the conceptus, contributing to fetal hypoxia (Robertson and Manning, 1974; Woessner, 1963), thus exacerbating the impact of alcohol. Increased age, however, appears to be the greatest risk factor (Abel, 1998a).

In relation to family planning, Astley and colleagues (2000b) found that, of the eighty birth mothers in their study, collectively they had given birth to 272 children. Seventy-three per cent of the pregnancies were reported by the women to be unplanned. Tait (2000a), in a qualitative study of women's experiences with substance addiction and pregnancy, found that the use of birth control among 'high risk' women living in Manitoba was very low, despite the women being relatively well-informed and having access to some form of birth control. The reasons given by women for not using birth control were: problems negotiating condom use with partners, a partner not wanting to use any form of birth control, difficulty remembering to take birth control pills because life was too chaotic, side effects from birth control pills and Depo Provera® (e.g., nausea, weight gain or loss, prolonged menstruation, mood swings and depression), fear of using an IUD, and thinking oneself to be infertile. Some women in the study had tubal ligations because they were unable to cease their use of alcohol and/or drugs and did not want to have an affected child. Other women in the study were either actively trying to become pregnant or were indifferent to the possibility of becoming pregnant despite them knowing that risks existed because of their substance abuse.

Psychological Factors

Studies have found that women who give birth to an alcohol-affected child (Astley et al., 2000b), women who continue drinking heavily while pregnant (Astley et al., 2000b) and pregnant women in treatment for substance abuse or dependence (Howell and Chasnoff, 1999; Howell, Heiser and Harrington, 1999; Poole, 1997), have high rates of psychiatric co-morbidity. This type of co-morbidity often leads to relapse and premature treatment drop-out, with adverse consequences to the mother and infant (Miles, Svikis et al., 2001; Svikis, Gorenstein et al., 1998). Nanson (1997) suggests that women rarely wish to harm their children; however, substance abuse and mental illness can cloud a woman's thinking so that harmful actions seem reasonable. Miles and colleagues (2001) point out that, to date, little is known about the psychological profiles of pregnant substance abusers and the studies conducted (Svikis, Gorenstein et al., 1998; Ingerscoll, Lu et al., 1995; Knisely, Barker et al., 2000) have focused on opiate and cocaine addiction. Miles and colleagues (2001) found that among pregnant drug-dependent women, those who had a co-morbid alcohol dependence diagnosis presented for treatment with greater psycho-pathology than drug-dependent women without an alcohol disorder. Rates of psycho-pathology were relatively high, with 97 per cent of women with an alcohol dependency and 89 per cent of those without having a least one clinically elevated scale (depression, hysteria, paranoia, schizophrenia, hypochondriasis,

---

[36]   See also Khera, 1987; Majewski, 1981; Sanchis et al., 1987.

psychopathic deviance, masculinity-femininity, psychasthenia, mania and social introversion). Sixty-nine per cent of women with co-morbid alcohol dependency and 54 per cent of those without had three or more clinically elevated scales.

In a sample of 299 women with a diagnosis of alcohol abuse (Kessler, Crum, Warner, Nelson, Schulenberg et al., 1997), lifetime co-occurrence of mental health disorders was found to be quite high: post-traumatic stress disorder (10.5%), depression (30.1%), simple phobia (28.2%), social phobia (24.1%), anti-social personality (2.1%), agoraphobia (9.3%), generalized anxiety disorder (8.4%), mania (3.8%) and panic disorder (7.3%). Kessler and colleagues (1997) found that social phobias, simple phobia, depression and drug dependence were highly predictive of subsequent development of alcohol abuse.

Astley and colleagues (2000b), in a study of eighty birth mothers living in Seattle, Washington, who had a child diagnosed with FAS or static encephalopathy, found that rates of mental health problems were significantly higher than those found by Astley and colleagues. The women were mainly Caucasian, although there was slight over-sampling of Native Americans and most (78%) had a gross annual household income of less than US $10,000 at the time of the index child's birth. Only one woman in the study had never experienced a mental health disorder. Three women (3.8%) had experienced one disorder, 33 (41.3%) women had experienced 2 to 4 disorders, 36 (32.5%) had experienced 5 to 7 disorders and 12 (15%) had experienced 8 to 10 disorders. The breakdown of mental disorder were as follows: post-traumatic stress (77.2%), major depressive episode (59.5%), phobia-simple (44.3%), phobia-social (43%), anti-social personality (39.2%), phobia-agoraphobia (36.7%), generalized anxiety disorder (34.2%), manic episode/bipolar disorder (21.5%), panic disorder (20.3%), bulimia (12.7%) and schizophrenia/schizophreniform (7%). In most cases, women experienced the onset of a mental health disorder prior to an onset of alcohol abuse. Ninety-five per cent of the eighty birth mothers had been physically or sexually abused during their lifetime.

Nanson (1997) reported that, among women she sees in a FAS clinic in Saskatoon, Saskatchewan, drinking is a way of coping with the emotional pain caused by unplanned, unwanted pregnancies, which are often the result of sexual assault. The women, she adds, are often too traumatized to consider the risks to themselves or their child that excessive drinking presents.

Abel (1998a) argues that maternal stress (marital discord, over-crowding, negative attitudes about pregnancy, etc.) and physical abuse are prominent correlates of poverty (Amaro et al., 1990; Polednak, 1991). He writes:

> Stress can impair maternal physiology and health and contribute to increased rates of spontaneous abortions (Scarpellini, Sbracia and Scarpellini, 1994), obstetric complications (Laukaran and VandenBerg, 1980), and low birth weight (Edwards et al., 1994). Stress can also potentiate alcohol's toxicity and may initiate or encourage continued alcohol abuse (Bresnahan, Zuckerman and Cabral, 1992). Whether by cause or effect, victims of violence during pregnancy are also more likely to be "heavy" drinkers (Amaro, et al., 1990) (Abel, 1998a:178-179).

Chapter 8

In a study of seventy-four women, most of whom were Aboriginal, who abused substances during one or more of their pregnancies, Tait (2000a) found that 92% reported chronic or long-term feelings of depression, stress, isolation and/or suicidal thoughts. Others reported mental health problems were suicide ideation, fear of leaving the house, obsession with cleanliness, extreme fear of physicians and dentists, anger, need for control, inability to cope with children, and violence toward other adults. Among the women, one-third reported being raped or sexually abused at some point in their lives, which they said contributed significantly to their substance abuse problems. Tait writes:

> For many of these women, their attackers had not been prosecuted, and in some cases, were individuals they still had to deal [sic] within their families, communities, or circles of friends. Many of the women felt silenced by the perpetrators, and the majority of women had received no informal or formal counselling for the abuse. In other cases, women reported that in some addiction treatment groups, they were pushed [by addiction counsellors] to discuss past abuse when they felt they were not ready to disclose what had happened (2000a:45).

Women, who did not experience sexual, physical, emotional abuse or neglect as children or adults (29%), reported fewer problems related to substance abuse, a more secure and stable childhood, a greater number of people in their support networks, better relationships with partners, friends and family, and better relationships with service providers (Tait, 2000a).

Culture/Ethnicity

Differences among ethnic or cultural groups, with respect to social or behavioural characteristics, may increase the risk of FAS for one group as compared to another. For example, patterns of drinking, particularly binge drinking, may be characteristic of some groups (Abel, 1998a). Abel writes:

> In cultures in which alcohol is consumed regularly at meals, infants are found to be at less risk for FAS than those whose culture encourage periodic drinking behaviour (e.g., concentrated on weekends), or where alcohol abuse is characterized by bingeing. Differences in diet can also influence the risk for FAS/ARBE when particular diets provide (or do not provide) nutrients (e.g., saturated fats, vitamins) capable of exacerbating (or attenuating) alcohol's effects (Abel, 1998a:179-180).

Abel (1998a) adds that ethnicity and culture are influenced by socio-economic status (SES) and, in turn, can influence patterns of alcohol consumption and diet.

Environmental Factors

Several studies have shown that the incidence of FAS is clearly related to socio-economic status (SES) (Abel, 1998a). Abel goes as far as to argue that "although FAS occurs in all races, poverty-stricken alcoholics are far more likely (one is tempted to say 'almost exclusively') to have children with FAS than affluent alcoholics" (1998a:176). In the United States, for example, much higher rates of FAS have been reported among African-American and American Indian populations, most of whose SES is characterized by poverty. Despite the fact that these groups are disproportionately poor, the focus of attention with respect to alcohol's effects has typically been on race, rather than SES.

In a review of the case studies and epidemiological literature, Abel found that, although racial susceptibility was highlighted by many studies, these studies were fundamentally flawed because they rested on a misconception that race reflects biological homogeneity, and genes determining race are linked to those affecting health (Abel, 1998a; Williams, Lavizzu-Mourey and Warren, 1994). Abel states: "Genes ... are easier to characterize and study than SES, and, because race is highly related to SES (Cooper 1993), investigators have largely ignored SES as a factor in FAS research in favor of race-related genetic susceptibilities" (1998a:172).

Abel (1998a) argues that environmental and social correlates of poverty that are directly provocative or exacerbate other provocative factors for FAS include inadequate diet or poor nutrition, inner-city residency, psychological stress, high parity, smoking and abuse of other drugs.

Tait (2000a) found that, of the seventy-four women in Manitoba who participated in a study on substance abuse and pregnancy, the majority lived in extreme poverty, particularly those living in Winnipeg. For example, twenty-eight of the forty-one women from Winnipeg reported incomes below $10,000 per year, with no woman reporting an income above $25,000 per year. Tait writes:

> The impact of poverty on the lives of the women was enormous, affecting not only their wellbeing but also that of their children. The poorer women in the study were typically single mothers receiving social assistance. Some women were working in low-income jobs that still kept them well below the poverty line. The poorest women were Aboriginal. For women living in poverty, daily life consisted of dealing with ongoing problems such as finding enough money for food, transportation, shelter, and clothing. Chronic poverty contributed significantly to feelings of helplessness and hopelessness, and contributed to women choosing to participate in illegal activities such as prostitution, theft, and drug-dealing-activities that are intertwined with, and often promote, substance misuse (2000a:37).

Tait (2000a) suggests that many women with children who participated in illegal activities often did so for very pragmatic reasons, mainly to provide extra goods for their home, such as food, household items and toys. Participation in illegal activities meant that a significant amount of money could be made fast and without the knowledge of social workers. In some cases, women preferred participating in illegal activities rather than trying to receive social assistance, because of the constant surveillance of their lives by social welfare agencies. Participating in illegal activities was generally viewed by service providers as irresponsible and was considered to be a sign of deficiency in a woman's character. While a few women did recall times when their participation in illegal activities could have brought potential harm to their children, most women kept these activities very separate from their lives at home with their children and were very protective not to bring their children in harm's way.

Tait (2000a) found that the activities of women receiving social assistance, particularly their substance abuse, were highly visible to service providers as compared to women who were either employed or whose partners were employed. This meant that women on social assistance were under greater scrutiny than women who were working, and at a greater risk of losing custody of their children because of their substance abuse. Even though some women who were not receiving social assistance reported similar significant financial challenges and similar substance abuse problems, the involvement of the state in their lives, because they were working or being supported by a partner, was significantly less. Once a woman became employed, she quickly became ineligible for support that she previously could receive when on social assistance, even though she still faced significant challenges in her life.

Women who were financially better off and who had higher levels of education were less likely to attend addiction treatment programs than poorer women or women with lower levels of education. Women who had higher incomes were less fearful of child welfare services using their substance abuse problems as a way to gain custody of their children, than were women on social assistance. For women on social assistance, fear that child welfare services would apprehend their child or place a 'birth alert'—apprehension order at the time of birth—on the child they were carrying was given as a common reason for not seeking addiction treatment and accessing prenatal care (Tait, 2000a).

Geographical location and environment were important considerations for some women in Tait's (2000a) study, particularly Aboriginal women. While Aboriginal women live in all regions of Manitoba, a large percentage live in isolated rural communities, which makes service delivery particularly difficult. Some of these communities have high rates of alcohol abuse, which is linked to chronic poverty and unemployment and to negative impacts brought on by colonialization. Tait found that pregnant women living in remote communities were reluctant to leave their home communities to attend addiction treatment programs. Most non-status and Métis communities did not have addiction treatment workers in their communities to provide counselling and after care addiction services were basically non-existent in most remote and rural communities.

Summary

Alcohol and pregnancy studies, in the past decade, have focused increasingly on determining the characteristics of women who are at high risk of giving birth to an alcohol-affected child. While there is still debate over 'safe levels' of alcohol use by pregnant women, researchers are increasingly arguing that the women who are at risk are a very specific population, namely women with an alcohol dependency problem and women who engage in binge drinking behaviour, particularly chronic binge drinking. Typically, these women are in poor health, socially marginalized and have given birth to previously affected children.

Many mothers of alcohol-affected children die at an early age from alcohol-related deaths. Researchers are increasingly finding that factors, such as tobacco use, age, parity, family planning, psychological distress and environmental factors, such as chronic poverty and geographical location, are important factors that intersect with alcohol abuse to produce negative birth outcomes. Authors, such as Abel (1998a), argue that the relatively low rate of occurrence of FAS among heavy drinkers means alcohol is a necessary, but not sufficient, cause of FAS. For this reason, he suggests that more research be conducted into the intersection between conditions, such as chronic poverty and the abuse of alcohol by pregnant women, in order to fully understand the occurrence of FAS/ARBEs.

Recent Alcohol and Pregnancy Studies Among Aboriginal People

> Traditionally in Aboriginal societies, women held a place of respect and honour for their role as keepers of the culture. Although their day to day responsibilities varied culturally across the country, the role as nurturer and teacher of the children was universal and very much respected and supported by local laws and practices. Today women carry the same responsibilities, but often the familial, social and community support are no longer there. In the absence of a strong support network women at risk, because of their personal and family histories or addiction, will be predisposed to consume alcohol during pregnancy (Van Bibber, 1997:33).

Over the past decade, fewer studies have been conducted that are specifically aimed at Aboriginal people in North America. Most of these studies set out to determine incidence rates (Habbick, Nanson et al., 1996; Williams and Gloster, 1999) and do not systematically attempt to determine risk factors. In many cases, Aboriginal people are a sub-group(s) of broader urban and/or rural based research (Godel, Pabst et al., 1992; Poole, 2000; Tait, 2000a).

Habbick and colleagues (1996) describe the incidence of FAS in Saskatchewan over a twenty-year period. Eighty-six per cent (n=178) of the individuals diagnosed were Aboriginal. Of the 207 cases, 149 had been in foster care at some time and many had been in multiple foster homes. Only 25.6 per cent were living with their biological parents; however, the authors do not give an ethnic breakdown of this group. Fifteen to twenty per cent of all births per year in Saskatchewan belong to Aboriginal women; however, eighty-six per cent of the FAS patients in the study were Aboriginal, indicating a major over-representation of Aboriginal cases. Habbick and colleagues give possible explanations for the higher incidence rates, including cultural influences, patterns of alcohol consumption and abuse, child-bearing at a later maternal age when alcohol abuse is apt to be greater, and "perhaps" dietary and metabolic influences.

The problem with the explanations given by Habbick and colleagues is that these fail to specify what is meant by 'cultural influences,' 'patterns of alcohol consumption and abuse' or 'dietary and metabolic influences,' so the reader is left to speculate on the meaning of these categories (Tait, 2003).

Some authors have suggested that Aboriginal women who live in remote areas are either unaware (Square, 1997) or hold false impressions about dangerous levels of alcohol use during pregnancy and about the biological mechanisms that contribute to FAS (Williams and Gloster, 1999). Kellner, through a series of interviews with Yukon residents, found that Aboriginal women are more likely than men or non- Aboriginal women to abstain from alcohol. However, when they do drink, they are more likely to drink heavily (1998 in Roberts and Nanson, 2000). Godel and colleagues (1992) found that Inuit and Indian mothers in their study were more likely than non-Indian and mixed race women to engage in binge drinking; they were also more likely to be heavy smokers.

Chapter 8

Lack of social integration has been identified as a risk factor for substance abuse (McKenzie, 1997), as has lower socio-economic status (Loney, Green et al., 1994; Health and Welfare Canada, 1989). Poor socio-economic conditions (Loney, Green et al., 1994; Health and Welfare Canada, 1989) coupled with loss of cultural identity are believed to be major contributors to the high prevalence of alcohol abuse among some Aboriginal groups (Loney, Green et al., 1994). In many instances, youth populations are believed to be most at risk, as indicated in a study by Williams and Gloster (1999), who found that teenagers in northern Manitoba communities reported the highest levels of smoking and alcohol use during pregnancy.

Summary

Studies in the past decade that have examined FAS/ARBEs among Aboriginal people in North America support findings in other more general studies. Aboriginal women at risk have been found to engage in heavy drinking, and binge drinking appears to be a common pattern of drinking in some sub-groups. Aboriginal women also tend to experience high levels of poverty, social marginalization and psychological distress. Tobacco use and poor nutrition are also common among women with alcohol abuse problems.

Conclusion: Residential Schools and Substance Abuse by Pregnant Aboriginal Women

The white population cannot point smugly at [A]boriginals and claim fetal alcohol syndrome is just a native problem. For one thing, we [non-Aboriginal people] helped to create the problem by refusing to acknowledge [A]boriginal culture and by sending Indian children to residential schools. People with low self-esteem often turn to alcohol for consolation (cited in Square, 1997:59).[37]

When pretending to wonder whether or not Residential School had a negative impact on at least some Aboriginal individuals, there are some notable blind-spots in evidence anecdotally called forth. Few people if any, for example, have noted the similarities between the informal symptomology literature that is developing with respect to former Indian Residential School attendees and the symptomology of Holocaust survivors, Japanese prison camp inmates, victims of torture and physical abuse, colonially oppressed peoples, and similarly aggrieved groups. But even a brief look at the literature on "concentration camp syndrome", the psychological consequences of torture, or the psychology of colonial domination establishes the correspondence: virtually nothing attributed to Aboriginal Peoples in the way of symptoms falls outside what has already been found for **any group of human beings subjected to severe and prolonged oppression and exploitation** ... the "question" of whether severe mistreatment of Aboriginal Peoples can be "passed on" to generations or individuals who didn't attend Residential School has already been examined in some of these groups, and, we might add, no one thought the notion preposterous (Chrisjohn and Young, 1997:79-80).

---

[37]   Quoted by the former president of the Canadian Medical Association.

Chapter 8

Alcohol and pregnancy studies have, in many instances, focused on Aboriginal women as a sub-group in North America who are particularly at risk for producing alcohol-affected children. In a review of the literature, however, it becomes clear that methodological problems exist in many of the studies that argue Aboriginal heritage is a risk factor for FAS/ARBEs.

Rather, factors that are experienced by women from all ethnic groups, such as chronic poverty and social marginalization, appear to be variables that are more important in identifying women at risk than ethnic identity. If this is true, then how do we understand intergenerational links between the residential school system and alcohol abuse by pregnant Aboriginal women? (Armstrong, 1998)

The above statement suggests that a unidirectional link can be made. Armstrong (1998) argues that the experience of Aboriginal students at residential schools caused them to have low-self esteem. The experience made these individuals, including pregnant women, turn to alcohol, thereby creating a 'problem' of FAS among Aboriginal people. The 'white' population is implicated in this 'problem' by it's refusal to acknowledge Aboriginal culture and by sending children to residential schools. As Chrisjohn and Young point out, the residential school system subjected Aboriginal children to "**severe and prolonged oppression and exploitation**" (1997:79). For them, this is not simply an issue of low self-esteem among individual former students; rather, it is about the collective experience of colonially oppressed peoples who were victims of severe mistreatment. Chrisjohn and Young (1997) point out that there should be no question about whether the impact of the experience of former students can be "passed on" to generations or individuals who did not attend the schools and they ask why, in light of other discussions of Holocaust survivors and Japanese prison camp inmates where intergenerational links are assumed, should questions be asked of the residential school experience and Aboriginal people.

Armstrong's (1998) statement suggests that we are now seeing the consequences of historical colonialist oppression of Aboriginal people. His statement can be seen to represent commonly held beliefs by most mainstream health and social service providers, in that they see the residential school experience for Aboriginal people as something located in the past. As service providers, they view their task as treating the consequences of past oppression, which are located in the physical bodies of individual Aboriginal patients or clients. Furthermore, when Armstrong states that the 'white' or dominant society failed to recognize Aboriginal culture in the past, this implies that this is no longer the case in present day Canada and that we have entered into a post-colonial era. In 'post-colonialist' Canada, Armstrong's statement suggests that oppression be re-labelled as 'treatable' conditions, such as fetal alcohol syndrome, low self-esteem and alcohol abuse, conditions which mainstream health and social services then focus on to 'improve' the lives of Aboriginal people.

While health and social service professionals, such as Armstrong, are well-intentioned, they fail to recognize that the residential school experience of Aboriginal people who attended the schools and for subsequent generations, is on-going. One only needs to look at how recently former students began to come forward to speak publicly about their experiences to know that this is not something of the past. The present day experiences of residential schools, for example, are manifest in community healing initiatives, lawsuits by former students and publications documenting what happened at the schools. They are also manifest, as has been shown in this report, in the health and well-being of Aboriginal people. Substance abuse, intergenerational alcohol abuse, individual and communal distress, chronic poverty, high unemployment, lack of social integration, poor education, apprehension of children and poor overall health are the links between residential schools and FAS/ARBEs. These intergenerational factors are situated within a colonialist, rather than a post-colonialist, context in which Aboriginal people continue to experience daily oppression in the form of racism, marginalization and lack of control and autonomy in their lives.

Aboriginal groups that have been able, in this context, to improve the lives of their people, are those who have found ways to engage in community development initiatives, thereby improving economic circumstances in their communities and who have gained local control over activities, such as education, health care, social service delivery and policing. While more research to look at ways in which improved local conditions interface with problems of alcohol abuse and pregnancy, and FAS/ARBEs more generally, is needed in Canada, there are strong indications that community development and local control of community services are important protective factors against pregnancy and alcohol abuse and FAS/ARBEs.

Chapter 9

'Best Practices:' Prevention

Introduction

Marginalization from dominant political, economic, social, and health sectors arises from and reinforces racial stereotypes that contribute to views of Aboriginal people as "others" (Frideres, 1991) ... Contemporary power relations are troubled further by a cultural legacy of mistreatment and abuses that arose in relation to residential school practices ... physical and sexual abuses create a lifetime of fear, humiliation, and mistrust (RCAP, 1996a). These abuses and the shame inculcated by the very strict teachings of sexual modesty and morality are compounded by the lived experiences of maltreatment. The social harm of enforced residential schooling is immense; of intergenerational alienation, the loss of siblings and other kin through death at the schools, and the pain of community and family disruption. In sum, the combination of these complex, strained social, economic, and political relations shape [Aboriginal] women's health care encounters and the capacity of women to be accepted as credible medical subjects (Browne and Fiske, 2001:131).

... I went to a [addiction treatment] program with her in my belly. If I didn't go she wouldn't have been normal. I guess. But then when she went to the hospital ... they said, "Your baby is okay, there's nothing wrong with her. When she gets older there's going to be nothing wrong with her." ... It makes me feel good ... that's what [my worker] said to me, "You've given your daughter a chance to have a good life by going to the program" (cited in Tait, 2000a:61).

A CFS [child welfare] worker came to see me and she told me, she said "It's the best that you get something to help you to not have babies because from now on you're always going to have this birth alert". She says "Every time you're going to have a baby, they're always going to apprehend the baby" (cited in Tait, 2000a:55).

This chapter discusses 'best practices' in relation to the prevention of substance abuse by pregnant women. The 'best practices' recently identified by Health Canada (Roberts and Nanson, 2000) will be examined in relation to Aboriginal people. To date, the report by Roberts and Nanson represents the most comprehensive attempt to identify 'best practices' for fetal alcohol syndrome (FAS) and other alcohol-related birth effects (ARBEs) in Canada. Three important points need to be made to frame this discussion. First, the 'best practices' identified by Roberts and Nanson, with the help of a national steering committee of professional and lay experts in the field of FAS/FAE and other birth disorders, are derived mainly from scientific articles.

Roberts and Nanson (2000), however, recognized that local FAS/ARBE prevention programs currently operating in Canada may have identified 'best practices' during the course of their work, but that descriptions of these practices and information on how and why they would qualify as a 'best practice,' were generally absent from the current scientific literature. The 'best practices' study attempted to address this gap by basing the determination of 'best practices' in areas of prevention, identification and intervention, on scientific evidence *and/or* the perspectives of consumers, expert practitioners and educators. A second report, by Leslie and Roberts (2001), addressed some of the gaps between identified 'best practices' in the community and the lack of published research literature. Their report, which was researched alongside the report by Roberts and Nanson, identified elements of 'good practices' as identified by service providers involved with Health Canada's community-based programs that address prenatal and early childhood issues. These programs include Community Action Program for Children (CAPC), Canada Prenatal Nutrition Program (CPNP) and Aboriginal Head Start (AHS). The programs are located across Canada (almost one-thousand) and support a range of community-based programs and services for pregnant women and their children, and families living in conditions of risk.

Second, the 'best practices' identified by Roberts and Nanson target the general Canadian population. Although they refer specifically at times to groups such as Aboriginal women, the report is aimed at the general population. This chapter will discuss the 'best practices' identified by Roberts and Nanson in relation to their applicability to Aboriginal groups in Canada. Information from the report by Leslie and Roberts (2001) will be used to support the discussion. This exercise will help build upon the identified 'best' and 'good' practices put forth in the two reports and help sensitize these practices, where needed, to the specific realities and concerns of Aboriginal people.[38]

Third, as stated in the introductory chapter, the question of what 'best practice' means for Aboriginal people in relation to traditional knowledge is an area that deserves more attention. This is particularly true when dealing with an issue as sensitive as pregnancy, substance abuse and FAS/ARBEs. In the following discussion of 'best practices,' issues relating to traditional/cultural beliefs and practices will be raised when these issues have been discussed in the research literature; however, an important future component of identifying 'best practices' for the topic areas covered in this report would involve reworking the identified 'best practices' in relation to local traditional knowledge and practices. Currently, there has been only limited discussion about the important role traditional Aboriginal knowledge could play in prevention and interventions aimed at substance abuse and pregnancy. Most discussions concerning the role of Aboriginal cultures have been quite negative, in that they identify 'cultural patterns of drinking' or identify 'cultural traits' among Aboriginal groups that promote and support substance abuse. However, in these accounts, what the authors regard as 'cultural' are, in fact, behaviours, attitudes and responses that have been shaped mainly by colonialist oppression, including social and economic marginalization and acculturation strategies, such as the residential school system (Tait, 2003). By invoking 'culture' in this limited sense, these accounts undermine the role of historical events and, also, in this specific example, the traditional roles of indigenous women, particularly as mothers. They also fail to acknowledge practices such as traditional child birth and child rearing, including the role of indigenous practitioners such as midwives. Inclusion of traditional Aboriginal knowledge and practices in discussions of FAS/ARBEs would greatly improve understandings of the issue and contribute significantly to prevention and intervention initiatives.

---

[38]   Rather than reviewing the same body of literature than Roberts and Nanson, the following discussion of 'best practices' will, in most cases, discuss the conclusions made by Roberts and Nanson from their review of the literature and apply them to the specific circumstances of Aboriginal people. For details of the review, see Roberts and Nanson, 2000.

Chapter 9

'Best Practices' and Primary Prevention

> ... my mother drank with all of us and all of us are healthy. I thought, ah, it's just BS what they say about alcohol ... And so I never thought it could really harm a baby (cited in Tait, 2000a:63).

Primary prevention refers to activities "undertaken with a healthy population to maintain or enhance physical and/or emotional health. Such activities focus on individual *behaviour* change, systems or environments" (Roberts and Nanson, 2000:3). Four primary prevention best practices were identified by Roberts and Nanson with the assistance of the National Steering Committee.

Alcohol Availability

'Best practice'

1. There is some evidence that measures to limit the availability of alcohol, such as bans on sales and importation that are broadly supported by the community or price increase can reduce heavy alcohol use by pregnant women, at least in the short-term.

Many Aboriginal communities in Canada have chosen to limit the availability or use of alcohol in their communities through bans on sales and importation of alcohol (Maracle, 1994; Brady, 2000). For example, occasional prohibitions have been attempted in northern Quebec, where municipal councils have the authority to impose periods of dryness by limiting shipment of alcohol supplies to local stores from particular towns. However, because the by-laws of the local Inuit councils are not legally binding on the stores who receive the alcohol, their non-compliance continues to undermine the council's authority (Brady, 2000). Other Aboriginal communities have created policies that regulate the sale and service of alcohol at public events (Lauzon, Gregoire, Gliksman, McKay and Douglas, 1991). 'Bootlegging' of alcohol, where bans exist, is often a serious problem for communities trying to impose bans and may contribute to episodic binge drinking, particularly in more isolated communities (Tait, 2003).

Bowerman (1997) reported that preliminary findings from a community-initiated FAS intervention program, which combined education about FAS with a regional village ban on alcohol in a group of American Indian communities, resulted in only limited success in relation to alcohol abuse by pregnant women in the villages. Although the ban had been extended to all villages, it did not apply to Barrow, the largest and most central village in the area. When the ban was extended to Barrow, significant drops in alcohol abuse by pregnant women were recorded (from 42% to 9%). Bowerman suggests this was due to Barrow's central location as a distribution point to the other villages.

Authors, such as Chiu and colleagues (1997) and Smart and Ogborne (1996), contend that alcohol prohibition in geographically isolated communities can be effective public health interventions (Brady, 2000). For example, O'Neil (1985) found that alcohol prohibition over a four-year period in an Inuit community resulted in an increase in family integrity and respect among generations, an increase in interest by youth in traditional values and lifestyles, and decreases in aggressive behaviours and abuse of other substances. While some drinking did occur, the difficulty with supplies of alcohol meant that even habitual heavy drinkers had to reduce their consumption level substantially (O'Neil, 1985 in Waldram, Herring and Kue Young, 1995).

In Canada, Aboriginal non-reserve and urban-based communities are under provincial jurisdiction, making it virtually impossible for alcohol restrictions to be implemented in these communities. Urban Aboriginal people have no more (or no less) influence than any other community group to implement alcohol bans or regulate sale and service of alcohol. Some opponents of alcohol bans and restrictions contend that these types of measures perpetuate a paternalism that fosters drinking as an oppositional and political act. What they suggest is that Aboriginal people must come to terms with living with alcohol, while simultaneously social, political and economic change must also be addressed to successfully curb abusive drinking (Brady, 2000).

May (1992) suggests that prohibition of alcohol, which is common tribal policy among American Indian communities (approximately 69% of tribes in the 1990s), may reflect the persistence of biological explanations for drinking among American Indians by the community members themselves. In a study by May and Smith (1988), they found Navaho participants were overwhelmingly against legalization of alcohol on their reservation, mainly because they believed all 'Indians' had a physical weakness for alcohol. Weibel-Orlando (1990) suggests that this 'new' prohibition in American Indian communities flies in the face of evidence that it does not work and may contribute to alcohol abuse and racial discrimination, and may foster binge drinking. In discussing prohibition among American Indian communities, she suggests that the earlier benevolent paternalism of the American federal government has been 'co-opted' by tribal governments, making it more of a moral or ethical stance than an effective social policy (Weibel-Orlando, 1990 in Brady, 2000). For example, May (1992) argues that prohibition of alcohol can result in the substitution of alcohol with other substances, such as methylated spirits and hair spray.

There are no studies in Canada that specifically examine whether alcohol bans limit the use of alcohol by pregnant women. While alcohol bans could result in a decrease in drinking among pregnant women, they could also lead to the use of other substances, such as solvents, to secretive binge drinking, to under or non-reporting of alcohol use to health care providers, or to women at highest risk moving from the community to places where they can obtain alcohol. In this context, a high risk woman may break ties with her support network, live in much more violent and dangerous circumstances, and increase her alcohol use (Tait, 2003; May, 1991). While community bans on alcohol may decrease the overall use of alcohol by the majority of pregnant women, May (1991) points out that policies such as these could lead to high risk women being ostracized in their community, which could contribute to increased substance abuse where alcohol is still available, or to women leaving their communities to find places where their drinking is less stigmatized.

A pragmatic and immediately effective strategy for reducing the impact of alcohol abuse is through the price control of alcoholic beverages (Abel, 1998a). Recent studies have consistently shown that all drinking levels, light, moderate and heavy, are responsive to price (Manning, Blumberg et al., 1995; Sutton and Godfrey, 1995; Godfrey, 1997). One study found that price elasticity was greater for women than men (Kenkel and Manning, 1996). The combination of public education and price increases could reduce alcohol consumption among those women most at risk (Abel, 1998d). However, it is not known if price increasing is effective in communities where alcohol abuse is endemic. Further research is needed to examine the impact of price increases in Aboriginal communities with high, moderate and low levels of alcohol abuse among its members. Important issues to consider are whether alcohol is replaced with less expensive substances, if community dysfunction and community response to price increases are related. Another issue to consider is what impact price increases have on families, particularly children, when alcohol abuse is not decreased after prices rise.

Revised 'best practice'

1. There is some evidence that measures to limit the availability of alcohol, such as bans on sales and importation that are broadly supported by the community, or price increase, can reduce heavy alcohol use by pregnant women at least in the short-term. These measures should be undertaken along with added measures to address the problem of 'bootlegging' of alcohol, which may contribute to increased binge drinking among pregnant women. Also, include measures that would address the use of replacement substances, such as solvents. Bans on sales of alcohol will be more effective if they are combined with a multi-component strategy that builds upon individual and community strengths. Research is needed to examine the impact of alcohol bans and price increases in Aboriginal communities with high, moderate and low levels of alcohol abuse among their members to better determine the effectiveness of these prevention strategies in local settings.

Public Health Prevention Strategies

'Best practice'

1. There is some evidence to support warning labels and posters as a means of increasing awareness and effecting short-term behaviour change among low-risk women. However, women who drink heavily during pregnancy do not appear to be affected by warning labels.

Controversy exists over the extent to which the behaviour of pregnant women who consume alcohol can be influenced by primary prevention initiatives, particularly warning labels on alcoholic beverages, and poster and media campaigns.

Warning Labels

In the United States, federally mandated warning labels on alcoholic beverages and point-of-sale signage laws has been a central strategy for distribution of public health warnings aimed at reducing alcohol use during pregnancy. Studies assessing the impact of these initiatives have shown some impact upon light drinkers and only a minimal deterrent effect upon heavy drinkers, as a result of the messages (Hankin, Sloan et al., 1993a; 1993b; 1996; Scammon, Mayer et al., 1991; Kaskutas and Greenfield, 1992; Graves, 1993). Awareness of FAS/ARBEs has increased since the introduction of warning labels and public health prevention posters, but this has not necessarily resulted in any long-term decreases in consumption, particularly among high risk women. Abel (1998a) suggests that warning labels have been ineffective, in part, because FAS is generally associated with compulsive, involuntary drinking behaviour. He adds, women with heavy drinking problems are also in greater denial about the dangers of alcohol abuse and are more likely to attribute FAS/ARBEs to factors other than their alcohol use.

Chapter 9

In 1992, the *House of Commons Standing Committee on Health and Welfare, Social Affairs, Seniors and the Status of Women,* focused national attention in Canada on FAS. The committee called for mandatory labels on alcoholic beverages to warn women about the dangers of consuming alcohol while pregnant. They also argued for a ban of lifestyle advertising of alcoholic beverages, despite research that found warning labels had limited effect in decreasing alcohol consumption among pregnant women in the United States (Loney, Green et al., 1994).

Loney and colleagues (1994) argue that a warning label that focuses specifically on pregnant women and FAS/ARBEs excludes the contribution of alcohol to other serious health and social problems. They argue that an emphasis on this form of education may reinforce the perception that women face an uncomplicated choice about alcohol consumption during pregnancy, thereby further stigmatizing pregnant alcohol abusers as weak or deviant. Abel (1998a) argues that primary prevention efforts will only be successful if a woman's drinking has not reached a compulsive stage and if she is prepared to cut down on her drinking. However, the compulsive and heterogeneous nature of alcohol abuse undermines primary prevention efforts among high-risk women. Pregnant women may drink for various reasons; for example, to cope with spousal abuse, mental health problems or poverty (Abel, 1995; 1998a; Tait, 2003).

Research suggests that warning labels have a limited impact on consumer consumption patterns; however, supporters assert that the labels are worthwhile because they contribute to greater awareness of the dangers of alcohol use by pregnant women and may lead to decreased use of alcohol. Whether or not this occurs, supporters contend that the presence of warning labels does not present any harmful consumer effects (Abel, 1998a). However, some studies suggest that alcohol and drug use may increase after the introduction of warning labels (Plant and Plant, 1997). Abel (1998a) argues that this increase may occur because individuals are asserting their individuality and personal freedom or because they are reacting to the stress of having possibly harmed their child. The implication of warning labels that there is no 'safe' level of alcohol use by pregnant women could also create unnecessary guilt, stress and anxiety among low-risk women, and could cause them to seek therapeutic abortions of wanted pregnancies (Abel, 1998c; Loney, Green et al., 1994; Tait, 2003). Loney and colleagues argue that, instead of focusing on warning labels, support should be given to policies that improve access to the basic determinants of health, since "policy initiatives can do more than directly address consumption through restrictions on alcohol consumption and distribution" (Loney, Green et al., 1994:249). However, Loney and colleagues support a ban on alcohol lifestyle advertising, as they believe this type of measure better addresses the broader effects of alcohol consumption.

Mass Media Campaigns

The mass media has been used to distribute information and warnings regarding alcohol use during pregnancy. Waterson and Murray-Lyon argue that: "The mass media are particularly effective in bringing topics to public attention and in promoting cognitive change" (1990:355). American studies in Seattle, California and Boston all reported some decrease in alcohol use during pregnancy after public education campaigns (Little, Streissguth, Guzinski, 1980; Rosett, Ouellette et al., 1978; Weiner, Rosett, Weiner et al., 1983; Kuzma and Kissinger, 1981). However, it is impossible to differentiate between the effects of the campaigns and the influence of generally changing social norms, though they are likely to interact (Waterson and Murray-Lyon, 1990).

Chapter 9

A study by Ihlen and colleagues (1993) found substantial changes in public attitude toward alcohol consumption during pregnancy after a five-year awareness campaign directed toward health personnel and the general public by the Norwegian National Directorate in 1984-85. Ihlen and colleagues found a reduction in alcohol consumption between pregnant women surveyed at the beginning of the campaign and those surveyed five years later.

Mass media messages have been criticized for being unduly alarming. A study by Koren and colleagues (1996) found that, after watching a one-minute video released by the Manitoba Medical Association, most participants believed that even a single drink of alcohol could harm the developing fetus. Koren and colleagues argue that the video successfully advised against scientific evidence that suggests no increased risk to the fetus exists as a result of rare social drinking. While it may seem safe to err on the conservative side, some argue this could cause unnecessary anxiety for women who are at limited or no risk and possibly result in the termination of wanted pregnancies (Koren, Koren et al., 1996; Abel, 1998a; Tait, 2003).

A study by Oei and colleagues (1986), to determine young adults' attitudes and awareness of FAS, reported that mass media campaigns, especially among young males, was a preferred method of disseminating knowledge about the dangers of drug and alcohol use during pregnancy. Both female and male participants chose medical practitioners as the best people to present information in a media campaign.

In a study of pregnant women in Manitoba, Tait (2000a) found that women, including high risk women, were generally aware that drinking alcohol or using drugs during pregnancy could potentially harm the developing fetus. However, women who were dealing with a substance addiction and various other life problems found it difficult, in most cases, to decrease or stop their use, even when pregnant. The women also reported receiving varied public health messages about risk behaviour in relation to 'safe' levels of alcohol and risks associated with consumption during various stages of pregnancy. Women reported that some public health campaigns were not clear in their message and focused too strongly on the individual woman, rather than including her family and community. Public health messages in the form of posters and pamphlets produced by Aboriginal organizations tended to take a community perspective, focusing much more on the community and family, as well as the pregnant woman (Tait, 2000a).

There has been no research that examined the effectiveness of public awareness approaches on levels of alcohol consumption by pregnant Aboriginal women. However, within Canada, particularly in western and northern regions, most Aboriginal communities have a general awareness of FAS and the dangers of alcohol consumption by pregnant women. While warning labels and public awareness materials may contribute to increased awareness, issues, such as the general accessibility of the language used in these campaigns, a cost-benefit analysis of warning labels and public awareness materials, as well as cultural sensitivity to how the issue is presented, need to be addressed. In Aboriginal communities, the creation of public health campaigns may be most effective if they are conceived of, designed by and distributed by local community organizations and members, including women at risk for having an affected child. Prevention may be located as much in the process of having community members involved, invested and controlling the creation and dissemination of the public health message, than in the actual end product itself.

Chapter 9

Revised 'best practice'

1. There is some evidence to support warning labels and posters as a means of increasing awareness and effecting short-term behaviour change among low-risk women. However, women who drink heavily during pregnancy do not appear to be affected by warning labels. Public health prevention messages in Aboriginal communities need to be culturally sensitive to local communities and their success may be enhanced by community involvement, investment and control of the creation and dissemination of the public health message.

Multi-Component Community-Wide Initiatives

'Best practice'

1. There is some evidence to support multi-component community-wide initiatives as a means of increasing awareness generally, reducing consumption for pregnant women and promoting referrals.

Multi-component community-wide initiatives generally combine various strategies of prevention aimed at increasing awareness in all segments of the community. An example of such an initiative is the Tuba City, Arizona, Fetal Alcohol Syndrome (FAS) Prevention Project (Masis and May, 1991; LeMaster and Connell, 1994). The program used a comprehensive approach to prevention and intervention through the following objectives: 1) to increase the knowledge of FAS among Navajo Division of Health personnel; 2) to train Indian Health Service Tuba City Service Unit (TCSU) providers in FAS; 3) to double the number of pregnant women from TCSU who complete residential treatment for alcoholism; 4) to demonstrate that TCSU officials show a positive attitude change towards the need to educate their constituents about FAS; 5) to establish an effective screening mechanism for alcohol use by pregnant women; 6) to implement a protocol for intervention and follow-up of pregnant women using alcohol; 7) to double assessment and treatment of FAS children; and, 8) to increase the number of FAS/FAE mothers or care takers participating in treatment of children (Masis and May, 1991). Although the various components of the project were not individually evaluated, the overall program was effective in promoting referrals and abstinence among pregnant women (Roberts and Nanson, 2000; Masis and May, 1991).

Multi-component community-wide initiatives are increasingly being tried in Aboriginal communities and communities with large numbers of Aboriginal people. For example, the city of Prince George, British Columbia, which has a large Aboriginal population, created in 1998 the FAS/FAE Prevention Community-Based Policy Development Project. The initial task of the project was to research and review FAS prevention community-based strategies, in order to identify future strategies for prevention, intervention and identification. The Prince George FAS Community Collaborative Network was the base for the project and was made up of over fifty individuals representing thirty different organizations, groups, agencies and stakeholders in the community.

Chapter 9

Community readiness was determined through participatory action research (PAR), guided by the FAS Community Collaborative Network. Six indicators were identified and examined:

1. expressed need for change by the community;

2. agreement by the community on the goal, objectives and initiatives of the project, followed by a commitment of time and resources. A commitment of a core group of community members who were available to take on the tasks associated with the project was also sought;

3. awareness of the issue that involved groundwork to educate and disseminate information to the community about substance abuse and pregnancy and FAS;

4. community readiness, including the acceptance that there is a 'problem' to be addressed, community openness to seeking solutions, a broad range of support from within (and outside) of the community and mechanisms put in place for ensuring community input around collective actions;

5. resource availability, including organizational, structural and human resources that could support project initiatives; and

6. organization of supporting structure, including conflict resolution, reputable, reliable and inclusive organization and a positive public profile.

The experience of the community of Prince George illustrates that a multi-component community-wide initiative requires the willingness of key actors, including local political leaders, to participate and support the project. In some Aboriginal communities where high rates of alcohol abuse exist, it may be difficult for this type of broad-based strategy to take root, particularly if community leaders do not prioritize the issue. These communities may lack organizational structures to move the project along, and, therefore, the assistance of outside Aboriginal agencies that deal with community capacity building may be required. However, unless a core group of community members want the project and are involved and invested in the creation and implementation of it, outside assistance will have limited benefit. Other factors, such as available financial and human resources, are important in determining if a community can support such a strategy. Also, a commitment of adequate funding from government bodies is essential for the success of any initiative.

Multi-component community-wide strategies fit well with traditional Aboriginal approaches to individual and community wellness. For example, in a widely distributed publication produced by the Aboriginal Nurses Association and disseminated by Health Canada, the Medicine Wheel illustrates ways in which Aboriginal communities can address FAS prevention and intervention (Van Bibber, 1997). Another important publication, which outlines a community-wide initiative, is the *Community Action Guide: Working together for the prevention of Fetal Alcohol Syndrome* (BC FAS Resource Society, 1998). This report provides information on working with high risk women and planning effective community-based initiatives to prevent FAS.

Chapter 9

Revised 'best practice'

1. There is some evidence to support multi-component community-wide initiatives as a means of increasing awareness generally, reducing consumption for pregnant women and promoting referrals. These initiatives must be driven by a combination of community readiness, sufficient human and financial resources to sustain the initiative, and must be characterized by sensitivity to local beliefs and customs.

Multi-Component School-Community Substance Use Prevention Programs

'Best practice'

1. There is moderate evidence to support the use of life-skills-based and multi-component school-community substance use prevention programs as a means of preventing or delaying substance use among youth and, in turn, reducing substance use problems among adults.

Roberts and Nanson (2000) argue that substance use prevention initiatives could have significant benefit if they delay the age at which children or adolescents begin to use alcohol or other substances. For example, an American study found that age, at onset of alcohol use, was a powerful predictor of later alcohol problems. In this study, researchers found that 40% of those who began drinking alcohol at fourteen years of age or younger experienced alcohol dependence at some point in their lives, compared to 10% who began drinking at age 20 or older (Grant and Dawson, 1997 in Roberts and Nanson, 2000).

Studies of substance use among adolescents in Canada have found that Aboriginal adolescents are more likely than their non-Aboriginal counterparts to use a range of substances (e.g., marijuana, solvents and other hallucinogens). Alcohol use rates, however, are comparable between the two groups (MacMillan, MacMillan et al., 1996; Gfellner and Hundleby, 1995; Lalinee-Michaud, Subak, Ghadirian and Kovess, 1991), but high rates of binge drinking, coupled with high rates of adolescent pregnancies among Aboriginal adolescents, has raised concern about FAS/ARBEs.

Life skills training targeting adolescents has been found to be an effective primary prevention strategy in some contexts (Botvin et al., 1995 in Roberts and Nanson, 2000). Generally, these programs are school-based initiatives that teach personal and social skills, in combination with specific skills, to resist social influences to use substances (Roberts and Nanson, 2000; Botvin et al., 1995; Pentz et al., 1989; Perry et al., 1996). Some programs have involved media, community leaders, parents and the business and religious communities in their design (Paine-Andrews et al., 1996 in Roberts and Nanson, 2000). Roberts and Nanson add:

> FAS-specific content should be accommodated in health education and family living courses. Topics at the high school level should include pregnancy planning, the teratogenic effects of alcohol, early symptoms of pregnancy, the importance of routine physical exams of sexually active female adolescents, the problems of confronting parents, and understanding the needs of those affected by prenatal alcohol exposure (2000:18; Murphy-Brennan and Oei, 1999).

These initiatives will also benefit from consideration of local cultural and traditional beliefs about pregnancy and should involve the recognition of competing views about sexuality and pregnancy, which may exist in a community (e.g., Traditional vs. Christian views vs. images seen on television) and impact upon adolescent attitudes and behaviours.

Within Canada, a great deal of attention and resources have been directed toward Aboriginal youth, particularly initiatives aimed at giving youth more control and input into programs that target them as a group. Urban and rural youth groups, specifically those that provide outreach to high risk youth, including youth who have dropped out of school, play an important social, educational and support role in the lives of many Aboriginal adolescents. In some instances, these groups may be one of the only supports accessed by youth who are at risk of substance abuse and/or becoming pregnant. They may also be important sites for the dissemination of information on issues such birth control, substance abuse and prenatal care (Tait, 2003).

Caution should be taken when implementing FAS prevention programs targeting children and adolescents. Programs should ensure that trained personnel are available to correctly answer questions about FAS/ARBEs, in order to avoid the dissemination of misinformation about the illness. Special concern should be given to the possibility that some youth will be labelled by their peers (or others in the community) as alcohol-affected, particularly in communities where histories of maternal alcohol abuse are generally known, once a discussion of FAS/ARBEs begins in the community. Informal labelling, particularly among adolescents, could lead to the marginalization and stigmatization of some youth.

Revised 'best practice'

1. There is moderate evidence to support the use of life-skills-based and multi-component school-community substance use prevention programs as a means of preventing or delaying substance use among youth and, in turn, reducing substance use problems among adults. An important component of these initiatives should be Aboriginal youth groups and outreach programs, specifically those that target high risk youth who have dropped out of school and are accessing few services. Special attention should be given in these programs to reducing the possibility of informal diagnosing of individuals in the community as alcohol-effected once a discussion of FAS/ARBE prevention begins.

Conclusion

In general, primary prevention, through public health promotion strategies, does not work on its own. However, when combined with other prevention and intervention strategies, it can be beneficial. Central to primary prevention is the involvement of the target audience, whether specific local community members or sub-groups, such as adolescents or high risk women. Multi-component initiatives that involve and engage community members can be effective prevention strategies. However, these strategies must convey information about risk that is based on the most up to date scientific findings and deliver it in ways that are easily understandable by the majority of community members. They must also avoid the temptation to exaggerate risk associated with alcohol use by pregnant women and, thus, unduly alarm women who are at limited or no risk of producing an affected child.

Chapter 9

'Best Practices' and Secondary Prevention

> ... and I was pregnant with a baby back then when they took my younger son, the one I did have in my care. They don't know what they do to women when they take their children away ... Like, nothing mattered to me anymore and I, like, I drank occasionally, I admit that, but after they took my kids, my son, like, nothing mattered to me anymore. Not even the baby that I was carrying. And I started drinking more and started doing cocaine and I started shooting cocaine and I did that right through my pregnancy ... In other words, they took my life away when they took my kids. So they don't know what they are putting women through when they do that (cited in Tait, 2000a:69).

> Realizing I'm an alcoholic, I have a drinking problem, and trying to understand that I'm an alcoholic and I feel too young to be an alcoholic. All this stuff has happened to me ... I really didn't know who to talk to about it. That was when I was still pregnant with my last daughter (cited in Tait, 2000a:63).

Secondary prevention is defined as "efforts to slow or stop the progression of the problems through early detection and early treatment" (Poole, 1997:15). Early intervention involves identification, brief therapeutic attention and referral to treatment services of those with substantial problems (Poole, 1997). Secondary prevention, when applied to the issue of substance use during pregnancy, involves activities that target women of child-bearing ages who use substances and includes outreach, screening, referral and brief intervention activities (Roberts and Nanson, 2000). Roberts and Nanson state that the intent of secondary prevention is to "promote the health of the mother and prevent or minimize harm to the fetus" (2000:19).

Secondary and tertiary prevention occur within the larger framework of health care services provided to Aboriginal people. For Aboriginal people, the delivery of health care services, particularly for those living in First Nations communities who receive federally-run services, has been founded on colonial ideology and emphasize paternalism, dependency, victim blaming and medicalization (Browne and Fiske, 2001; O'Neil, 1986; Speck, 1987; Waldram, Herring and Kue Young, 1995; Young, 1984). Reproduction has always received a great deal of attention from colonialist interests, particularly the control of Aboriginal women's bodies and their reproductive experiences.

For example, Browne and Fiske (2001) point out that an extreme example of oppression and paternalism in northern health care was the sterilization of Aboriginal women in the early 1970s, reportedly without their full consent (O'Neil, 1988; RCAP, 1996b). A recent example is obstetric policies that require Aboriginal women from northern and remote communities to give birth in southern or regional centres. Browne and Fiske write:

> More recently, control and medicalization has been exercised through obstetrical policies developed by the Medical Services Branch (the federal department responsible for First Nations health) which requires all women from northern and isolated Aboriginal communities to deliver their babies in southern or regional centers, which are typically 1 to 4 hours by plane from their home communities (O'Neil and Kaufert, 1990). These policies are slowly changing, and Aboriginal communities are actively reclaiming control

over health services. Current 'health transfer' arrangements, however, must be viewed with caution: They have been critiqued as attempts to off-load federal responsibilities for health care that may disadvantage communities as they inherit underfunded, medicalized systems of health care (2001:128-12).

Tait (2003) suggests that new forms of colonizing Aboriginal women's bodies may be linked to prevention of FAS/ARBEs. For example, mainstream biomedical responses to large numbers of teen pregnancies in some northern Aboriginal communities and urban sub-populations in Manitoba has been the prescription of birth control methods, particularly Depo Provera®,[39] to adolescent girls, some as young as thirteen years old (Tait, 2000a). Some health and social service providers, in Tait's study, viewed this type of birth control as a positive measure to prevent FAS/ARBEs, in addition to pregnancies (2000a; 2003). Tait points out that, while Depo Provera® may eliminate problems for young women, such as negotiating condom use with partners or remembering to take a pill everyday, it does not protect them from sexually transmitted diseases, particularly HIV. Tait adds:

> Some service providers felt that prescribing Depo-Provera® was a responsible response to help prevent FAS and related illnesses in social environments where teen pregnancies and substance misuse were particularly high. Both service providers and consumers [women interviewed] pointed out that Depo-Provera® was prescribed to Aboriginal women at much higher rates than non-Aboriginal women, which raised questions about the underlying motivation behind these higher rates of prescription. From the perspective of some service providers, Depo-Provera® or any long-term birth control intervention did not address addiction problems among the target population, and therefore was only beneficial as a short-term solution in the prevention of illnesses related to substance use during pregnancy. They argued that Depo-Provera® did nothing to address the negative health and wellness consequences of addiction for women beyond the prevention of harm to the fetus (2000a:15).

Secondary prevention for Aboriginal women may present certain challenges for service delivery. Browne and Fiske point out that "the colonial legacy of subordination of Aboriginal people has resulted in a multiple jeopardy for Aboriginal women who face individual and institutional discrimination, and disadvantages on the basis of race, gender, and class" (2001:127, Dion-Stout, 1996; Voyageur, 1996). Poole (2000) writes that Aboriginal women are strongly affected by the pervasive, negative attitudes of society toward women who abuse substances, an attitude that has been brought to bear specifically on Aboriginal women with substance use problems.

Benoit and Carroll, in a study of the perspective of Aboriginal women who live in the downtown eastside of Vancouver, one of the poorest and most troubled neighbourhoods in Canada and one which has a high concentration of Aboriginal women, illustrate that specific sub-groups of Aboriginal women may be particularly marginalized within the larger society and within the general Aboriginal population.

---

[39]   A prescription of Depo Provera® lasts for three months and is given to a patient through injection. Several side-effects have been associated with Depo Provera®, such as weight gain or loss, and is typically not seen by health care practitioners as an appropriate form of birth control for adolescent girls (Tait, 2003).

Chapter 9

These women face formidable barriers to services, including systemic racism (2001; Tait, 2000a). Some of the literature on secondary prevention has been discussed above in the section on risk and protective factors for women and, therefore, will be reviewed only briefly in this discussion. Specific prevention initiatives will be reviewed in relation to each identified 'best practice,' as well as what the implications are for similar initiatives directed toward Aboriginal people. With the assistance of the National Steering Committee, Roberts and Nanson identified six 'best practices' concerning secondary prevention.

Screening

'Best practices'

1. There is a consensus among experts to support routine screening of pregnant women for use of alcohol and other substances in various settings, including justice, housing and health settings.

2. There is moderate evidence to support the use of the T-ACE and TWEAK, and some evidence to support the use of CAGE and AUDIT alcohol dependence instruments in a supportive milieu to identify women who would benefit from intervention for their alcohol use during pregnancy.

3. There is some evidence and a consensus among experts to support selective use of bio-markers by physicians, with the informed consent of the client, as a follow-up to a written screen.

The purpose of screening pregnant women for substance abuse problems is to provide a preliminary evaluation about whether or not key indicators of alcohol or drug problems are present (BC FAS Resource Society, 1998). Screening gives service providers, such as outreach workers, physicians and other health care providers, the opportunity to refer women at risk to prenatal education and counselling and to other services, such as substance addiction treatment programs (Roberts and Nanson, 2000; May, 1995). Browne and Fiske (2001) suggest that Aboriginal women may be reluctant to participate in screening programs because of a general feeling that the health care system is not culturally safe and does little to acknowledge or counter patterns of individual or institutional discrimination. Roberts and Nanson (2000) point out that some women may not acknowledge substance use problems due to a lack of motivation or fear of discrimination by health care providers. They suggest that screening needs to occur "in a supportive milieu that is sensitive to the circumstances of pregnant women, particularly substance users, and that will permit open questions and honest responses" (2000:21-22; Leslie and Roberts, 2001; Russell et al., 1996; Lieberman, 1998b; BC FAS Resource Society, 1998).

Roberts and Nanson (2000) describe screening instruments that "are simple and easy-to-use" for determining whether a woman may have an alcohol use problem. The tools have been used primarily in health care settings, but have been used in other settings by outreach health and social service providers. The most common and generally accepted screening instruments are AUDIT, CAGE, T-ACE and TWEAK (see Appendix C for a description of each instrument). In their review, Roberts and Nanson found that these particular screening instruments could be quickly and easily used in a variety of settings to identify women who would require further assessment (2000; Sokol and Clarren, 1989). A study, which examined the use of T-ACE among a group of pregnant American Indian women, recommended adjustments to the instrument so that it would be culturally sensitive to this population; however, without the adjustments, the instrument still showed a high degree of sensitivity for the group (Gale, White and Welty, 1998 in Roberts and Nanson, 2000).

Roberts and Nanson (2000) point out that a limitation of the screens is that women may under-report their use of alcohol. They write:

> To minimize under reporting the T-ACE and TWEAK do not ask women about actual quantities of alcohol used or about current use. Another limitation is that increasing the specificity of screens (that is, the effectiveness in correctly screening out women who do not have alcohol problems) usually means identifying fewer mothers who drink less heavily, but whose drinking nevertheless puts them at risk for delivering a FAS/FAE infant. It has been suggested that clinicians err on the side of increasing the sensitivity of the instrument (even if non-drinkers are identified as well) in order to ensure all problem drinkers are identified, recognizing that more women will need to be given follow-up assessments to verify the screen results, and this will require more resources (2000:22-23).

Project staff in a prevention program, surveyed by Leslie and Roberts (2001), explained that screening interviews were an opportunity to get to know women, to build trust and to emphasize the strengths of the woman. The staff found that, during screening, it was not necessarily the *nature* of the questions they asked women that determined whether the process was perceived by the clients as threatening or not, but *how* the questions were asked. Front-line prevention workers argue that screening must involve the acknowledgement of the woman's strengths and capacities and aim at building, rather than diminishing, her self-esteem. The tone of the interview screens must be non-judgmental and seek to normalize the behaviour by speaking openly and truthfully about the issue in a supportive safe context.

Research continues to search for an ideal bio-marker of alcohol exposure (Stratton, Howe et al., 1996). Roberts and Nanson (2000) found several studies that suggest two tests for alcohol use, carbohydrate-deficient transferrin (CDT) and gamma glutamyl transpeptidase (GGT) that, when applied together, show increased sensitivity than the use of one test alone, without reducing specificity.[40] This type of screening can reduce problems associated with under-reporting of alcohol use; however, because they can be applied without a woman's knowledge, ethical concern arises over their use. For this reason, Roberts and Nanson argue that bio-marker testing be conducted only with a woman's informed consent.

Screening for drug use that is brief and can be easily administered is not as developed as brief screening for alcohol use. Some toxicologic tests are effective in providing evidence of current or recent drug use; however, these tests do not distinguish between occasional and heavy use and, depending on the timing of the use, test results may lack sensitivity (Roberts and Nanson, 2000). Roberts and Nanson caution that, because these screens can be applied without a woman's knowledge, their use raises ethical and legal concerns that must be considered.

---

[40]   For a detailed description of these tests, see Stratton, Howe et al., 1996.

Chapter 9

Calls for initiatives to screen pregnant Aboriginal women, and women more generally, for alcohol use, imply that there are services currently available for women who are identified as needing further evaluation or in need of immediate and easy access to specialized services, such as detoxification and addiction treatment programming. It also assumes that women will willingly want to go on to the next step of evaluation or to receive treatment if they are identified by an initial screen. However, recent studies have found that inadequate detoxification services for women exist in some regions (Poole, 1997; Tait, 2000a) and that several barriers, including long waiting lists, prevent women from accessing addiction treatment programs (Jacobs and Gill, 2002; Poole, 1997; Tait, 2000a).

Research has also shown that high risk women may be reluctant to access health services if they feel they will be pressured or forced to accept services that they do not want (e.g., pregnant women who are screened may not want to leave their home community to go to a residential addiction treatment program far from where they live) or if they fear information gained by health care or social service providers will be used against them (e.g., to gain custody of their children) (Tait, 2000a; 2003; Benoit and Carroll, 2001; Browne and Fiske, 2001).

Roberts and Nanson (2000) argue that, in higher risk communities, outreach, identification, referral and appropriate support be incorporated into overall strategies for prevention and early intervention (Leslie and Roberts, 2001). In a review of a comprehensive local program for the prevention of FAS at the Tuba City, Arizona, Indian Medical Centre between January 1988 and July 1989, Masis and May (1991) found that women referred to the program showed a high rate of acceptance. A key element in the acceptance of the program, by both the community as a whole and by individual clients, was the status of the program staff members as trusted community residents. Masis and May write:

> Their skills in bridging the gap between the dominant culture and the Navajo culture were indispensable in gaining support by the community as well as the cooperation of pregnant clients. Such community leaders have been called "natural helpers" ... A family-oriented approach has been a strong asset to this program. Not only has it aided in the identification of additional mothers likely to produce FAS-FAE children, but it has fostered an understanding of the problem (1991:489).

Other key elements contributing to high acceptance of the program was that it was designated as a prevention, rather than an alcoholism or social work program, and that compliance was enhanced by having the program based in a hospital or prenatal clinic. Follow-up at the end of the eighteen-month period found that, of the thirty-two women remaining in the program, 18 (56.3%) were abstinent, 4 (12.5%) were drinking less and 10 (31.2%) were still drinking as heavily as before. Roughly, ten per cent of the women were using birth control and fifteen per cent had voluntary tubal ligations. It should be noted that 33.3% per cent of participants said they did not use birth control because of traditional Navajo beliefs (Masis and May, 1991). This finding supports the need for consideration of local cultural beliefs and their intersection with the defined problem, as well as re-evaluation of mainstream solutions that lack cultural sensitivity.[41]

---

[41] A limitation of this study, as pointed out by Roberts and Nanson (2000), was the lack of control groups in the research design, which may have shed further light on the program's impact.

Chapter 9

Revised 'best practices'

1. There is a consensus among experts to support routine screening of pregnant women for use of alcohol and other substances in various settings, including justice, housing and health settings. However, routine screening is only beneficial if follow-up evaluation and appropriate intervention services exist that pregnant women are willing to participate in and can easily access.

2. There is moderate evidence to support the use of the T-ACE and TWEAK, and some evidence to support the use of CAGE and AUDIT alcohol dependence instruments in a supportive milieu to identify women who would benefit from intervention for their alcohol use during pregnancy. In all settings using such instruments, measures must be taken to ensure that the women being screened are: 1) properly informed about the reasons behind the screen; 2) clearly ensured that the information obtained will remain strictly confidential; and 3) properly informed what follow-up evaluations or interventions (e.g., addiction treatment programs) may be recommended to them and that participation in these services is voluntary on their part. Screening instruments should be tested locally to gauge their sensitivity and cultural appropriateness.

3. There is some evidence and a consensus among experts to support selective use of bio-markers by physicians, with the informed consent of the client, as a follow-up to a written screen. Obtaining informed consent must be preceded by a very clear explanation given to women about the purpose of the tests, the confidentiality of the information and what follow-up evaluations or interventions (e.g., addiction treatment programs) may be recommended to them, and that participation in these services, as well as the screening interview, is strictly voluntary on their part. Special attention must be given to ways in which informed consent is obtained, including consideration of how best to fully inform women of what they are agreeing to (e.g., information given in Aboriginal languages) and the role that Aboriginal customs or historical influences of Aboriginal and non-Aboriginal relations may play in this process.

Prenatal Interventions

'Best practices'

1. There is good evidence that brief interventions in prenatal settings, based on cognitive-behavioural principles, are effective low-cost means of helping pregnant women with early-stage alcohol problems to reduce or eliminate alcohol use during pregnancy.

2. There is some evidence to support the effectiveness of drug education programs in reducing substance use among pregnant adolescents attending prenatal clinics.

Prenatal interventions can occur in various settings, including clinical, outreach, school and home settings. They can also be incorporated within activities at Aboriginal wellness and healing centres. Because many women are reluctant to seek help for their substance abuse problems, particularly when pregnant, general services may be settings where women at risk can be identified and assisted in finding appropriate services for their abuse problems. Although many Aboriginal women with substance abuse problems have some knowledge of, or experience with, addiction treatment programs, this background does not necessarily mean that they will try to access these services when pregnant and struggling with substance abuse. For example, Tait (2000a) found that women reported being less willing to go to an addiction treatment program when they were pregnant, as opposed to when they were not. This was specifically true for pregnant Aboriginal women who would be required to travel out of their community to a treatment centre located far away from where they lived.

For pregnant women struggling with substance abuse, increased stigmatization associated with substance abuse during pregnancy and fears that child welfare services could apprehend their babies at birth or their other children if they knew about the abuse problem, may influence decisions by pregnant women to avoid prenatal care and other outreach services (Tait, 2000a). This is illustrated in a woman's account of her decision not to seek help from service providers to access addiction treatment:

> Oh, yeah. There was lots of opportunity. But like I said I didn't want to lose my kids. I was so scared of the initial, okay if I trust these people, I go, right, what's going to happen? What if they don't think I'm good enough? What if they think, "Oh she did this, she did that?" I was scared of Child and Family. I've always been scared because when I was eleven I got taken away for nothing (cited in Tait, 2000a:62).

A study by Kowalsky and Verhoef (1999 in Roberts and Nanson, 2000) illustrates that inherent difficulties exist for pregnant women living in isolated Aboriginal communities. Fear of stigmatization, lack of awareness of the issues and specific community social problems contributed to women not accessing services. Kowalsky and Verhoef found that substance use was endemic in the community and, because it was intertwined with other social problems, it was difficult to address separately. Jordan (1998 in Roberts and Nanson, 2000), in a discussion of similar problems in a Navajo community in New Mexico, suggested the use of family advocates, indigenous languages and resource material published in local indigenous languages as strategies to help break down barriers.

In a study that examined the service needs of pregnant women with substance abuse problems in Manitoba, Tait (2000a) found that community services for women varied greatly, with the largest number and variety located in Winnipeg. The range of services included women's resource centres, shelters, transition housing, youth programs and services, support and self-help groups, and outreach centres. This group of service providers were key in supporting women before, during and after their pregnancies, in many instances, had initial contact with women and, in some cases, represented the only contact by a service provider throughout the pregnancies of high risk women. Many service providers pointed to several breakdowns in the continuum of care for pregnant women as contributing to substance abuse problems. Difficult access to addiction treatment programs (e.g., no available spaces) and lack of after care services for pregnant women who had completed addiction treatment were two common problems. Tait writes:

> One of the major factors is the level of comfort that women have with the services they access combined with the fact that services are located in various places. For example, typically a pregnant woman who accesses a service such as a shelter cannot receive counselling for substance misuse problems. She has to go to another program that deals with addiction treatment. She cannot receive pregnancy information and support at the addiction treatment program and must access that elsewhere ... Because most services for

women are designed to deal with a specific issue that impacts upon their lives—such as domestic violence, pregnancy, or addiction—they are left to negotiate their way through a maze of service options. This is not always easy, especially for women who are dealing with substance addiction and who may be fearful of the implications of becoming visible to service providers in the first place. As well, women from certain groups, such as First Nations or Métis women, may not feel comfortable accessing services provided by non- Aboriginal service providers and organizations (2000a:24).

For Aboriginal women, who live in settlements or reserve communities where they have very limited service options in their community, the complete opposite problem may exist. In cases where Aboriginal women are transported out of their communities to give birth in urban settings, these women may have very limited information about support services while away from home or may be reluctant or fearful to approach organizations who could support them. In some instances, pregnant Aboriginal women are living outside of their communities for two to four weeks while awaiting to give birth. Women, put in this circumstance, can experience a range of strong emotions, including depression, boredom, loneliness, isolation and fear, all of which can place women with past or present alcohol abuse problems at risk for further abuse. This is particularly true if appropriate supports do not exist for them in the centres where they give birth (Tait, 2003).

Barriers that may prevent pregnant women from accessing prenatal clinical and outreach services can be varied. For example, Tait (2000a) found that inappropriate location of services, such as a pregnancy outreach services being located in the same building as the child welfare services, could discourage pregnant women from attending certain programs for fear that their pregnancy would become visible to child welfare services. This is particularly true in small urban and rural communities where limited space is available to house programs. Transportation problems and lack of child care services were barriers for some women, particularly women living in rural areas who wanted to access services in urban centres. Supplying bus tickets and day care services may be simple low-cost interventions that increase participation by women and, therefore, outreach services should be given appropriate budget allocations for these supports.

An important finding in the study by Tait was the distinction between 'programs' and 'place.' Unlike specific programs, some outreach services operate as drop-in centres. Examples of such services include Aboriginal Head Start programs, Native and Métis Friendship Centres and women's resource centres. Typically, women access these services on a drop-in basis. What makes this service unique is that it operates as a *place* rather than a *program* (Tait, 2000a). Women are not required to attend a program such as a parenting or prenatal class; however, these programs may be offered if a woman chooses to attend. *Street Connections*, a service for street-involved women and transgender persons living in Winnipeg, is an example of a 'drop-in' service designed specifically for women. Tait writes:

> Community-based outreach centres such as Street Connections ... begin with the notion of community and build their programs and services from that base ... Women are encouraged to identify with the service as a place that they can come to and see other women who are experiencing similar life challenges. Places such as these have the capacity to build positive support networks for women and a sense of ownership or belonging in an environment that is non-threatening or judgmental. Various service providers are

available to women at outreach service centres. For example, Street Connections has a nurse on site so that women can access primary health care in a setting where they feel comfortable. They see the same nurse each time they have an examination, and are able to build a level of trust with her. Social workers and counsellors who work at the centre mix with clients who come to the house to 'hang out'. The women who access this service reported that they would often speak with workers at Street Connections before anyone else about what was happening in their lives because they trusted them to keep their conversations confidential. The women also respected the workers' opinions, and felt that they were non-judgmental and listened to them rather than pushing them into programs and activities in which they did not want to participate. Service providers ... also made themselves available to accompany women to appointments, and to advocate on behalf of women with other service providers when necessary. However, as with other similar programs, they are constrained by staff shortages and limited financial resources to meet client demand (2000a:25).

Outreach services that provide communal space for women to relax, laugh and talk with one another can break the isolation and loneliness that women who are street-involved may experience. They can also facilitate the building of community in urban centres where Aboriginal women come from a variety of Nations and backgrounds. An important component of these services is to provide a safe place for women and their children, which is best facilitated through women-only centres. Although community-based centres are also important, women may not access these services if they are fearful of running into male individuals (Tait, 2003).

Once women access prenatal services, service providers are in the position to work with women who are at risk of having an alcohol-affected child. Several qualitative studies have shown that Aboriginal women respond best to service providers who approach them in a non-judgmental manner, treat them with respect and include them in the decision-making process (Benoit and Carroll, 2001; Browne and Fiske, 2001; Tait, 2000a; 2003). In a qualitative study, which examined barriers to addiction treatment facing women in British Columbia, Poole and Isaac found that supportive professionals from a wide range of services, including justice, health and housing, helped women access treatment (1999 in Roberts and Nanson, 2000).

Carr emphasized the need to intervene at the level of the interpersonal needs of the client (e.g., self-esteem issues, family violence), rather than just providing facts on the risks of drinking during pregnancy (1995 in Roberts and Nanson, 2000). In the particular case of high risk women, who have a history of distrust of health and social services, building trust in order to provide appropriate services may take a great deal of time and special attention from individual service providers (Leslie and Roberts, 2001). In Tait's (2000a) study, many Manitoba service providers reported they did not have enough staff and funding to deal with the demands by clients for individual counselling, outreach services or follow-up after care programs for women with substance abuse problems, despite a clear need for these services (Leslie and Roberts, 2001). The identification of 'best practices' will have far less benefit unless issues pertaining to adequate human and financial resources are addressed by government funding bodies.

Chapter 9

In their review of the literature, Roberts and Nanson (2000) found several studies, which examined the use of brief interventions that may motivate pregnant women to decrease or stop their use of substances. Yahnee and Miller (1999 in Roberts and Nanson, 2000:25) reviewed the literature on brief interventions and identified the following elements for success, identified by the acronym FRAMES:

Feedback: effective, but brief interventions provide clients with personal feedback regarding their individual status.

Responsibility: effective brief interventions emphasize personal responsibility for change and the individual's freedom of choice.

Advice: effective brief counselling that includes a clear recommendation on the need for change, in a supportive, rather than authoritarian, manner.

Menu: a menu of different strategies for change is offered, providing options from which clients may choose what seems sensible to them.

Empathy: emphasis is placed on an empathetic, reflective, warm and supportive practitioner style.

Self-efficacy: effective brief interventions reinforce self-efficacy, e.g., the client's expectations that she can change.

Other approaches focus on psycho-social stressors, teach stress management skills and alternatives to smoking, drinking and other substance use, in culturally appropriate ways (Mehl, 1993 in Roberts and Nanson, 2000; Leslie and Roberts, 2001). With few exceptions, these interventions have been tried with non-Aboriginal women and no study was found among Aboriginal women in Canada. Adoption of brief interventions, based on cognitive-behavioural principles for Aboriginal women accessing prenatal services, will require adjustment to the specific local circumstances (e.g., culture and language, geographical consideration), which impact upon women's perception of the service. However, this will be much more difficult in urban centres, where Aboriginal women come from diverse cultural and social backgrounds.

The incorporation of traditional Aboriginal approaches to pregnancy and child birth into prenatal intervention services for Aboriginal women may motivate pregnant women to decrease or stop their use of substances. Central to this is the role of traditional practitioners, such as midwives and Elders. The integration of traditional practitioners into prenatal services, including a recognition by biomedical practitioners of traditional knowledge and the benefits of traditional practices, should be included in both rural and urban centres. Aboriginal health practitioners, who are trained in biomedicine, and organizations such as the Aboriginal Nurses Association and the Aboriginal Physicians Association, could play a central role in this integration process. For example, Aboriginal nurses, for several decades, have worked in local community settings and have maintained a national dialogue on Aboriginal health issues. They are in a key position to work with communities to identify ways in which local traditional knowledge can be integrated with biomedical prenatal care.

Chapter 9

It Takes a Community: A Resource Manual for Community-based Prevention of Fetal Alcohol Syndrome and Fetal Alcohol Effects (Van Bibber, 1997), which was sponsored by the Aboriginal Nurses Association, is an excellent example of this process. The manual integrates Aboriginal traditional knowledge and practices with biomedical conceptions of FAS/ARBEs and situates these within a historical and social framework that recognizes the impact of colonialism upon Aboriginal people. The manual is also published in Inuktitut, which not only makes it accessible to a wider audience, but also acknowledges the importance of Aboriginal languages in the dissemination of information and resources aimed at Aboriginal people.

Pregnant adolescents may require special programming based on their age and, possibly, substance of choice. Among some Aboriginal youth, solvent use, particularly gasoline sniffing, is a serious problem (Waldram, Herring and Kue Young, 1995) and poses a unique challenge for secondary and tertiary prevention. While some studies suggest that drug education programs for pregnant adolescents attending prenatal clinics may provide the opportunity for secondary prevention (Sarvela and Ford, 1993 in Roberts and Nanson, 2000), these programs may have only limited or, in some cases, no benefit in communities where serious problems, such as adult substance abuse, family dysfunction and poverty, are endemic. Furthermore, in situations such as these, the addiction problems are likely to be so severe that education programs will not begin to make an impact upon behaviour. However, in communities where substance abuse is less widespread, programs targeting adolescents may help to reduce adolescent substance abuse and pregnancies if they are presented in ways that are meaningful to participants. A second way to approach questions concerning adolescent substance abuse and pregnancies is to consider Aboriginal communities where these issues are less common. Identifying risk and protective factors by comparing and contrasting variables, such as social integration, community control and autonomy in high, moderate and low risk communities, could yield important information on adolescent behaviour and attitudes, thus better informing prevention and intervention strategies for these groups and their communities.

Revised 'best practices'

1. There is good evidence that brief interventions in prenatal settings, based on cognitive-behavioural principles, are an effective low-cost means of helping pregnant women with early-stage alcohol problems to reduce or eliminate alcohol use during pregnancy. These interventions must be developed in ways that are sensitive to both the individual and collective experiences of Aboriginal women and include, where possible, the integration of traditional Aboriginal knowledge and practices, as well as Aboriginal practitioners, such as midwives and community Elders.

2. There is some evidence to support the effectiveness of drug education programs in reducing substance use among pregnant adolescents attending prenatal clinics. Before these programs are adopted, they must be culturally sensitized to the needs of the local community. A community assessment should be undertaken to determine if these programs are the proper strategy, given the local level of substance abuse in the community. Research examining risk and protective factors in high, moderate and low risk communities that compare and contrast variables, such as social integration, community control and autonomy, could yield important information on adolescent behaviour and attitudes, thus better informing prevention and intervention strategies for this group and their communities.

Chapter 9

Health Care Training

'Best practice'

1. There is some evidence and a consensus among experts that training can be effective in helping physicians and other professionals work with women who have substance use problems.

Health care providers have been named as key service providers who can identify and assist women who have substance use problems. However, research indicates that a number of health professionals are reluctant to question and counsel pregnant patients with regards to their alcohol use (Funkhouser and Denniston, 1985; Weiner, Rosett et al., 1985; Waterson and Murray-Lyon, 1990; Nanson, Bolaria et al., 1995; Leslie and Roberts, 2001). Nanson and colleagues (1995) conducted a survey of pediatricians, family physicians and general practitioners in Saskatchewan, which has a large Aboriginal population and where the prevalence of FAS is thought to be high. They found pediatricians and more experienced family and general practitioners were more likely to feel comfortable discussing alcohol-related topics with patients than their less specialized and less experienced colleagues. Funkhouser and Denniston suggest that the reluctance of some physicians to advise women of the dangers of alcohol use during pregnancy could be a result of a lack of detailed information about the specific risks associated with a variety of drinking patterns of pregnant women. While physicians may want to offer accurate and realistic advice, they may feel ill-equipped to do so because they lack clear knowledge about the risks involved (Funkhouser and Denniston, 1985; Tait, 2003). Weiner and colleagues (1985) suggest that increased physician awareness of available community resources to which they can refer patients, could help physicians feel more comfortable with inquiring about the alcohol use of a pregnant patient.

An analysis of personal health habits of physicians found that those with better personal health habits counsel a broader range of patients and do so more aggressively (Funkhouser and Denniston, 1985). An early study by Wechsler and colleagues (1985) found that 74 per cent of physicians believed it was their responsibility to educate their patients about smoking, alcohol, drugs, exercise, stress and diet. However, some physicians remained reluctant, embarrassed, felt they were not knowledgeable enough or had limited time to inquire about alcohol abuse. Waterson and Murray-Lyon suggest "the medical profession has shown little desire to take over the management of alcohol problems unless physical damage has already occurred" (1990:358). Early American studies emphasized the importance of discussions between pregnant women and medical personnel in fostering a reduction in alcohol consumption (Minor and Van Dort, 1982; Waterson and Murray-Lyon, 1990).

A lack of understanding of class differences by health practitioners could be a barrier to identification and treatment for poor women. Handwerker (1994) found that, while health practitioners were aware of class differences, this did not seem to lead to greater understanding of the difficult life circumstances of their patients. The health care practitioners in her study consistently placed the burden of blame for pregnancy outcomes on women and expected them to have control over their life circumstances, regardless of their socio-economic status or poor social environment. Handwerker points out that "[p]atients' understanding of risk often differs from that of medical professionals and depends on their values, education, class and other markers affecting their location in the social structure" (1994:669).

Chapter 9

She adds: "Thus, reasons why individual women fail to take action to reduce their risk may be, in part, because they are acting on a concept of risk that is qualitatively different from clinical risk as discussed in a prenatal setting" (Handwerker, 1994:671).

The tension that emerges when medical professionals recommend changes in behaviour that their patients are unwilling or unable to follow may result in fewer poor pregnant women seeking prenatal care (Handwerker, 1994). This is illustrated in one woman's account of her interaction with health and social service providers while pregnant. In this example, the woman locates greater risk with the threat of child welfare apprehending her baby than with her not seeking addiction treatment and continuing to use substances:

> I first went to this doctor and I didn't get a very good feeling from her because at that time I had tried shooting up a few times and I had told her. And instead of her being a counsellor, she basically ridiculed me. Told me I was stupid and crazy for doing that. "Aren't you thinking of that baby?" ... So I kind of backed off from doctors for a few months ... I never told anybody because I was so worried about getting my baby taken away. I never told the obstetrician that I was using. The hospital found out because my counselor told them. She warned me ahead of time ... I kind of backed off, away from her when she said that about me. I just wanted to cut myself away from her. I was so scared about CFS [child welfare] getting involved and taking my baby. But that didn't stop me from using. Every day I'd tell myself this is it (cited in Tait, 2000a:65).

Waterson and Murray-Lyon found that, within prenatal clinics, medical staff are seen by women as sources of information; however, "the literature is full of complaints about lack of communication between obstetricians and mothers, which are partly due to perceived status differences" (1990:356). Browne and Fiske found that Aboriginal women typically experience discriminatory judgements levelled against them, particularly in their role as mothers and with regard to substance abuse problems. They write:

> Perhaps the most troubling consequence of the colonial legacy in health and social service sectors are the discriminatory judgements levelled against Aboriginal women as mothers. Repeatedly, stories were shared that described how participants were viewed as negative stereotypes, an act that denies the centrality of mothers within this First Nation community (Fiske, 1993) ... Participants who worked in health care also described the discriminatory attitudes displayed by providers toward Aboriginal women with substance abuse problems and homeless persons who received services in emergency departments or hospital wards. In some cases, participants who worked in health care described how services were sometimes withheld from known alcoholics or street people [even when a First Nation support worker challenged the physicians to provide care] (Browne and Fiske, 2001:136).

Waterson and Murray-Lyon (1990) suggest that midwives are likely to be seen as more helpful by pregnant women. An increased role in prenatal preparation and the imparting of health education advice may be incorporated into their current practices (Tait, 2000a). The role of midwives and traditional child-birth practices are experiencing a renewal in some Aboriginal communities and, therefore, they should be considered in FAS/ARBE prevention efforts. For example, some Aboriginal communities are attempting to revive and maintain traditional teachings and practices with regard to pregnancy, child-birth and parenting, in hopes that they will form an important foundation for personal and community development. Pauktuutit, the Inuit Women's Association, conducted research into traditional child-birth practices in hopes of bringing back the practice of home births and the use of traditional midwives (Van Bibber, 1997).

The Skookum Jim Friendship Centre in Whitehorse, Yukon, has developed a traditional parenting program that is a combination of two pilot projects dealing with traditional motherhood and fatherhood. Traditional laws and practices of child rearing have been researched for use in the program and circle discussions as effective, traditional ways of sharing knowledge. The Native Health Unit on Manitoulin Island, Ontario, has developed a series of teaching models using Anishnabe teachings in prenatal education. The teachings involve the seven gifts of the Creator—respect, humility, compassion, honesty, truth, wisdom and love—and incorporate the Circle and the Medicine Wheel (Van Bibber, 1997).

Revised 'best practice'

1. There is some evidence and a consensus among experts that training can be effective in helping physicians and other professionals work with women who have substance use problems. Training must seek to address questions of racism and discrimination and aim at making biomedical health care practitioners sensitive to the specific needs of Aboriginal women. Support for traditional Aboriginal practitioners in rural and urban Aboriginal communities, along with traditional child-birth and rearing practices, can be important factors in assisting pregnant Aboriginal women who have substance use problems.

Conclusion

Secondary prevention is defined as "efforts to slow or stop the progression of the problems through early detection and early treatment" (Poole, 1997:15). Within the framework of secondary prevention that targets pregnant women who abuse substances, it is important that the emphasis of prevention be placed on the woman and not just her pregnancy. Research has shown that women, who are at risk for having a child with FAS, have generally poor health and are likely to suffer from one or more alcohol-related illnesses (Abel, 1998a). They are also likely to die within a very short period of time after giving birth to a FAS child if they do not receive treatment for their substance dependency and other health problems. While a great deal of concern, which at times is expressed as outrage, has occurred in Canada over the birth of children with FAS/ARBEs, there has been far less concern (and even less outrage) over young women, many of whom are Aboriginal, dying of alcohol-related illnesses or accidents (Tait, 2003). As with FAS/ARBEs, these illnesses/accidents are one-hundred per cent preventable.

This suggests that a re-thinking of secondary prevention of FAS/ARBEs should occur in which the problem to be addressed is conceived first as a women's health issue and then as a health issue related to pregnancy and birth outcomes. In this context, women at risk do not become of interest only when they are pregnant, but on-going efforts are made to assist them in improving their life circumstances, including addressing their addiction problems. Prevention strategies, which re-conceive the issue as such, will not only improve birth outcomes, but will also have the potential to decrease mortality rates among this group of women and to reduce the chance of subsequent alcohol-effected children from being born.

'Best Practices' and Tertiary Prevention

Tertiary prevention refers to activities that "target those for whom FAS is already a concern. The aim of tertiary prevention is to minimize the damage to the fetus, reduce the likelihood of further affected pregnancies, and increase the capacity of the mother to care for her FAS children effectively" (Roberts and Nanson, 2000:28; Astley et al., 2000b). Tertiary prevention involves several interacting strategies, such as substance abuse treatment, birth control and parenting programs (Roberts and Nanson, 2000). In this context, strategies are aimed at high risk women and their offspring. Roberts and Nanson state:

> Those considered at high risk are women who drink heavily, and/or have mental health problems and/or histories of physical or sexual abuse and are of childbearing age. Also at high risk are women who have already given birth to an FAS child. Studies show that women who have given birth to one FAS child and who continue to drink, are at risk of having subsequent children that are progressively more severely affected (2000:28; Jacobson et al., 1998; Astley et al., 2000a; Abel and Hannigan, 1995).

Women, who are at high risk for giving birth to an alcohol-effected child, typically have very complex histories, with substance abuse being only one of a number of factors impacting upon their lives. Because of the range of problems these women experience, they may access a number of different services, such as women's shelters, addiction treatment programs, pregnancy outreach programs or mental health services. Therefore, it is important that service providers build links between one another, in order to assist women in accessing the full range of services they need. However, in some cases, high risk women may access only limited health and social services; therefore, it is important that service providers are given adequate resources to allow them to take the necessary time to connect with these women when they do arrive for services.

Aboriginal women, who are at high risk, often have very complex relationships with their bodies, which may not necessarily be understood by health care practitioners (Browne and Fiske, 2001; Tait, 2003). This is illustrated in a quote from a young Aboriginal woman who participated in a study that examined encounters between First Nations women from a northern reserve in British Columbia and mainstream health care services. Browne and Fiske found that intergenerational experiences of sexual abuse were central to the experience of some women when accessing health care. Feeling vulnerable when having to expose their bodies for physical examinations was one such example expressed by a young woman:

> There's lots of sexual abuse too that happened, probably still happens in the community. [A]nd younger women, they hide their bodies. They don't want to draw any attention to themselves or to their physical ailments or whatever, or because they're afraid to let anybody touch them because of the sexual abuse that's happening ... And the doctors are not sensitive to this. You know, they don't know the full picture of what goes on behind closed doors, what happens in this community ... And the same thing with

physical abuse ... Again, that's where you find really shy women. Especially when you have a male doctor talking like an authority to you or feeling that you're being talked down to (cited in Browne and Fiske, 2001:139).

In situations such as this, the reluctance of a woman to participate in a clinical examination, particularly if she is pregnant, will most likely be understood by health care providers as non-compliant behaviour or as the woman being indifferent to the health of the fetus. If she is having trouble with substance abuse, this may further add to her anxiety about being examined. In situations involving women at high risk of having a child with FAS/ARBE, compounding factors, such as past sexual abuse, the woman's alcohol addiction, racism and fear that her child will be apprehended when born, may contribute to her not seeking prenatal care or addiction treatment services (Tait, 2003). High risk women generally do not have a long-term trusting relationship with a family physician and, for women living in remote and isolated communities, the physicians they see generally change frequently, including physicians who visit the community or physicians women see when they are required to travel to urban centres for health care. For Aboriginal women from remote areas, choosing to see a female, rather than male, physician or a physician who is Aboriginal is not generally an option.

Women face a number of barriers when trying to access prenatal care or addiction services, and gaps in services are common, particularly for women living in isolated or rural areas. In a study examining the service needs of pregnant women with substance addiction problems in Manitoba, Tait (2000a) identified six types of barriers that women face when accessing addiction treatment: psychological barriers, barriers related to a woman's children, barriers related to social networks, socio-geographic barriers, barriers related to stigma and addiction treatment program barriers. Many of the barriers also apply to the experiences of women in accessing other services, such as prenatal care, outreach services and shelters. The range and availability of services also vary, depending on whether a woman lives in a rural or urban community, on or off-reserve, and where the community is located within the country. This means that Aboriginal women will face differing barriers and gaps in services, depending on the community they live in. Levels of community dysfunction, specifically for isolated and remote communities, but also within urban Aboriginal communities, will impact upon the types of services available that are culturally sensitive and inclusive of traditional Aboriginal knowledge.

Generally, there are two types of addiction treatment programs available for women: out-patient and residential treatment. Out-patient programs typically operate over a number of weeks, with participants living at home and attending treatment on a daily basis. Residential programs are either short (approximately 30 days) or long term (a number of months) and participants stay at the treatment facility for the duration of the program. These programs vary in their treatment philosophies and most try to offer some type of follow-up program after participants complete the program.[42] Within Canada, there are several successful treatment programs run by Aboriginal organizations and based on Aboriginal cultural values. These programs tend to combine traditional knowledge with mainstream addiction philosophies that have shown to be successful with Aboriginal clients, although variations in philosophies do exist between the programs.

---

[42]   A review of the different treatment programs in Canada and their philosophies is beyond the scope of this report. For a recent review, see Roberts and Ogborne (1999a; 1999b).

Chapter 9

Aboriginal women access a range of addiction treatment services, some are Aboriginal-specific and others have a general clientele. Although there is no specific research, it appears that Aboriginal women, specifically poor Aboriginal women, are more likely than non-Aboriginal women to access addiction treatment services. Tait (2000a) found that a range of barriers prevent women from accessing addiction treatment. For example, even though pregnant women in Manitoba have been prioritized by the majority of addiction services, numerous barriers exist that prevent them from entering and completing treatment programs.

Some of the psychological barriers women identified were directly related to their pregnancies, including not wanting to go to treatment because of being pregnant, fear of being stigmatized if they admit being pregnant and addicted, and a belief that their substance use would not harm the fetus. A number of other psychological barriers have been identified by women: denial of having a substance abuse problem; not being ready to quit using substances; believing they could quit on their own without treatment; giving up trying to change their life; fear, guilt and shame preventing them from telling people they need help; fear of the shame and stigma that would be brought to bear on them and their families if they admit to having a problem; fear of trying new things; not being referred to treatment by people they trust; and fear of going through detoxification.

Several authors have found that women often fail to access addiction treatment for reasons concerning their children (Astley et al., 2000b; Roberts and Nanson, 2000; Tait, 2000a). For example, in the study by Tait (2000a), women reported the following barriers related to their children: fear that their children will be apprehended by child welfare services if they admit to needing treatment; fear that if they place their children in temporary care with child welfare services while they are in treatment, the children will not be returned to their care after they complete treatment; fear that if they place their children in temporary care and then cannot complete treatment, child welfare services will not return their children to their care; fear that they will not complete treatment if their children are living away from them in foster care; fear that they will be seen as 'bad mothers' if they admit to needing help for their abuse problems; fear that their children will have the same negative experiences they had as a child while staying with a foster family; having no child care for their children while they are in treatment; and their children not wanting them to go away, but there being no treatment services available in their community.

The role of child welfare services in the lives of high risk women is an important consideration in secondary and tertiary prevention. More attention should be given to the relationships women have with these agencies. Because the mandate of child welfare service agencies is to protect children, which has informally been extended to the fetus by some workers, this places social workers in a difficult position *vis à vis* the building of trusting relationships with high risk women (Tait, 2000a; 2003). Despite this, the relationship women have with child welfare workers is often seen by them as the most significant relationship they have with service providers, as child welfare has the power to apprehend their children. This relationship influences the help-seeking behaviour of women, as is illustrated by one woman in her discussion of accessing services while pregnant: "I didn't tell them [obstetrician, outreach workers etc.] what I really wanted to tell them because I look at them and they all work with Child and Family. I don't know who doesn't and who does. And they might say something to them" (cited in Tait, 2000a:64).

Chapter 9

Tait (2000a; 2003) found that Aboriginal women were particularly afraid of child welfare services finding out about their substance abuse problems and then using this as justification to apprehend their children. Many of the women had been in foster care as children, some in multiple homes, and they recounted a range of negative experiences they had and were afraid this would happen to their children if they lost custody. This fear, which is grounded in the historical experience of Aboriginal people, based on the apprehension of their children through residential schools and, later, child welfare agencies, creates a type of paradox in which women end up avoiding those service providers and treatment programs that are mandated to help them. Tait writes:

> When women spoke about barriers that prevented them from accessing treatment that were related to their children, they were not saying that problems related to their substance use did not warrant concern, and [at] times, some type of intervention by service providers. *For the majority of women, the characteristics of the relationship they had with a service provider, not the necessity of the relationship itself, was problematic.* Women reported that the nature of their relationships with many service providers, particularly CFS [child welfare] workers, was antagonistic rather than supportive. Because the mandate of CFS is to protect children ... they are in a difficult position *vis-à-vis* the mothers of these children. Women often view CFS and related service providers as oppressive and threatening to their families. As a result, the women end up juggling a number of things simultaneously, such as their substance misuse, parenting, relationship problems, and the threat of apprehension by CFS, in an effort to keep their families together. Accessing addiction treatment, in the view of many women, cannot be prioritized if it results in their children being removed from their care (2000a:69).

Apprehension of children is a necessary measure at certain times and child welfare workers are not purposely pitting themselves against women (Tait, 2000a). Rather, it is their mandate to protect children and, therefore, they must be vigilant to ensure the safety and well-being of children. However, very limited research has been conducted that examines the role child welfare agencies play in the lives of women, particularly pregnant women, with substance abuse problems. For example, Tait (2000a) found some pregnant women increased their use of alcohol significantly when they had other children apprehended, which suggests this is a risk factor for FAS/ARBEs; however, there are no studies which have systematically looked at apprehension of other children and risk. It is also unclear at this point if prevention programs are conceptualizing the help-seeking behaviour of high risk women within a context that includes the important role child welfare agencies play.

An example of a service that has acknowledged the role of child welfare services is the *Stop-FAS* mentor program run by the Aboriginal Health and Wellness Centre in Winnipeg. This program works with Aboriginal women who have substance abuse problems and are of child-bearing age. The program assists women in negotiating their relationships with service agencies, including child welfare agencies. This program, while providing an important link between high risk women and various health and social service agencies, has also gained valuable knowledge about the ways in which women experience their interaction with service providers, cope with their life circumstances and make decisions related to their children, substance abuse, pregnancies and general well-being. This program has the potential to inform the creation of similar services in urban and rural, and reserve and non-reserve Aboriginal communities.

Chapter 9

A woman's social network (friends, family, social service providers, etc.) can play a central role in whether or not she accesses addiction treatment. A range of barriers exist that relate to a woman's social network. For example: most people in her social network are abusing substances, including her family and/or friends; she is dealing with other life crises, such as poverty, relationship problems and providing for her children, with limited support from those in her social network and, therefore, addiction treatment cannot be a priority; and she experiences opposition from key individuals in her social network, including her partner, friends and/or family, to her participating in an addiction treatment program (Tait, 2000a). High risk women typically have very few people in their support networks and, generally, the people they interact with are also substance abusers (Tait, 2000a; Jacobs and Gill, 2002). Male partners can have a significant amount of influence over women and can be a major barrier to women not accessing addiction treatment.

Certain socio-geographic barriers exist, which prevent women from accessing addiction treatment. For example: limited choice of treatment programs that are accessible in or near the community where she lives; losing her housing (e.g., does not have money to pay rent when in treatment, requirement of subsidized housing that she be living in the house) if she enters a residential treatment program for an extended period of time (usually more than a month); difficulties placing her personal belongings in storage due to lack of money, storage options and/or help to move her belongings; no services in her community to help her prepare for treatment (e.g., information about programs, arranging care for her children); cannot financially afford to take time off work to go to treatment; and enrolled in school and cannot take time off to go to treatment (Tait, 2000a). Because many Aboriginal women who live in isolated communities are faced with having to travel far to access treatment services, typically, these women have very limited choices or, in some instances, none at all in the type of program they attend. Stigma is a major barrier that pregnant women face when considering addiction treatment. Tait writes:

> Because women who misuse substances while pregnant are part of the larger society, they too share and internalize the moral beliefs held by the general population. As increased medical and social attention is directed toward the problem of substance misuse during pregnancy, women who use substances while pregnant are increasingly condemned and stigmatized for their behaviour. During the course of this project, it was found that pregnant women who misuse substances are one of the most despised groups in Manitoba. This has resulted in women feeling guilt and shame about their substance use, and in many cases, causes them to isolate themselves from the services that could help them (2000a:73).

Numerous barriers exist that are directly related to addiction treatment programs. Some examples given by women in Tait's study were related to the woman being pregnant: long waiting lists and no priority for pregnant women; many treatment centres do not accept pregnant women, specifically those in their last trimester of pregnancy; and if she gives birth during the time she is attending a residential program, the program cannot accommodate her with her newborn in order to complete the program. Other barriers were also identified by women: detoxification or withdrawal management services not existing close to where she lives; no detoxification or withdrawal management services for women only; no residential treatment in or near her community; problems of confidentiality (e.g., everyone knows who is in treatment) in smaller urban centres and rural communities; not speaking or understanding the language used at the treatment centre; problems accessing information about different treatment programs; problems finding one-on-one counselling; treatment programs not being designed to accommodate individuals with certain physical disabilities (e.g., people who are blind or deaf) or individuals with diagnosed psychiatric problems; most treatment programs are co-ed and some lack women-specific programming; and no transportation to out-patient or residential treatment (which is especially difficult for pregnant women) (Tait, 2000a).

The experience that women have when attending residential and non-residential addiction treatment programs plays a central role in their recovery. In Tait's study, women reported a number of positive aspects about the treatment programs they had attended: long-term individual counselling services; programs that accommodate women with their children or accommodate whole families; treatment based on Aboriginal traditions; treatment programs for couples who both have an addiction; treatment programs specifically for women; participating in women's groups; other Aboriginal people being in the program; the structure, schedule and daily routine of the program; learning how to talk about problems; and feeling that they are doing positive things for their unborn baby while in treatment (Tait, 2000a).

Women in Tait's study also reported several negative aspects concerning the treatment programs they attended. Some of their concerns were directly related to pregnancy: not receiving special consideration because they are pregnant (e.g., extra time to rest, relief from doing chores at the centre, such as dishwashing and general cleaning); coerced by counsellors to disclose to other clients, male and female, that they are pregnant and abusing substances; feeling workers at the treatment centre stigmatized pregnant women who were in treatment; being pregnant while in treatment, but having to leave the centre after completing the program, even though not feeling confident about maintaining abstinence; wanting information about FAS but none of the workers would give them information; and the counsellors treating addiction differently when a woman was pregnant, with it becoming a moral issue rather than being seen as an illness or disease.

Other concerns were also expressed by women: most treatment centres do not have facilities to accommodate children and/or families; no preparation before entering treatment; programs not addressing women's needs; treatment programs having all male counsellors; being the only woman in the treatment program; loneliness; program only dealing with the addiction and not with other things, such as past sexual abuse and relationship violence; not being able to find a treatment centre with a harm reduction philosophy; feeling threatened by the men in the program; treatment philosophy being too clinical; program being too institutionalized; having problems discussing past sexual abuse when there were men in group sessions; treatment program not being long enough; and detoxification centre not being clean, but being the only option available (Tait, 2000a).

Of the 58 women in Tait's study who had been to an addiction treatment program, 18 (31%) had either dropped out or been asked to leave a program. Reasons for leaving a program included the following: feelings of helplessness and hopelessness because they were not with their children; their partner wanting them to come home; not being prepared for treatment and not being able to cope with the program; still using and not being ready to be in treatment; not comfortable with mixed (male/female) treatment and having to talk about difficult issues, such as past sexual abuse, in front of male clients and/or counsellors; not being able to complete out-patient programs when living in a home and/or community environment where there was a lot of substance use around them; not feeling comfortable in the program; and feeling lonesome for their family (Tait, 2000a). Clients who were asked to leave programs were generally asked to do so because they were caught using substances or because of problems with other clients (e.g., aggressive behaviour, having an affair with a male client).

Addiction service providers point out that pregnant women attending out-patient treatment often have the responsibility of child care, attending prenatal appointments, negotiating their relationship with partners and family members and dealing with employers and social workers. Juggling these other responsibilities can be overwhelming for women when they are also required to attend a daily treatment program. These could contribute to women dropping out of programs prematurely (Tait, 2000a). A lack of shelter for intoxicated women, including pregnant women, can also be a problem; however, it is very difficult for women's shelters to accommodate clients who have been drinking, as this can be very disruptive and sometimes dangerous for other clients.

In some cases, pregnant women are picked up by police because they are intoxicated in a public place and, depending on the police involved, may be taken to an addiction treatment facility. However, addiction experts point out several problems with the police doing this, mainly that the women involved are generally not ready to address their substance abuse problems and will most likely leave the facility the first opportunity they get (Tait, 2000a). Where addiction programs and shelters cannot accommodate pregnant women who either present while intoxicated or are picked up by the police, these women risk being put in jail over night, being involved in an accident or being a victim of violence. This gap in service can be very frustrating for service providers involved, as they have no positive avenues in which they can assist women.

Once a woman completes a residential treatment program, she returns to her home or, in some cases, to a new home, to begin to build a life without alcohol. Tait (2000a) found that, overwhelmingly, the reason given by women for relapse, including relapse by pregnant women, was a lack of after care services. For many women, maintaining sobriety while in treatment was manageable; however, upon returning home, their ability to stay substance-free could quickly change, particularly if there were no after care supports. This was expressed by one pregnant woman who recounted the events around her completing a treatment program:

> 'Cause I just want to keep my baby this time. I don't want nothing to go wrong. But I'm really struggling too because I went to treatment. I was there in May. I finished in June, and then I came back [home]. I was doing okay for awhile and then I fell off again. So I started using again ... It's like, easier if you just stay in the program until as long as you can. See, I was thinking if I stayed in there through my whole pregnancy then it would have been a lot easier ... You got to go out a month [when you finish], then come back or whatever. So I was going to go but my boyfriend didn't want me to go back (cited in Tait, 2000a:81).

A number of reasons given by the women for relapse include: loneliness; she was not ready to quit using; all her friends around her were using; depressed about being on welfare and living in poverty; a twenty-eight day program was not long enough for her to maintain sobriety afterwards; isolation and/or boredom; her children were in the care of child welfare services and alcohol helped her to grieve for the loss she was feeling; her partner came back into her life and he was using; she had no positive supports in her life; she had nothing else in her life but alcohol; she had to use in order to be able to work the streets; she was frustrated with child welfare services because she was trying to get her children back, but they kept breaking their word about returning them; using was a way to cope with her partner rejecting her; she had too much stress and too many problems in her life to deal with; her children were apprehended by child welfare service and so she started using right afterwards (this explanation was given by some pregnant women); and she experienced guilt and shame that she had used while she was pregnant (Tait, 2000a).

The findings by Tait have been echoed in other studies in both Canada and United States (Astley et al., 2000b; Poole and Isaac, 1999; Poole, 2000; Howell and Chasnoff, 1999; Howell, Heiser and Harrington, 1999; Messer, Clark and Martin, 1996; Ernst et al., 1999) and point to the complexities involved in trying to address the service needs of high risk women who live in various geographical and regional settings. In relation to Aboriginal women, it is encouraging that a great deal of moral support within Aboriginal circles exists that encourages women to address their substance abuse. However, many challenges exist in providing easily accessible services where Aboriginal women will feel comfortable and confident in accessing.

In relation to residential schooling, some concern should be given to addiction treatment programs that are highly institutionalized and structured,[43] as they may unwittingly recreate a similar context for clients through the adoption of practices similar to those found in residential schools. Examples of such practices would be punitive measures for certain behaviours (e.g., clients being put on a 'hot seat' to account for their behaviour towards other clients or counsellors, clients who cannot stop using substances being forced to hide their problem and then being kicked out of the program if they cannot maintain abstinence); clients being *assigned* and *required* to do daily chores, which administrative and counselling staff members do not participate in, such as food preparation and cleaning, which consume a significant amount of the time clients spend at the treatment centre;[44] and clients not being able to call or see friends or family members during the initial days of treatment (in some cases 30 days) or not being allowed to leave the treatment facility and grounds.

While there is no research that has examined this issue, there are indications that Aboriginal people should be very concerned with treatment programs that target their people, but are not Aboriginal-run. In some instances, these programs 'adopt' Aboriginal traditional practices into their programming, which may mask some of the concerns raised above (Tait, 2003).

Roberts and Nanson (2000), with the assistance of the National Steering Committee, identified six 'best practices' related to tertiary prevention of FAS/ARBEs:

---

[43]   These programs generally service clients who are Aboriginal and non-Aboriginal, and many of their Aboriginal clients live in non-reserve communities.

[44]   The chores, generally, are assigned to cut budget costs for support staff. Their 'therapeutic' value is questionable and concern should be given when the assignment of chores is deemed by administrative staff to be part of the treatment program (Tait, 2003).

Chapter 9

Culturally Appropriate and Women-Centred Services

Punitive Measures

'Best practice'

1. There is no evidence to support the use of punitive measures, such as mandated treatment, as being effective in improving maternal and fetal health. A consensus among experts suggests that such measures deter pregnant women from seeking needed services.

Within Canada, significant debate has occurred as to whether a pregnant woman, who is abusing substances, should be mandated into addiction treatment in 'exceptional circumstances,' in order to protect her unborn child. In 1997, this question was taken to the Supreme Court of Canada, based on a case involving a twenty-two year old, pregnant Aboriginal woman living in Winnipeg, known as 'G.' In this particular case, the social service agency traced a long history of addiction, including events surrounding the permanent removal of three previous children from G's custody, at various times, due to her addiction. The Supreme Court of Canada ruled against mandatory treatment for pregnant women, as it deemed the fetus was not a person until born alive and, therefore, a pregnant woman did not have a legal 'duty of care' with regard to her unborn child.[45]

Legal cases in Canada of mandatory addiction treatment for pregnant women, which have been pursued by child welfare services, illustrate that ethnicity, along with socio-economic status, are important factors. Women most likely to be subjected to judicial intervention are disproportionately poor, Aboriginal or members of a visible ethnic minority (Royal Commission on New Reproductive Technologies, 1993). The reasons for the majority of court cases in Canada involving women with similar socio-economic and ethnic background is complex and points toward the possibility of racial discrimination and to the life circumstances of these women, being such that their behaviour when pregnant is more likely to come under surveillance (Royal Commission on New Reproductive Technologies, 1993; Women's Legal Education and Action Fund, 1997). These two factors are especially true for poorer urban Aboriginal women, who are more likely to have a long history with governmental agencies and institutions (Swift, 1991; 1995; Gurstein, 1977; Williams, 1997; Whiteford and Vitucci, 1997). Furthermore, these women are often isolated from social support networks in the urban milieu, such as band councils, to advocate on their behalf (Gill, 1995; Williams, 1997). Ironically, this vulnerability has also limited the number of cases of court-imposed treatment[46] that actually reach the courts, as most women who are likely to encounter this situation are in no position to resist and, therefore, comply with the wishes of physicians or social workers (Royal Commission on New Reproductive Technologies, 1993).

Despite the ruling by the Supreme Court of Canada, Tait (2000a) found that pregnant women were still being coerced into attending addiction treatment programs. A common form of coercion was the use of 'birth alerts,' where child welfare service workers places a 'birth alert' on a woman so that her baby

---

45   For further details, see Tait, 2003.

46   While the Supreme Court of Canada ruled against mandated treatment, women who use illicit drugs can still be mandated into treatment, based on drug charges and sentencing requirements.

would be apprehended at birth if she was known to be abusing substances. A way in which a woman could prevent apprehension of her baby was to complete an addiction treatment program. A significant number of women in Tait's study (53%) reported going to treatment to regain custody of their children. Addiction specialists report that, clients who are forced or coerced into treatment, are more likely to have difficulty in treatment than individuals who enter on their own volition. Tait writes:

> Even when a pregnant woman enters treatment to decrease the risk of harm to the fetus, there is a greater chance she will not complete the program than if she enters treatment because she feels she wants to improve her own health and well-being. Many women, especially those who are entering treatment for the first time, have little or no preparation for participating in treatment programs ... Women who are forced or coerced into treatment usually do not see treatment as much more than a means to an end. Even though many women in this situation would say that addiction treatment is a valuable and positive way for people to deal with substance misuse, they do not necessarily relate this to their own lives. In many cases, women are so preoccupied with filling the immediate requirements of social assistance, the courts, or CFS [child welfare], that they do not focus on their substance misuse problems while in treatment. The reality is that they perceive the situation as a battle between them and an oppressive agency in which they have only one option, and that is to comply with the requirements (2000a:58).

Pregnant women who fear they will be mandated into treatment or will have their baby apprehended if they do not enter addiction treatment are likely to avoid accessing services that will draw attention to their pregnancy. Therefore, it is common for high risk women to seek very few services while pregnant, including prenatal care and outreach pregnancy services (Tait, 2000a; Astley et.al., 2000c).

Revised 'best practice'

1. There is no evidence to support the use of punitive measures, such as mandated treatment, as being effective in improving maternal and fetal health. A consensus among experts suggests that such measures deter pregnant women from seeking needed services. Poor Aboriginal women may be particularly vulnerable to forms of coercion and measures should be taken to ensure that more positive and meaningful supports are given to those women who are struggling with substance abuse. These could include: assisting women in preparing to enter treatment by emphasizing the benefits to her health and the health of her unborn baby; listening and assisting her to address the concerns she has about entering treatment; and identifying a treatment program that will best meet her needs.

Multi-Component Strategies

'Best practice'

1. There is moderate evidence and a consensus among experts that combining prenatal care with other services, including substance abuse treatment, shows positive outcomes for women with substance use problems and their newborn child.

Chapter 9

In review of the literature discussing programs that serve pregnant substance-using women and their families, comprehensive care strategies have been identified as particularly important in addressing the needs of high risk women (Poole, 2000; Roberts and Nanson, 2000). Poole writes: "Instead of focussing narrowly on change in substance use patterns, programs have found it useful to combine alcohol and drug treatment with other services such as prenatal care, other medical care, parenting education, family planning services, nutritional support, advocacy on housing needs and counseling on violence and relationship issues" (2000:39; Creamer and McMurtrie, 1998; Garm, 1999; Grella, 1996; Kerson, 1990; Egelko, Galanter, Dematis and DeMaio, 1998; Finkelstein, 1994; Grayson, Hutchins and Silver, 1999; Ryland and Lucas, 1996; Mosley, 1996; Schumacker, Siegal, Socol, Harkless and Freeman, 1996; Brindis, Clayson and Birkowitz, 1997; Namyniuk, Brems and Clarkson, 1997; Rivadeneira, Hamilton, Pressley, Turner, Cress et al., 1998; Whiteford and Vitucci, 1997; Young and Gardener, 1998). She adds that, because of the formidable barriers women may face in accessing addiction treatment, "engaging women in care through other avenues that have the impact of reducing harms related to substance use is effective" (Poole, 2000:39).

An example of a multi-component strategy is the Tuba City *FAS Prevention Project* located in a Navajo community in the southwestern United States (Masis and May, 1991). A family physician, a Navajo-speaking prevention worker and a Navajo-speaking clerk joined the community health services staff to provide a three-pronged approach to FAS prevention, involving community, family and individual based techniques. Tertiary prevention consisted of detailed case management and support for the client through counselling, personal support and social services. A FAS diagnostic clinic was held five times during the year between 1987 and 1988 and initial counselling of the mother or care taker of the diagnosed individual was provided.

Employees from Navajo and Hopi tribal agencies and schools were trained in FAS recognition and awareness. The community participated in these and other presentations. Some of the women who had received counselling were found at follow-up to be drinking less than they were before contact. Clients referred at the time of pregnancy were more likely to accept help with their drinking. Having the program staff consist of community members aided in acceptance of the program and in bridging the culture gap between the health providers and the clients. A family-oriented approach was also found to strengthen the success of the program (Masis and May, 1991) Masis and May conclude: "The effectiveness of this program depends not only on knowledge, case finding, and treatment efforts both inside and outside the clinic and hospital, but also on the involvement of multiple constituencies in the community" (1991:489).

An example of an urban-based multi-component program is the *Sheway* project. The *Sheway* project is an outreach program located in the Downtown Eastside of Vancouver (DTES), which provides holistic services to pregnant women with substance abuse problems and supports for mothers and their families. The DTES of Vancouver is well-known for its high crime rate, drug and sex trade, violence, sub-standard housing and high rate of HIV/AIDS. *Sheway's* service philosophy and values are to provide services in a flexible, non-judgmental, nurturing and accepting way, while supporting the self-determination and choices of women. The program has a large Aboriginal clientele (60%) and has, therefore, sought to understand Aboriginal cultures, histories and traditions, in order to better meet the needs of this group. The program is based on a harm-reduction approach and offers a safe, accessible and welcoming drop-in environment that links women to a support network. In an evaluation of the project, Poole found that

194

clients often mentioned the level of support given to them by the *Sheway* program as a critical factor in them seeking help from this service (Poole, 2000). This was echoed in a recent study by Benoit and Carroll, which examined the experiences of Aboriginal women living in the DTES of Vancouver:

> A welcoming, group-oriented approach to service delivery, such as that offered at Sheway, was highlighted by many women as an important factor in determining their comfort with accessing services. More than an 'open door', this program practices a non-task-oriented philosophy of care critical to getting women through the front door, as a first step in preventative health. For instance, many women initially approach Sheway for non-medical reasons, such as to access wholesome food and to socialize with other new mothers. In time, once trust with staff has been developed, they begin to address their health issues. Were they faced with numerous personal and medical questions upon first arriving, as is the norm in medical offices, most would not enter the site at all or would not stay long enough to begin a treatment program (2001:15-16).

In 1998, *Sheway* carried an active client list of 60 to 70 women and 20 to 30 children. By January 2000, the active caseload had increased to 100, the set maximum number of women and families that could be effectively served. According to data from the Community Health Area, *Sheway* is reaching approximately fifteen per cent of women giving birth in this health area (Poole, 2000) and, according to Loock and colleagues (1993), an average of sixteen per cent of infants born to women in the DTES of Vancouver have been exposed to alcohol or drugs in-utero. From these numbers, *Sheway* is reaching the majority of women in the target group (Poole, 2000). *Sheway* has been very successful in helping women access prenatal care and other supports during pregnancy and in assisting women and families to improve their nutrition and housing situations. Reducing risk behaviours has been more challenging, Poole suggests, but improvement in areas where the program had more success may create the necessary conditions for changing risk behaviours. The program has also achieved only moderate success in the promotion of the health, nutrition and development of the children born to women accessing care (Poole, 2000).

Revised 'Best Practice'

1. There is moderate evidence and a consensus among experts that combining prenatal care with other services, including substance abuse treatment, show positive outcomes for women with substance use problems and their newborn child. For smaller, isolated communities where services are limited, efforts should be made to modify this strategy at the local level to prevent women from having to travel outside the community for support services. Elders and midwives could play a central role in building and implementing local strategies.

Gender-Specific Substance Abuse Treatment

'Best practice'

1. There is some moderate evidence and a consensus among experts that gender-specific substance abuse treatment is more effective for women than programs serving both men and women.

Chapter 9

Debate exists around the need for gender-specific substance abuse treatment programs. Only a few studies have looked at treatment outcomes by gender and they tend to show no difference in outcomes between female and male alcohol-dependent persons in traditional western-based treatment programs (Roberts and Nanson, 2000). However, the effectiveness of approaches, such as family therapy, group therapy, separate rather than combined treatment with men, and female rather than male therapists, have not been systematically examined in the research literature. In relation to Aboriginal women, gender-specific programs may be beneficial for some women, particularly if they experienced child or adult sexual and/or physical abuse and do not feel comfortable being in treatment with male clients or counsellors.

Unfortunately, most Aboriginal women who go to addiction treatment have very limited choices as to the type of treatment program they attend and requesting to attend a women-specific program is, in most cases, not an available option. While more research into the value of gender-specific treatment is needed, specifically in relation to Aboriginal women, some contend that more gender-specific treatment programs are needed for high risk women (Poole, 1997; 2000; Tait, 2000a).

'Revised 'best practice'

1. There is some moderate evidence and a consensus among experts that gender-specific substance abuse treatment is more effective for women than programs serving both men and women. Gender-specific treatment targeting Aboriginal women should be sensitive to specific intergenerational experiences of Aboriginal women, particularly with regard to past sexual and physical abuse and the removal of children from their care. While Aboriginal women and men share similar intergenerational experiences, acknowledgement of experiences specific to women because of their gender and incorporation of this into mainstream and traditional addiction treatment and mental health/wellness services are essential.

Harm Reduction Strategies

'Best practice'

1. There is some evidence and a consensus among experts that treatment services employing a respectful, flexible, culturally appropriate and women-centred approach, open to intermediary harm reduction goals and based on client circumstances, are effective in engaging and retaining women in supportive programming and in improving the quality of their lives.

Women who are at highest risk of abusing substances while pregnant generally have long histories with substance addiction and many have been in and out of numerous addiction treatment programs. For some women, complete abstinence is simply not an option and, increasingly, service providers are adopting harm reduction approaches to assist these women. A harm reduction approach:

> ... is a public health alternative to the moral/criminal and disease models of drug use and addiction. It recognizes abstinence as an ideal outcome but accepts alternatives that reduce harm. This includes encouraging reduction of substance use without requiring abstinence, and giving a 'less is better' message to clients. A harm reduction approach recognizes the complex needs of the client rather than focusing solely on the substance use issue (Leslie and Roberts, 2001:39).

Chapter 9

Breaking the Cycle in Toronto and *Sheway* in Vancouver both employ a non-judgmental harm reduction approach in their work with substance-using pregnant women. The *Stop-FAS* programs in Manitoba—mentor programs for high risk women and their children—also adopt a similar philosophy, as does *Street Connections* in Winnipeg, discussed earlier. While harm reduction is controversial within addiction treatment circles, for this particular group of women and because of the numerous other risk factors in their lives, it provides the opportunity to decrease risk to them and their unborn child through a number of supports, such as improved nutrition, assistance in accessing prenatal health care and advocacy for women with other service providers, such as child welfare services. Leslie and Roberts write:

> A harm reduction approach takes into account woman-centred and family-centred approaches. It recognizes and respects the ability of the family, and assists the family to regain ability after trauma (such as residential school experiences). It recognizes the complex needs of the woman, and the various interventions that may promote better outcomes for herself and her fetus (2001:40).

The success of this type of strategy may be undermined when women interact with health care and social service professionals and with others in their support network (e.g., family members) who convey negative and judgmental messages about their behaviour (Leslie and Roberts, 2001). This is why, as suggested by Leslie and Roberts, it is important for communities to agree upon a common approach to the problem of substance abuse and pregnancy.

Women at high risk can be very difficult to work with at times and may be extremely resistant to assistance from service providers, family and friends. Furthermore, many communities, particularly isolated rural and reserve communities, may face numerous difficulties in securing appropriate treatment for women, particularly when they are pregnant. Their efforts could be undermined further by most treatment centres requiring abstinence on the part of clients and refusing treatment to anyone who breaks this rule, including pregnant women (Leslie and Roberts, 2001).

Leslie and Roberts (2001) contend that the best treatment option for women, including high risk pregnant women, is a program utilizing women and family centred approaches to treatment; however, these are uncommon and, where available, often have long waiting lists. They also point out that a harm reduction approach becomes much more problematic when a woman has a child in her care. Women who abuse substances, most specifically those on social assistance, have a great deal of fear about their children being apprehended because of their substance use. In advice to service providers facing this challenge, Leslie and Roberts write:

> Indeed, substance use can present an impediment to appropriate parenting, and children of parents who use substances are at greater risk for developmental problems as well as for abuse and neglect. Providing clients with education and information about how children can be affected by their parents' substance use can be a strong motivator for change for some clients. Be clear with clients about your relationship with child welfare services, and outline your responsibilities should you be concerned about the child's safety or well-being. Be open about how you will involve clients and inform them about any discussions you might have with other agencies regarding your concerns. Advocating for the client is an important role for staff; however, this advocacy becomes much more

Chapter 9

complex when there is a child involved who may be at risk. In all good practice projects, the needs of the child are recognized as paramount in the work that is done with women and their children. Balancing the role of supporting and advocating for the woman with that of advocating for the child when necessary is the most challenging work to be done. The good practice projects have been able to process these difficult issues and concerns with women honestly, openly and directly, and in a manner that does not rupture the trusting relationship that has been developed (2001:40).

Research studies on harm reduction strategies that target Aboriginal people in Canada are currently not available; however, consideration of the perceptions and responses of Aboriginal people to this type of intervention strategy should be given before it is adopted locally into programming initiatives. Further research is needed to examine the interface of local understanding—for example, of alcohol abuse vs. abstinence—and how these understandings relate to the ways in which historical processes within the community, such as colonization, acculturation and local identity, have been experienced by members of the community.

'Revised 'best practice'

1. There is some evidence and a consensus among experts that treatment services employing a respectful, flexible, culturally appropriate and women-centred approach that is open to intermediary harm reduction goals, based on client circumstances, are effective in engaging and retaining women in supportive programming and in improving the quality of their lives. However, little is known about how effective harm reduction approaches are among members of urban and rural Aboriginal communities, particularly in communities where alcohol abuse is endemic. Further research and evaluation is needed in this area.

Multi-Component Community-Based Initiatives

'Best practices'

1. There is some evidence and a consensus among experts that services with a single point of access addressing the range of social and health needs of pregnant women with substance use problems (e.g., assistance with transportation and child care, education, vocational training, job placement, housing, getting food, income support and help in accessing health care and mental health services), through collaboration between relevant service providers, are effective in engaging and retaining women in treatment.

2. There is strong evidence that intensive case management or coordination services that advocate for women can be effective in promoting family planning, access to substance abuse treatment, retention in treatment, reduced consumption and connections to community services for high-risk pregnant women.

Multi-component, community-based initiatives for the prevention of FAS/ARBEs in Aboriginal communities will look very different, depending on geographical location, the size of the community, the existing services and community decisions on how best to address prevention. Van Bibber (1997) writes that some communities will use traditional laws and practices to change behaviour, while others will strive to improve economic conditions, develop special programs or design school curriculums. Generally, Aboriginal communities who use traditional teachings emphasize a holistic approach that reflects the teachings of the Medicine Wheel (Van Bibber, 1997). Treatment for high risk women within this context includes a community-wide approach to healing and recovery with the involvement of community members and organizations, along with family members, to support the woman on her healing journey. Central to the process is a rediscovery of cultural and spiritual traditions (Roberts and Nanson, 2000).

Leslie and Roberts point out that community readiness is essential for programs to be effective. They write:

> If a community is not ready to deal with it [FAS], the issue can be forced underground. A case in point is when a community believes that it has dealt with the problem simply by declaring itself to be a dry community. There is a need for openness to all perspectives and to all groups at this stage to see what might work (2001:17).

Roberts and Nanson (2000) suggest that a single point of access addressing the range of social and health needs of pregnant women with substance use problems (e.g., assistance with transportation and child care, education, vocational training, job placement, housing, accessing food, income support and help in accessing health care and mental health services), through collaboration between relevant service providers, are effective in engaging and retaining women in treatment. Coordinating such an effort is an enormous undertaking and generally requires the commitment of multiple funding agencies. Leslie and Roberts (2001) found that securing funding involved communities and organizations building strong associations with different levels of government and with different community groups. Multiple-funding sources were positively correlated with a number of successful FAS-related initiatives and activities operating in Canada.

Provincial/territorial support for FAS programs, however, is more prevalent in the western regions of Canada. Leslie and Roberts (2001) found that no provincial government east of Manitoba allocated resources towards FAS activities, although the Government of Newfoundland and Labrador, at the time of their report, had announced plans to invest some of its federal Child Tax Benefit toward FAS-related initiatives. The prairie provinces, the Yukon and British Columbia had several province-wide initiatives over the past few years that supported local community initiatives.

Revised 'best practices'

1. There is some evidence and a consensus among experts that services with a single point of access addressing the range of social and health needs of pregnant women with substance use problems (e.g., assistance with transportation and child care, education, vocational training, job placement, housing, getting food, income support and help in accessing health care and mental health services), through collaboration between relevant service providers, are effective in engaging and retaining women in treatment. These initiatives should be based on local community priorities and traditions (including the involvement of local traditional practitioners and Elders), which should be reflected in their efforts to support women and their children.

2. There is strong evidence that intensive case management or coordination services that advocate for women can be effective in promoting family planning, access to substance abuse treatment, retention in treatment, reduced consumption and connections to community services for high-risk pregnant women. Organizations, such as Friendship Centres, Aboriginal Health and Wellness Centres, Aboriginal Head Start Programs and other wellness and healing services, can play an important role in providing this support for women. This service must be provided in a non-judgmental context where women feel safe accessing the service.

Conclusion[47]

Several challenges exist in addressing tertiary prevention for high risk women. This is particularly true for Aboriginal women, who collectively come from various Nations, geographical locations, live on and off-reserve and who have varying life experiences. An important component of tertiary prevention is the involvement of local communities and the interaction of the community with service providers, such as addiction treatment programs. Also central is the value brought to addressing substance abuse by pregnant women of the inclusion of traditional Aboriginal knowledge and practices.

Numerous barriers and gaps in services have been identified that prevent pregnant women from accessing addiction treatment services and prenatal care. Barriers are directly related to the social context in which a woman lives, including the level of the coordination of services that are available to assist her. In many cases, child welfare services play a central role in the lives of high risk women. More needs to be known about how this relationship influences the help-seeking behaviour of these women. Gender-sensitive addiction treatment programs are also important components of tertiary treatment, specifically for Aboriginal women who have experienced child or adult sexual or physical abuse. Aboriginal-run treatment programs that involve the use of traditional teachings in their service delivery are key in addressing the needs of high risk women. These programs need to be supported by strong follow-up after care programs once the woman returns home. Further research is needed in different regions of the country, in order to further identify breaks in the continuum of care for pregnant women, and women more generally, with substance abuse problems.

---

[47]   Two 'best practices' dealing with other substances, identified by Roberts and Nanson, have not been reviewed here. They are: 1) there is some evidence that a contingency management approach is effective in reducing cocaine use and increasing attention to prenatal care among cocaine-dependent women; and 2) there is moderate evidence that providing methadone maintenance therapy (MMT) in the context of comprehensive care has a positive impact on the health of mothers and birth outcomes for mothers who are opiate-dependent. Priority access to MMT for pregnant women and program components that address barriers to treatment should be considered in program design. Guidelines for methadone dosage and regimen should take into account changes in methadone metabolism that may occur in the later stages of pregnancy. For further discussion, see Roberts and Nanson, 2000.

Chapter 9

Conclusion

The prevention of substance abuse by pregnant women that results in alcohol-related birth defects among their offspring is currently of great concern in most regions of Canada. Typically, prevention has focused on preventing damage to the developing fetus and, therefore, the emphasis has been on the pregnancy, rather than on the health and well-being of the woman. The research reviewed in this report illustrates that women at risk for giving birth to a child with FAS generally have poor health and many will die shortly after giving birth to an affected child if their substance abuse problems are not addressed. This suggests that all efforts should be made to address substance abuse by women at risk, rather than maintaining a narrow focus on these women only when they are pregnant.

The 'best practices' identified in this report overwhelmingly support the involvement of local communities and coordination of services in order to improve upon the continuum of care for women struggling with substance abuse problems. Ideally, multi-level approaches would best address this need. Leslie and Roberts (2001) write that, because of the complexity of the problem of FAS/ARBEs, the issue requires a multi-level approach involving community, regional, provincial and federal agencies and governments. They write:

> Given the complexity of needs from a population health perspective, the multiple needs of women who are using substances prenatally, and the limited timeframe of pregnancy in which to address these issues, an intersectoral partnership approach is required. Many informants spoke of the importance of the commitment and passion of even one person who can spearhead the FAS agenda in a community or in a region as a critical catalyst for development of initiatives (Leslie and Roberts, 2001:14).

While Leslie and Roberts are right in pointing out the need for intersectoral partnerships, in many Aboriginal communities, shaving-off resources to address an 'FAS agenda' will not make sense, given the history and the myriad of issues confronting the community. Van Bibber suggests that it is important to place community-based FAS/ARBE strategies in a wider context. She writes:

> People designing community-based FAS/E strategies need to consider the root causes of alcohol abuse and the community responses. Recognizing the root causes will help community participants design an approach that truly reflects the communities history and its current needs. Because each community is at its own stage of development as it strives to become healthy and self-sufficient. The strengths of the community can be found in its efforts to regain control—and an important principle of community development is building new initiatives on the strengths of the community. Effective strategies recognize the issues that community members deem important. They also consider actions that the community has already taken and actions they plan to take to address these issues. Likely the important initiatives in the community involve efforts to counteract the debilitating impact of colonialism—the root causes of many social ills such as loss of lands, language, culture and resources. If possible and appropriate, these factors should be integrated into the strategy. This means that an FAS/E strategy could have linkages to a number of ongoing community initiatives such as affordable housing, education, cultural programs or recreation (Van Bibber, 1997:13-14).

Chapter 9

Within current national and provincial funding contexts, a common problem for Aboriginal communities is that they envision the issues to be addressed in their community differently than government funding bodies. For example, governments are accustomed to funding programs for specific health issues, such as FAS, rather than funding multi-dimensional initiatives that are based on priorities set by communities, such as those discussed above by Van Bibber. Furthermore, as governments announce funding for particular issues, such as FAS/ARBEs, Aboriginal communities find themselves scrambling to access a portion of the funding, even though they may have very limited knowledge about the actual depth of the problem in their community. When governments decide what community problems and priorities should be, they, in effect, take control away from the communities, minimizing local knowledge and reinforcing an unequal relationship in which priorities determined by the government are imposed upon Aboriginal people (Tait, 2003).

Furthermore, when a health problem and the risk associated with it are presented to communities as being based on scientific knowledge that is without controversy, when, in fact, a great deal of controversy and uncertainty exists among medical experts, such is the case with FAS/ARBEs, then there is less likelihood that communities will question the priorities set by the government.

In the example of FAS, Tait (2003) argues that Aboriginal communities, urban, rural and reserve, have been confronted with creating an 'FAS problem' among their community members, in order to access certain funding announced by federal and provincial governments. She argues that many communities constructed a FAS problem when it was actually unclear to them if a problem existed (e.g., they had very limited knowledge of the illness, very few women who abused alcohol when pregnant, few or no individuals were medically assessed as having FAS and limited opportunities to have individuals medically assessed for FAS/ARBE, particularly individuals who were older children, adolescents or adults). Despite this, communities were asked by governments to define the 'FAS problem' in their community and then propose projects to address the problem. More pressing issues for a community, such as chronic poverty, which has been identified as a significant contributor to FAS/ARBEs (Abel, 1998a), did not fall within the limited scope of this funding (Tait, 2003). As Van Bibber states above, FAS/ARBEs is an intergenerational wellness issue, which involves more than preventing pregnant women from consuming alcohol, but rather involves whole communities to gain control over their lives through the development of community-based institutions in the areas of culture, education, health, economies and justice. Taking a narrow focus on a specific illness, particularly one that is so ill-defined as FAS/ARBE, ignores the root causes underlying substance abuse, minimizes local priorities and contributes to dependency relationships (Tait, 2003).

FAS/ARBE programs also maintain a certain degree of surveillance over community members (Tait, 2000a). The contradiction, O'Neil (1993) points out, is that public health surveillance systems perform disciplinary and regulatory functions in a community, independent of their overt purpose of tracking health conditions. Therefore, they can construct knowledge about sectors of society that reinforce unequal power relationships. "[I]n other words, an image of sick, disorganized communities can be used to justify paternalism and dependency" (1993:34). Furthermore, external agencies and academic researchers have the power to interpret data and construct images of Aboriginal communities as desperate, disorganized and depressed environments (Tait, 2003). "This image is created ostensibly to support lobbying efforts to secure a larger share of national resources for community development. However, this image is reflected through the Canadian media and general public and is to some extent internalized by Aboriginal communities, reinforcing dependency relationships" (O'Neil, 1993:34). In this context, Tait (2003) adds, negative images of pregnant Aboriginal women abusing alcohol and then giving birth to 'epidemic' numbers of brain-damaged offspring, undermine efforts by Aboriginal people to secure self-government.

Aboriginal communities face different challenges, depending on whether they are rural or urban-based, First Nations, Inuit or Métis, the degree of substance abuse in the community and the range of other issues confronting them, including challenges related to substance abuse during pregnancy and FAS/ARBEs. Aboriginal communities, with the involvement of national Aboriginal political and professional organizations, are better equipped than government ministries to identify the priorities to be addressed within their communities. The example of substance abuse, pregnancy and FAS/ARBEs, more generally, illustrate how federal and provincial governments continue to set priorities in Aboriginal health (Tait, 2003). While substance abuse during pregnancy and FAS/ARBEs are health concerns for Aboriginal people, this report has illustrated the need for a cautious approach, including critiquing the scientific and policy literature, and the importance of taking a broad-based perspective that situates the issue within a larger historical and social context.

Chapter 10

Persons with Fetal Alcohol Syndrome and Other Alcohol-Related Birth Effects

Introduction

"Not all our children are fetal alcohol syndrome" (cited in Tait, 2000b:96).

A recent study conducted on a First Nations Reserve in Manitoba indicates that 1 in 10 children is the victim of alcohol teratogenesis. And that, says a researcher involved in a seminal investigation of fetal alcohol syndrome (FAS) and possible fetal alcohol effects (FAE) in Canada's [A]boriginal population, is just the tip of the iceberg (cited in Square, 1997:59).

This chapter discusses the identification of persons with fetal alcohol syndrome (FAS) or other alcohol-related birth effects (ARBEs), the life trajectory of these individuals as recorded in the research literature, and 'best practices' for identification and interventions over the life span of affected individuals. As is indicated by the statements above, FAS/ARBEs are of great concern for Aboriginal people in Canada on a number of levels. First, there is concern over the actual number of individuals who are affected by in-utero alcohol exposure, how best to prevent more babies from being born who are affected and how best to address the needs of high risk pregnant women and alcohol-affected persons. Second, there is concern over the lack of adequate resources (financial, human and information) to address the problem. Third, in light of diagnostic inconsistencies and the lack of standardized diagnostic tools for assessment, there is growing concern about possible under and over-diagnosing, informal labelling[48] of Aboriginal individuals and populations (e.g., epidemic numbers of brain damaged individuals in a community) and the use of this group of diagnostic classifications to effectively transform colonialist oppression, such as chronic poverty, poor education, systemic racism, child welfare practices and the impact of the residential school system, into a medical problem that implicates Aboriginal mothers and effectively labels high numbers of Aboriginal people as having permanent brain damage (Tait, 2003). This chapter will discuss each of these concerns in relation to the life span trajectory of affected individuals and with regard to the identification of 'best practices' for intervention services and supports.

Chapter two dealt with some of the problems concerning identification and diagnosis of individuals affected by in-utero alcohol exposure. This chapter will expand upon the previous discussion by looking at the three diagnostic criteria for FAS/ARBEs, as well as other birth outcomes that are associated with the diagnosis, but not part of the criteria. As stated earlier, the difficulty with diagnostic categories as ill-defined as FAS/ARBEs is that they present the possibilities of mis-classification of individuals, either through under or over-diagnosing. Because they are relatively new diagnostic classifications, only limited knowledge exists as to how these illnesses manifest themselves over the life span given differing environmental influences, such as family stability/dysfunction and educational programming and supports (Royal Commission on Aboriginal Peoples, 1996b). This chapter will seek to address some of

---

48   Informal labelling refers to individuals being identified by service providers, such as social workers or teachers, or by lay persons, as having FAS/ARBEs without a medical assessment and diagnosis. This also occurs with specific populations, such as communities with high rates of alcohol abuse being identified as having high prevalence rates of FAS/ARBEs before medical assessments are actually conducted in the community.

Chapter 10

these questions. Although, as stated in the introductory chapter, the reader may find there are more questions than answers when examining this body of literature from a broad-based historical and social perspective.

Studies that focus on individuals with FAS/ARBEs have attempted to determine specific risk and protective factors that affect the developing fetus, and the affected offspring during the various stages of their life. Animal studies have played a central role in this process, particularly with regard to risks to fetal development. Studies involving human subjects have focused on perinatal problems, primary disabilities (mainly functional deficits that reflect central nervous system dysfunctions inherent in FAS diagnosis) among affected offspring, and secondary disabilities, particularly among older children, adolescents and adults (Streissguth et al., 1997). The following chapter reviews this body of literature with specific attention paid to risk and protective factors related to Aboriginal people with FAS/ARBEs. The chapter begins with a brief discussion of diagnosis of FAS/ARBEs, including a discussion of the 'best practices' identified by Roberts and Nanson (2000). This will be followed by a review of studies that focused on birth outcomes and the various life stages of affected individuals. The 'best practices' identified by Roberts and Nanson (2000), with regard to interventions for persons affected by in-utero alcohol exposure, will be included in this review.

Identification of Fetal Alcohol Syndrome and Other Alcohol-Related Birth Effects

> So many of the children have not been diagnosed that we don't want to create an atmosphere where teachers and staff are going back and labelling these kids when they have not been diagnosed (cited in Leslie and Roberts, 2001:20).

The history of how the diagnostic criteria for FAS/ARBEs came to be generally agreed upon by medical researchers was reviewed in chapter two. This review pointed out that controversy still exists over current practices of diagnosing individuals, and medical researchers are attempting to address the lack of diagnostic validity and reliability through the development of more sophisticated diagnostic tools that will decrease the likelihood of misclassification through under and over-diagnosing of patients.

Chapter two also points out that specific concerns exist for Aboriginal people in Canada with regard to diagnostic criteria, particularly concerning the pattern of facial features proposed as markers of FAS, the use of standard growth measurements to determine FAS/ARBEs and the use of mainstream psychological testing for neuro-behavioural dysfunction among Aboriginal children.

The use of 'secondary disabilities,' which are believed to be the result of the interaction between primary disabilities, particularly neuro-developmental anomalies, and the environment in which the person lives, as markers for FAS/ARBEs are problematic in relation to Aboriginal people, as this group of problems occur disproportionately among the general Aboriginal population. Secondary disabilities that have been identified are: mental health problems, disrupted school experience (suspended, expelled or dropped out), trouble with the law, confinement (in-patient treatment for mental health or addiction problems or incarceration), inappropriate sexual behaviour and alcohol/drug problems (Streissguth et al., 1997).

This is specifically true when diagnosis is heavily weighted toward behavioural problems and when confirmation of levels of maternal alcohol-exposure cannot be determined when there is an absence of other diagnostic markers, such as the pattern of facial features and growth retardation and when the individual has experienced negative environmental influences (family dysfunction, multiple foster-placements, child physical or sexual abuse, poor education and/or chronic poverty). These environmental influences have all been linked to some or all of the 'secondary disabilities' of FAS, apart from in-utero alcohol damage. For example, the literature concerning children of alcoholics documents the adverse impact of living with an alcoholic father. Abel writes:

> Growing up in an alcoholic environment in which a child has no opportunity to become socialized results in many of the same conduct disorders currently associated with FAS/ARBE. Such children do not form intimate lasting relationships and do not develop a sense of remorse. In their behavioural profiles, these children bear a striking similarity to those with FAS. Both have been described as impulsive, hyperactive, aggressive, disobedient, antisocial, insecure, emotionally disabled, academically delayed, and so on (Steinhausen, et al., 1984). However, when assessing the home environment, the father's role is typically ignored in FAS/ARBE studies ... If a father's alcoholism is ignored, the validity of the results provided for the potential impact of the home environment by these [home assessment] instruments is meaningless. In the context of alcoholism, this is especially so when the home itself is not observed (1998a:138).

This suggests that caution should be taken with regard to diagnosis based on behavioural problems and the occurrence of 'secondary disabilities,' as the potential for mis-labelling individuals as permanently brain damaged will have significant repercussions on their self-perception and their ability to improve the quality of their life (e.g., educational and employment opportunities). Furthermore, longitudinal studies have not yet determined how significant environmental influences are, but the studies that do exist argue that behavioural problems can be greatly diminished among affected persons with early interventions, most importantly, a stable home environment, with few or no disruptions in living circumstances.

Screening, referral and case management activities by various professionals (e.g., public health nurses, teachers, social workers), as well as expert diagnosis of individuals (newborns, children, adolescents, adults) affected by alcohol exposure during pregnancy, are all used in the identification of FAS and ARBEs (Roberts and Nanson, 2000). Roberts and Nanson point out that, apart from the concerns raised above in relation to Aboriginal groups, other more general problems exist with identification of individuals. They write:

> Clinically, many of the anomalies associated with prenatal alcohol exposures are not unique to FAS and related effects and can be confused with other disorders or conditions, particularly among children with partial FAS, and Alcohol-Related Effects (i.e. ARBD and ARND). Examples of conditions often easily confused with FAS include Aarskog syndrome, fragile-x syndrome, fetal hydantoin syndrome and Noonan syndrome (Astley and Clarren, 1999). Presentation of FAS anomalies varies widely among individuals, with growth retardation seen in most, but not all, diagnosed children, intelligence scores ranging from severely disabled to normal, and a range of behavioural difficulties

that generally but do not always co-occur (Aase, 1994; Stratton et al. [eds.], 1996). Consequently, Aase acknowledged that diagnosing FAS in a specific patient is often difficult even for an experienced clinician because the diagnosis depends on recognition of a consistent pattern of minor, often subtle physical anomalies, generalized but disproportionate growth retardation, and non-specific developmental and behavioural problems—some of which change with time and in severity among individuals (Roberts and Nanson, 2000:53).

Roberts and Nanson add that further complications arise because of the influence of environmental factors, "making it difficult to determine whether behaviours problems are due to the child's living environment, the result of prenatal alcohol exposure, or some combination of the two" (2000:53). Abel (1998a) points out that cognitive and behavioural problems associated with poverty, for example, are the same kind of cognitive and behavioural problems one encounters with FAS/ARBEs; therefore, it is not surprising that children with FAS/ARBEs from different homes vary so much in their intelligence or their behaviour. He adds: "FAS/ARBES is not simply the result of being born to an alcoholic mother. It is also the result of being raised by an alcoholic mother; and it is especially the result of being born and raised by a poverty-stricken alcoholic mother" (1998a:138). Being raised in an unstable environment exacerbates underlying biological problems and most persons described in the FAS/ARBES literature have lived in very tumultuous home environments, including during the early stages of infancy and childhood (e.g., Streissguth et al., 1985; 1991).

Leslie and Roberts (2001) point out that receiving a formal diagnosis can take a very long time and, in the meantime, little can be happening to help the child. They recommend that service providers and family members not wait for a formal diagnosis before intervening with an affected child. Service providers can support family members in obtaining an assessment and throughout the process. However, FAS diagnosticians interviewed by Tait (2003) reported having many referrals of children to their clinic who were not alcohol-affected, but whose physical and behavioural profiles appeared as FAS to social service providers and family members.

This suggests that caution should be taken when interventions are made prior to assessment and labelling the child as FAS or ARBES should be avoided. Supports, such as improved home and school/day care environments, will benefit children with developmental and behavioural problems apart from whether or not they warrant a diagnosis of FAS/ARBES. The knowledge of care givers about their child's behaviour and the supports needed to address the needs of the child should also be respected and supported by social service agencies, even when an assessment or diagnosis has not been made.

Three 'best practices' concerning identification were identified by Roberts and Nanson with the assistance of the National Steering Committee:

Prenatal Screening

'Best practice'

1. There is some evidence that prenatal screening for FAS is most effective when initiated by routine, collaborative screening of mothers during prenatal care.

Chapter 10

Early identification and diagnosis of individuals affected by in-utero alcohol exposure are believed to be key in the prevention of future affected pregnancies and in the quick referral of infants to appropriate services (Roberts and Nanson, 2000). Because there are several problems identifying affected infants, particularly those with less severe damage, knowledge of the mother's alcohol use history is of great importance. As discussed in the previous chapter, prenatal screening of pregnant women for alcohol abuse can help determine the level of risk to an offspring. Roberts and Nanson (2000) suggest that routine, collaborative screening of mothers during prenatal care can facilitate identifying those offspring who are at risk.

Within this context, issues of confidentiality regarding the woman's use must be maintained (Van Bibber, 1997). Not only will this assist health care practitioners to build trust with the woman and facilitate referral to addiction treatment or other supports, but it will also encourage women to access prenatal care, particularly high risk women, who may be fearful that their use will be reported to child welfare services. The role of service providers, such as mentors and outreach workers, who can assist high risk women in accessing prenatal care and advocate for them, when necessary, with other service providers, such as obstetricians, are key to this process (e.g., attending prenatal appointments with high risk women until they feel comfortable attending alone, ensuring that confidentiality of screening information is maintained, assisting obstetricians in referring women to addiction or mental health services).[49] Traditional practitioners, such as midwives, could also play an important role in screening practices targeting pregnant women, as could Elders and other local health practitioners, such as nurses.

Hart suggests that service providers who work with First Nations communities "should establish an environment of support in the here-and-now, as opposed to focussing upon assessments and desired outcomes and dictating direction" (1999:77; Nelson, Kelley and McPherson, 1985). He adds:

> Support may be demonstrated by spending time to get to know the people with whom you are working directly and indirectly, exercising patience, especially when communicating, and being willing to include Elders and community healers in the provision of services (Hart, 1999:77; Janzen, Skakum and Lightning, 1994).

In this way, the strengths in Aboriginal identity and traditional practices can be drawn upon to holistically address the needs of the woman, her unborn child and the community (Hart, 1999; Hampton, Hampton, Kinunwa and Kinunwa, 1995).

Revised 'best practice'

1. There is some evidence that prenatal screening for FAS is most effective when initiated by routine, collaborative screening of mothers during prenatal care. The inclusion of traditional practitioners, along with service providers being familiar with the local cultural beliefs and practices and the history of Aboriginal communities, are key in screening and identification strategies. The involvement of mentors and outreach workers, who can assist and advocate for high risk women when accessing prenatal care, will help to build trusting relationships between pregnant women and health care practitioners.

---

[49]   See chapter nine for a more in-depth discussion.

Chapter 10

Diagnostic Services

'Best practice'

1. There is a consensus among experts that the availability of diagnostic services can be enhanced through mechanisms, such as specialized training, consultation and support, telemedicine and travelling clinics.

Receiving an assessment for FAS/ARBEs is difficult to obtain in many regions of Canada and, when available, there are generally long waiting lists because of limited health resources. Roberts and Nanson report that non-specialist physicians and nurses are in key positions to assist in screening and referral when they "obtain information on prenatal exposure history, sequential growth measurements, and help to provide photographs of an affected individual over time" (2000:55). Astley and Clarren (1995 in Roberts and Nanson, 2000) have developed a screening tool based on facial phenotype that could potentially be used in various clinical settings to assist in identifying individuals for further assessment. The tool has shown high sensitivity and specificity with two racially mixed samples of children ranging in age from two to ten years; however, the tool requires further evaluation (Roberts and Nanson, 2000).

The use of multi-disciplinary teams has been useful in identifying persons with FAS/ARBEs. Generally, these teams include a physician, usually "a pediatrician or geneticist to assess growth and dysmorphology—and a psychologist to assess the behaviours that would support the finding of central nervous systems anomalies, such as mental retardation, learning disabilities or adjustment problems" (Roberts and Nanson, 2000:55). Travelling clinics have been used in some remote Aboriginal communities in Saskatchewan in which a specialized team visits the community to assist with diagnosis and with the development of local resources. The FAS team includes a pediatrician, psychologist, social worker, physiotherapist, occupational therapist and speech therapist. The team, as much as possible, incorporates local professionals, such as nurses and dieticians; however, there is no information on whether local traditional practitioners and/or Elders are included in team activities. Roberts and Nanson write:

> These traveling clinics have been independently evaluated (Adrian and Fisher, 1997). High levels of client and community satisfaction with the model were reported, although some parents reported enjoying the opportunity to leave isolated northern communities to attend appointments in a larger centre, particularly when they have extended families to visit there. Concerns were expressed with the limited numbers of families who can receive services at a clinic and the limited length of the appointments. A similar outreach service delivery model is offered in BC through the Children and Women's Hospital. Patients are seen by a developmental pediatrician, psychologist, geneticist and psychiatrist (C. Loock, personal communication, 1999) (2000:56).

Manitoba has operated a telediagnostic program for the past few years, which links through teleconferencing specialists in Winnipeg with physicians and other health care providers in remote communities (Square, 1999). There is, however, no comprehensive evaluation of the program in terms of its effectiveness, costs or client and professional satisfaction (Roberts and Nanson, 2000).

Chapter 10

Specialized diagnostic programs, such as travelling clinics and teleconference facilities, help to expand diagnostic services to remote areas of the country. However, the lack of standardized diagnostic tools and these services not being sensitized to local populations (e.g., adjustments to psychological testing and standardized measures) due to time constraints suggest that the validity and reliability of diagnostic assessment may be somewhat unreliable. Follow-up testing of identified individuals at various age-related stages, where the diagnostician is blind to a previous diagnosis, would help determine the reliability of this form of assessment.

The targeting of remote communities for diagnostic assessment must involve a strategic plan for support and intervention of persons identified as having FAS/ARBEs. This strategy must be directed by the community and developed with the assistance of the diagnostic team and other local health care and social service providers. Diagnosis without appropriate follow-up services could potentially cause a great deal of anxiety, guilt and frustration among family and community members and, therefore, a well thought out plan must be in place before diagnostic services are made available. Within this context, difficult questions, such as how the needs of affected persons will be met in a remote community, particularly the needs of infants and children, must be asked and positive assessments of FAS/ARBEs must be questioned as sufficient grounds to remove children from their homes.[50]

This concern was raised by the Royal Commission on Aboriginal Peoples, which pointed out that "family caregivers in Aboriginal communities are often forced, by lack of private means or public programs suitable for their children as they grow up, to place their children in provincial care facilities" (1996b:133). This situation results in families and communities, once again, having to give up their children and in children experiencing being removed from their homes and living apart from their family. Instead, resources should be made available to support the community in its efforts to address the needs of affected children within the community (Fournier and Crey, 1997; Tait, 2003).

Revised 'best practices'

1. There is a consensus among experts that the availability of diagnostic services can be enhanced through mechanisms such as specialized training, consultation and support, telemedicine, and travelling clinics. Included in this process should be the sensitization of diagnostic tools to the local community context (e.g., psychological testing, standard measurements). Prior to the commencement of assessments diagnostic initiatives must develop intervention and support strategies, driven by the priorities of the community that will be put in place for affected individuals and their families. A collaborative effort between diagnosticians and local traditional practitioners, Elders and health and social service providers, in conjunction with community leaders and their constituents, should be prioritized in any assessment and intervention initiative, even when time and financial constraints would suggest otherwise.

---

[50] This question did not arise in the research literature, but given the long history of Aboriginal children being over-represented in child welfare systems in Canada and the fact that a number of services recommended for infants and children with FAS/ARBEs are not available in remote or rural communities, the potential for arguments advocating the removal of children from these communities based on the child's 'best interest' could be very compelling.

Chapter 10

Other Substances

'Best practice'

1. There is a consensus among experts that, in the presence of particular maternal characteristics (including lack of prenatal care, previous unexplained fetal demise, repeated spontaneous abortion, severe mood swings and precipitous labour) or infant attributes (including prematurity, unexplained intra-uterine growth retardation, neuro-behavioural abnormalities, urogenital anomalies, myocardial infarction and blood flow restriction), selective screening for maternal substance use by taking a detailed maternal history in a supportive atmosphere can be effective in identifying children affected by prenatal use of substances other than alcohol.

The use of substances (e.g., cannabis, opiates, stimulants, inhalants, hallucinogens) other than alcohol is a concern for poor Aboriginal women, particularly those women who live in urban centres, are street involved and struggle with addiction problems (Tait, 2000a; Jacobs and Gill, 2002). Inhalant use, namely gasoline sniffing among youth populations, is also of concern for some Aboriginal groups. However, there is limited information about inhalant use and pregnancy. Polysubstance use–the use of more than one substance during the same period – is common among women with addiction problems (Loock, 1998; Poole, 1997; 1998; Tait, 2000a), with alcohol generally being combined with another licit or illicit drug. The use of self-reporting for illicit drug use has been found to be unreliable in clinical and research settings (Jacobson, Jacobson, Sokol, Martier, Ager et al., 1991) because women may fear that their use will be reported to the authorities. However, information gained in respectful, non-judgmental contexts appears to be more reliable (Roberts and Nanson, 2000; Chasnoff, 1992; Russell et al., 1996; Lieberman, 1998a).

Identification of children affected by prenatal use of substances, other than alcohol, and the determination of the life span trajectory of these effects, are problematic for a number of reasons (Roberts and Nanson, 2000). Roberts and Nanson write:

> Prenatal exposure to other substances does not produce an identifiable pattern of anomalies that has been clearly identified as a syndrome as has FAS (Lester et al., 1996). Because effects range so widely, identification of exposed children often relies on evidence of maternal use of substances ... Consequently, selective screening by a trusted clinician taking a careful maternal history may currently be the best way to screen for substance-exposed children (US Preventive Services Task Force, 1996). Characteristics of the mother that might indicate screening include lack of prenatal care, previous unexplained fetal demise, repeated spontaneous abortion, severe mood swings and precipitous labour. Although there is not a typical profile of a drug-exposed child (Sinclair, 1998), infant characteristics indicating possible prenatal substance use are prematurity, unexplained intra-uterine growth retardation, neuro-behavioural abnormalities, urogenital anomalies, myocardial infarction and blood flow restriction (American Academy of Pediatrics [Committee on Drugs], 1998). Newborn withdrawal from a substance may be confused for a common neonatal problem such as colic if the physician is unfamiliar with neonatal effects, or is unaware of the mother's history (2000:57-58).

Chapter 10

With increasing access to and use of a range of substances, such as cannabis, opiates, stimulants, inhalants, and hallucinogens, either in communities or due to migration to urban centres, some Aboriginal women and their offspring are at risk for fetal drug exposure that could lead to a number of negative birth outcomes. Increased access and use of a range of drugs also places the health and well-being of women at risk due to a number of related health and social problems, including: increased family dysfunction and violence; transmission of infectious diseases, such as HIV and Hepatitis C; participation in illicit activities, such as theft and prostitution; and the risk of over-dosing. Programs that attempt to identify infants who are at risk of fetal drug exposure must include supports for the mothers of these children and seek to address the needs of the child and mother.

Revised 'best practice'

1. There is a consensus among experts that, in the presence of particular maternal characteristics (including lack of prenatal care, previous unexplained fetal demise, repeated spontaneous abortion, severe mood swings and precipitous labour) or infant attributes (including prematurity, unexplained intra-uterine growth retardation, neuro-behavioural abnormalities, urogenital anomalies, myocardial infarction and blood flow restriction), selective screening for maternal substance use by taking a detailed maternal history in a supportive atmosphere can be effective in identifying children affected by prenatal use of substances other than alcohol. Support for the mother must also be prioritized, including referral and follow-up, to culturally sensitive addiction treatment and after care services.

Persons Affected by Prenatal Alcohol Exposure

> Perhaps one of the most important points that service providers must realize and act upon is that culture is central to every person. While issues such as FAS/E deserve significant attention, the importance of this issue or any issue does not pre-empt the fact that culture has to be considered and incorporated when working with First Nations people, especially those facing the issue of FAS/E. People cannot hide behind excuses such as "It is less important" or "We know nothing about First Nations and therefore we cannot do anything about it." If you are going to work to address FAS/E, you can expect to work with First Nations people. If you are going to work with First Nations people, you had better prepare yourself to learn about their culture and their histories, and how to best support them (Hart, 1999:78-79).

> A clinical one-to-one approach does not work well for us [Métis], [because] we cannot divorce the healing of individuals from the healing of families and communities. Indian people often find spiritual wholeness in a return to their traditional ceremonies. That rarely works for us. Traditionally, our people were Roman Catholic or Anglican … We desperately need the resources, money and man power to develop our own culturally appropriate programs (cited in Royal Commission on Aboriginal Peoples, 1996b:211).

> We found that Inuit Women or Inuit communities need different solutions … That's why we decided to have different solutions, a different section for Inuit [in the report of the Canadian Panel on Violence Against Women]. But it was very hard for me to try to get the Inuit section, because I was lumped with other Aboriginal groups all the time.

Chapter 10

> I fought and fought. I kept saying ... "I am not like other Aboriginal people ... I am not white, I am not Indian, but I am Inuk" (cited in Royal Commission on Aboriginal Peoples, 1996b:211).

There is a growing body of research literature that examines the life trajectory of individuals affected by prenatal substance use. The following discussion will review this literature in relation to perinatal problems, and in relations to the three diagnostic criteria for FAS—cranio-facial characteristics, growth deficiency and CNS damage—and their manifestations during the various life stages: infant and early childhood, later childhood, adolescence and adulthood. Emphasis will be given to issues specifically confronting Aboriginal communities and their members; however, there is a dearth of research literature that specifically examines Aboriginal people affected by in-utero alcohol damage.

Interventions for persons affected by prenatal substance use are defined as "activities intended to prevent and reduce harmful effects associated with primary and secondary disabilities among persons exposed to alcohol and other drugs *in-utero*. Intervention also aims to promote the development of individuals exposed to alcohol or other substances prenatally, during the various life stages and to support those caring for them" (Roberts and Nanson, 2000:62). Intervention is generally believed to be best addressed by a number of inter-related strategies because of the range of potential difficulties that can arise. Research that has evaluated the effectiveness of intervention strategies has been quite limited, particularly for interventions directed toward adolescents and adults (Roberts and Nanson, 2000).

The following review will include a discussion of the 'best practice' interventions for individuals with FAS/ARBEs identified by Roberts and Nanson (2000). Because of the limited number of intervention strategies that have been evaluated, Roberts and Nanson identified several 'best practices' by relying significantly on the observations of experts, mainly from their National Steering Committee, that work or live with alcohol-affected individuals. This discussion will be supported by the report by Leslie and Roberts discussed earlier (see chapter nine), which identified 'good practices' based on the opinions of service providers who have been involved with FAS/ARBES programming and services. The aim of the following discussion is to review the 'best practices' and to discuss these in relation to the lives of Aboriginal people in Canada. Special attention will be paid to risk and protective factors that prevent or improve upon the delivery of effective and appropriate programs and services for this population. However, as indicated by the above statements, risk and protective factors, as well as 'best practices,' may be different for each of the three Aboriginal groups. They will also be different depending on historical circumstances, geographical location and community characteristics, such as the level of social integration.

Perinatal Problems

Several perinatal problems, such as stillbirths, preterm birth, intrapartum problems, neonatal withdrawal, and placenta pathology and size, have been studied in relation to in-utero alcohol exposure.

Chapter 10

Stillbirth

Prospective studies have failed to make an association between in-utero alcohol exposure and stillbirth rates among women clinically characterized by alcohol abuse (Abel, 1998a; Sokol, Miller et al., 1980). High rates of alcohol consumption by pregnant women were examined in several studies that found consumption of an average of three (Gibson, Baghurst et al., 1983) or five or more (Davis, Partridge and Storrs, 1982; Giso, Roman, Inskip, Beral and Donovan, 1984; Plant, 1985) drinks a day found no significant increases in stillbirths. The conclusion from these studies was that alcohol consumption during pregnancy did not increase the risk for stillbirths (Abel, 1998a).

Preterm Birth

About one-half of the children with FAS described in the clinical case literature were born preterm (Abel, 1990). Preterm birth is the most important factor affecting neonatal mortality (Abel, 1998a). A study in France found that 46% of a group of children with FAS were preterm, compared with 29% for non-FAS children (Dehaene, Crepin et al., 1981 in Abel, 1998a). A second study in Sweden also recorded a high rate of preterm birth among children with FAS (Olegard et al., 1979 in Abel, 1998a). In a critique of this literature, Abel writes:

> Because cirrhosis is associated with alcoholism, studies relating preterm births to drinking during pregnancy, especially among alcoholics, should control for this factor. As in the case of spontaneous abortions, cirrhosis is also one of the most important factors increasing the likelihood of preterm birth (Scholters, 1979). Other than mentioning the fact that some mothers may have the disease, no studies have considered cirrhosis when preterm births have been examined in the context of FAS/ARBEs (1998a:38-39).

Studies have varied as to whether preterm birth is associated with maternal alcohol abuse in the absence of FAS. A study of 202 women and their offspring found that infants of alcoholic women and of heavy drinkers had a shorter gestation than those of moderate and light drinkers; however, the difference was only significant for women who were alcoholics (Rostand, Kaminski et al., 1990). In a review of the literature, Abel (1998a) concluded that the relationship between maternal alcohol consumption and preterm birth was tenuous and, even when statistically significant, the association was weak.

Intrapartum Problems

Intrapartum complications, such as breech birth, occur at a higher frequency among children with FAS. For example, three per cent of all births are breech (Barden, 1975 in Abel, 1998a), while this occurs in fifteen per cent (Majewski, Bierich, Loser, Michaelis, Leiber et al., 1976 in Abel, 1998a) to thirty-five per cent (Abel, 1990) of all cases of FAS. Abel suggests that the percentage may be even higher because fetuses in the breech position are often delivered by Cesarean section, which also occurs with relatively high frequency in FAS (e.g., 36%) (Abel, 1990). Abel writes:

> When twins are differentially affected with ARBEs, including FAS, it is the twin in the breech position who is primarily affected (Riikonen, 1994). Because breech birth is associated with many of the behavioural effects of FAS, such as hyperactivity and

mental retardation (Abel, 1984a), the higher prevalence of these behavioural effects in children with FAS may be due to their having been born as breech babies rather than the direct effects of alcohol on the nervous system (1998a:41).

Abel suggests that the involvement in births by Caesarean sections of anaesthetics and analgesics, which exhibit cross-tolerance to alcohol (Han, 1969), may result in alcohol-abusing women requiring higher doses to produce maternal narcosis or analgesia than those required by non-abusers (Abel, 1998a; Han, 1969). Behaviour effects that have been associated with these medications are newborn depression, altered EEG activity, poorer performance on newborn test measures, such as orientation to novel stimuli, and increased irritability and altered motor activity lasting several days after birth (Abel, 1984; 1998a). Abel (1998a) suggests that newborn behavioural effects reported in conjunction with maternal drinking during pregnancy may be due to intrapartum exposure to obstetric medication, rather than directly related to maternal alcohol abuse.

Neonatal Withdrawal

In a review of the scientific literature, Abel (1998a) found that relatively mild neonatal withdrawal symptomatology was reported for children with FAS and for children without FAS who were born to alcoholic women. Withdrawal was characterized by jitteriness and tremulousness, increased muscle tone, increased respiratory rates, hyperacusis, exaggerated reflexes and sleep disturbances. These symptoms were also entirely different in magnitude and severity compared with those associated with neonatal withdrawal from narcotics (Zelson, 1975 in Abel, 1998a). Because the symptoms have been noted to last up to ten days to a month after birth, Abel (1998a) suggests that they are not likely to be symptomatic of withdrawal, as is commonly believed.

Placenta Pathology and Size

In a review of the scientific literature, Abel (1998a) concluded that, although placenta pathology is associated with alcohol abuse, this relationship is only indirect. Changes in placental size, however, were found to be directly affected by alcohol abuse, but further research to determine the extent to which these changes directly impact the embryo/fetus is still needed (Abel, 1998a).

Risk and Protective Factors for Persons with Fetal Alcohol Syndrome

The following discussion will focus on risk and protective factors for alcohol-affected individuals.[51] Miscellaneous alcohol-related birth effects that are commonly found among alcohol-affected individuals, but are not part of the diagnostic criteria, will be discussed first, followed by a brief review of the literature concerning sex ratios and FAS. Two of the diagnostic criteria, growth deficiency and cranio-facial characteristics, will be briefly touched upon in relation to risk. The remainder of the chapter will focus on the third diagnostic criteria, central nervous system (CNS) damage, as it is the most serious outcome for affected individuals, in terms of risk for primary and secondary disabilities.

---

[51]   A discussion of each of the three diagnostic criteria for FAS and other ARBEs occurred earlier in this report (see chapter two).

Chapter 10

Miscellaneous Alcohol-Related Birth Effects

Infants identified as having FAS often experience an array of physical complications associated with alcohol but are not necessarily part of the diagnostic criteria (Streissguth, 1997). Depressed immune function, for example, while not considered diagnostic of FAS, occurs at very high rates in FAS children (Abel, 1998a). A range of alcohol-related birth effects (ARBEs) have been discussed in the research literature; however, in most cases the small number of participants in the studies have led to inconclusive findings as to whether these effects are due to in-utero alcohol exposure. Several FAS clinical studies have reported brain tumours in children with FAS; however, in a review of the literature, Abel (1998a) found no direct association between FAS and spontaneous childhood tumours that could be found and that appeared to be coincidental.

Other health complications are heart defects, organ and skeletal malformations, particularly: cleft lips and palates; hip displacement and scoliosis; seizures; hyper and hypo-tonicity; hearing and vision problems; otitis media; and pneumonia (Streissguth, 1997). Some studies have noted an increase in the frequency of sudden infant death syndrome (SIDS) (the sudden and unexplained death of an infant or young child without apparent cause) with FAS or FAE or with maternal drinking during pregnancy (Hoffman, Damas, Hillman and Krongrad, 1988; Southall et al., 1987). However, Abel (1998a) points out that these studies were inconclusive as the mothers of the SIDS children were primarily of low socio-economic status and many were also smokers. Because SIDS is associated with these factors and with various other risk factors, which occur independently in these studies, the reported association between maternal alcohol consumption and SIDS is tenuous at best (Abel, 1998a; Kandall and Gaines, 1991).

Several other malformations have been noted in persons with FAS. Limb and joint anomalies are the most common structural anomaly in FAS, occurring in about eighteen per cent of all cases (Abel, 1990). If flexion problems and related movement problems were included in this estimate, the prevalence of this disorder in FAS would be even higher (Abel, 1998a). Cardiac anomalies in FAS are relatively high; Abel (1998a) suggests that this may be so because of the types of cases that are specifically referred for medical attention or, in other words, cardiac cases may not represent an unbiased sample of FAS cases.[52] Anomalies in the structure and function of the lungs have not been found in FAS cases. In relation to kidney and urological anomalies, a number have been noted: for example, hydronephrosis, hypoplastic kidney and renal agenesis (Abel, 1990). However, Abel (1998a) cautions that high rates of kidney anomalies among FAS patients may be misleading, as this appears to be due to these individuals becoming visible because of the problem requiring treatment. There are few case reports of liver damage in patients with FAS and no reports of gross pancreatic pathology in connection with FAS/ARBEs. Little evidence of structural damage to the pituitary or adrenal glands has been linked to maternal drinking during pregnancy and there is no evidence linking altered thyroid function and in-utero alcohol damage (Abel, 1998a). Although not common, the external genitalia are sometimes abnormal in both males and females with FAS (Abel, 1990; 1998a).

---

[52]   Abel adds that this is also true of rates of other malformations associated with FAS.

217

Chapter 10

Sex Ratios

Three studies were reviewed that attempted to estimate sex ratio for cases diagnosed with FAS/ARBEs. The first study found a male-to-female sex ratio to be 1:2.7 based on eleven clinic patients ranging in ages from one to seven years (Qazi and Maskawa, 1976). The larger number of female patients could be the result of a higher mortality rate of affected males in the first months of life or may be due to the male fetus or offspring being more vulnerable to the teratogenic effects of alcohol than their female counterparts. However, the results of the study are inconclusive, since they are based on a small sample size and on retrospective data. A second study found contradictory results to the first study. Male-to-female sex ratio was found to be 2.6:1 (n=25) (Vitez, Koryani et al., 1984). A third study in British Colombia found that the male-to-female ratio was 1.4:1 (n=22) (Robinson, Conry et al., 1987). At this point, it is inconclusive if men or women are more likely to be affected. However, there are indications in the research literature that more males than females are being identified as having FAS/ARBEs due to behavioural problems that bring them to the attention of medical researchers (e.g., Fast, Conry et al., 1999).

Growth Retardation

One of the three diagnostic criteria for FAS is growth retardation, which may occur prenatally and can be recognizable at birth or recognized postnatally when it is described as 'failure to thrive' (Abel, 1998a; Streissguth, 1997). Most children with FAS are shorter than the average child of the same age (Streissguth et al., 1985); however, since many of the children with FAS, whose growth has been monitored in follow-up studies, have been either Aboriginal or African-American children, their shorter stature may be related to their racial or socio-economic backgrounds (Abel, 1998a). Some follow-up studies have also noted catch-up growth, primarily in girls, during puberty (Streissguth, Aase et al., 1991; Spohr and Steinhausen, 1987; Spohr, Willms and Steinhausen, 1993; 1994). Studies that examined non-FAS offspring of mothers who drank during pregnancy, consistently find that catch-up growth is the rule rather than the exception, except when low socio-economic status is involved (Abel, 1998a).

Low socio-economic status has been identified by some researchers as linked to postnatal growth deficiency in children prenatally exposed to alcohol; however, consideration of factors, such as nutritional intake, are set aside and the relationship between maternal alcohol exposure and decreased growth measures are highlighted. For example, in a discussion of a study by Day and colleagues (1992), Abel (1998a) points out that the study authors fail to draw attention to their finding that persistent growth deficits associated with prenatal alcohol exposure were mainly found in children from low-income families (average income for 41% of the women in their study was $400 or less per month); whereas comparable effects were rarely seen in 'more advantaged' populations. Day and colleagues found that about 50% of the children in their study were consuming less than the recommended daily allowance (RDA) for dairy products, 46% were receiving less than the RDA for protein and 60% and 34% were receiving less than the RDA for fruits/vegetables and grains; however, they still concluded that nutritional factors did not effect the relationship between alcohol and growth measures.

This finding may be particularly important in relation to Aboriginal children, who are more likely than non-Aboriginal children to live in poverty and, in many geographical areas, may have only a limited supply of nutritious foods, such as fresh produce, much of which is very expensive for families to

218

purchase on a limited budget. In regions where environmental pollutants have minimized the use of traditional foods, this too can contribute to poor nutrition.

Cranio-Facial Anomalies

Cranio-facial anomalies have been described in several studies that generally focus on a particular aspect of the face (eyes; nose; mouth; throat, pharynx and dention; and ears). Several problems, such as abnormal curvature of the eye (Church and Gerkin, 1988; Miller, Israel and Cuttone, 1981; Stromland, 1985), strabismus—an inability of the eyes to focus parallel to one another (Abel, 1990; Majewski, 1993; Steinhausen, Nestler et al., 1982), esotropia—eyes turn inward or 'cross-eyed' (Jones et al., 1973; Miller, Israel and Cuttone, 1981), exotropia—eyes turn out (Walpole and Hoelig, 1980) and nystagmus— jerky eye movements—have all been found, to varying degrees, in FAS children (Abel, 1998a). Apart from the physical appearance of the nose (often described as short and upturned, the bridge low and broad), only one nasal disorder, persistent rhinorrhea, has been associated with FAS (Johnson, 1979 in Abel, 1998a).

Anomalies associated with FAS involving the mouth have been identified as indistinct or flat philtrum, thin upper lip, absence of 'cupid's bow' in upper lip, maxillar hypoplasia, mandibular hypoplasia, high arched palate, cleft palate, cleft lip and abnormal dentition (Abel, 1998a). Anomalies involving the throat have rarely been mentioned in FAS studies; however, feeding difficulties (dysphagia) have been mentioned in at least twenty cases of FAS (Abel, 1990). These feeding problems could reflect fine motor dysfunction, taking the form of impaired co-ordination of the tongue and pharynx (Aase, 1990 in Abel, 1998a).

A weak sucking reflex may reflect brain stem and autonomic nervous system dysfunctions and fine motor dysfunction. Malocclusion (the misalignment of the upper and lower jaws), crossbite and overbite, hypoplastic teeth and enamel and frequent caries, missing teeth, rotated teeth, overjets and crooked teeth have also been found among FAS patients. In relation to the outer ear, the most common mentioned anomalies are low set ears, posteriorly rotated ears, prominent ears, and poorly formed pinnae (Abel, 1998a).

A central risk related to cranio-facial anomalies for persons with FAS is that these features are not stable over the life span. For example, they may be difficult to identify in infancy as the features may not be apparent until the child's second year and beyond (Roberts and Nanson, 2000) and, once a child reaches puberty, may no longer be recognizable as FAS (Abel, 1998a). This may place infants, adolescents and adults who are not diagnosed at risk of going undetected and, therefore, not eligible to receive available services. Researchers have also pointed out that the characteristic facial features of FAS may occur independently in some Aboriginal groups, apart from maternal alcohol exposure in-utero (Roberts and Nanson, 2000; Abel, 1998a), which may result in over-diagnosis among these groups.

Neuro-Developmental Abnormalities

Neuro-developmental abnormalities are among the most serious health problems caused by maternal alcohol exposure (Abel, 1998a; Streissguth, 1997; Stratton, Howe et al., 1996). Information about affected children comes mainly from two sources: retrospective clinical studies of children referred with

Chapter 10

FAS and ARBEs; and, prospective research studies of children exposed to alcohol in-utero (Stratton, Howe et al., 1996). Stratton and colleagues point out that most of the children in prospective FAS studies are not dysmorphic (e.g., do not have the physical features associated with FAS) and would not qualify for a diagnosis of FAS, although some may have milder effects that are observable through focused testing or statistical analysis of group data. Stratton and colleagues state:

> In retrospective studies, there is usually much stronger evidence for the effect of a teratogen than in prospective studies, due to the systematic selection biases that occur when children are referred for special education or medical treatment. However, without statistical and experimental controls, it is difficult to discriminate the effects of the teratogen from that of other, associated factors. Despite these limitations, retrospective clinical studies are of great value because the characteristics of the affected individual can be observed much more clearly than among more moderately exposed children. In addition, the characteristics of clinically affected children include those problems that will require intervention and treatment (1996:158).

Prospective studies, on the other hand, allow some statistical control of confounding variables; for example, the use of contrast groups for variables, such as social class and race, and allow examination of factors that can be obscured in clinical studies (Stratton, Howe et al., 1996). Stratton and colleagues write:

> ... the sample selected for inclusion in prospective studies is often different from that included in retrospective and clinical studies. The level of prenatal alcohol exposure tends to be less than that found in retrospective studies of identified FAS individuals. This can lead to problems in interpretation of the findings. In interpreting the results of such studies, the problems of overgeneralization and interpretation of multiple comparisons should be considered (1996:159).

Neuro-developmental abnormalities caused by in-utero alcohol exposure manifest themselves as behavioural deficits referred to as 'primary disabilities.' Problems that have been identified are: attentional problems or hyperactivity (Morse, 1991; Nanson and Hiscock, 1990); academic problems, including specific deficits in mathematics and memory skills (Streissguth et al., 1993); very specific language deficits (Abkarian, 1992); and problems with adaptive functioning that grow more significant with age (Lemoine and Lemoine, 1992; Streissguth and Randels, 1989).

Stratton and colleagues (1996) point out that, while it is possible to have only one or two behavioural difficulties, individuals with a diagnosis of FAS generally have co-occurring problems in all identified areas. This makes program development and subsequent interventions difficult to implement.

Neuro-behavioural problems array along a continuum throughout the life span of the affected person (Warren and Bast, 1988). The following review will be divided into four age-related developmental stages—infant and early childhood, later childhood, adolescence and adulthood—and will specifically focus on neuro-developmental anomalies. Secondary disabilities and risk factors that have been identified in each of these age-related stages will be discussed, with special emphasis paid to those studies involving Aboriginal people.

Chapter 10

Infant and Early Childhood

Infancy and early childhood is an important period for influencing the life trajectory of affected children, including addressing medical and family needs. Roberts and Nanson (2000), with the help of the National Steering Committee identified five 'best practices' related to infancy and early childhood:

'Best practices'

1. There is a consensus among experts to support the use of a professional, multi-disciplinary team to address the range of complex health needs of affected children.

2. There is some evidence to suggest that a longer-term, stable living environment contributes to more positive outcomes for children affected by alcohol in-utero. This may be facilitated by family-centred substance abuse treatment, respite care, other support services and FAS-specific information and training for birth, foster and adoptive parents.

3. There is a consensus among experts indicating that child care programs for children affected by prenatal alcohol exposure employing a low staff-child ratio, following structured routines and regulating the amount of stimulation received by the child may be more effective.

4. There is some evidence that services offering a single point of access, combining services for the mother with attention to the developmental needs of the child, improve outcomes for the child.

5. There is some evidence from animal studies and studies of children experiencing developmental delay due to other causes suggesting that early educational interventions may contribute to improved outcomes for children affected by prenatal alcohol use, at least in the short-term.

Researchers have examined the period of infancy and early childhood to identify neuro-behavioural abnormalities in affected children, risk associated with those deficits and protective factors that can improve developmental outcomes. During infancy and early childhood, a significant amount of neurological development occurs and, therefore, it is a time when environmental factors, such as child care, home environment and nutrition, can have positive or negative impacts upon affected children (Roberts and Nanson, 2000; Coles and Platzman, 1992). Early diagnosis has been identified by some researchers as a protective factor against difficulties later on and have called for "early diagnosis and prompt intervention with families of alcohol-affected children to promote the development of these children and to minimize what are termed secondary disabilities" (Roberts and Nanson, 2000:62; Astley, Magnusson et al., 1999; Streissguth, 1997; Streissguth and Kantor, 1997).

Obtaining a medical assessment for FAS/ARBEs in infancy may be difficult for a number of reasons. In newborns, the specific facial characteristics of FAS may not be developed and they may only become evident in the pre-school period (Stratton, Howe et al., 1996; Clarren, Sampson, Larsen, Donnell, Barr et al., 1987). However, experts believe that trained observers can identify both the facial features and the behavioural signs associated with prenatal alcohol exposure during this period (Stratton, Howe et al., 1996; Abel, Martier et al., 1993).

Chapter 10

Early diagnosis may be particularly difficult for Aboriginal infants to receive due to many Aboriginal people living in remote areas. In many remote communities, pregnant women are transported out of their communities to give birth in a southern hospital and shortly after giving birth are returned to their community where medical assessment of the child for FAS/ARBEs is difficult or, in some cases, impossible. Unless the infant is taken to a medical centre that has trained personnel to make the assessment or diagnostic assessments are offered by travelling clinics in the community, the child will go unassessed. Leslie and Roberts (2001) found that many families had to travel long distances (sometimes out-of-province) for an assessment. In most cases, the families were also faced with delays of up to six months for an appointment due to limited health care resources. Although many births of affected children have complications during or shortly after delivery and many of the most severely affected infants are in need of specialized medical attention because of obvious health problems, both of which suggest the possibility of FAS/ARBEs, a lack of trained health care practitioners means that cases of FAS/ARBEs, particularly with less obviously affected children, go undetected.

Studies have found that inconsistencies exist in the identification of FAS/ARBEs in infancy and early childhood. For example, in one study, despite physical features consistent with FAS being described in medical records of a group of children born to women who abused alcohol during pregnancy, there was a 100% failure by hospital staff to diagnose the syndrome in the study sample (Little, Snell et al., 1990). Other authors have argued that certain ethnic groups, including some Aboriginal groups, may be over-diagnosed with FAS/ARBEs because certain facial features, which resemble the facial characteristics of the syndrome, show up naturally in these groups (Abel, 1998a). Jo Nanson, a Saskatchewan researcher, states:

> The facial dysmorphology in native children with FAS can be somewhat confusing as many [A]boriginal children have epicanthus and a depressed nasal bridge. This appears to occur so commonly in [A]boriginal children that the physicians I work with feel it is simply a genetic variant and is not representative of fetal alcohol syndrome (Nanson, 1995 in Abel, 1998b:74).

Studies have shown that affected infants, particularly those with FAS, have a range of neuro-developmental effects (Stratton, Howe et al., 1996). In a discussion of two cohort studies, Streissguth and colleagues (1989) found that affected infants exhibited poor habituation (the ability to tune out redundant stimuli); poor state control; poor sucking pressure and longer latency to suck after contact with the nipple; and increased frequency of body tremors, hand to face activity, head turns to left, opened eyes and a high level of activity. While the findings controlled for the effects of maternal smoking and other potential co-variates, in one of the studies, poorer operant learning in both a 'head-turning and a sucking paradigm' for only those infants whose mothers were both heavy drinkers and heavy smokers was found. At eight months of age, the children in the second study exhibited small decrements in mental and motor developments measured with the Bayley Scales of Infant Development, even after statistical adjustment for other relevant co-variates.

An early study by Jones and colleagues (1973) found that eight unrelated children from three different ethnic groups, all born to alcoholic mothers, exhibited lower than average intellectual performance. In a second follow-up study, which examined thirteen children at seven years of age belonging to a group of alcoholic women, Jones and colleagues (1974) found that children experienced deficits in intellectual performance, usually accompanied by diminished head circumference. The frequency of impaired intellectual performance was greater at the seven-year evaluation than at the four-year one; however, researchers were not able to ascertain the impact of the child's home environment. Of the twelve children where adequate information was available, the six who had lived with their mothers had a lower mean IQ at seven years of age (73) than the six who had spent some time living with relatives or in foster homes (IQ 84). However, the difference is not statistically significant.

Ernhart and colleagues (1995) found that, of eight infants who met the diagnostic criteria for FAS and were followed through the pre-school years with blinded assessment protocol, seven had no impairment in cognitive and language development when compared with their peers and were of average size. All eight children, as well as controls, had mothers who were disadvantaged and had relatively low verbal skills. While Ernhart and colleagues acknowledge several methodological weaknesses in their study (e.g., small sample group, other adverse effects of fetal alcohol exposure that were not measured), as well as the possibility of later-emerging impairments in more complex tasks for affected individuals, they suggest that their findings are a positive indication that not all children who present with FAS at birth will necessarily experience adverse outcomes.

Postnatal environment has been identified as influencing the development of affected infants and young children (Stratton, Howe et al., 1996; Weinberg, 1997; West and Prinz, 1987). Roberts and Nanson found that studies, which examined the background of alcohol-affected children generally, revealed a high degree of family upheaval that could worsen the child's development (2000; Abkarian, 1992). Family upheaval is often marked by lack of consistent child care taking, healthy and secure attachments, and environmental stability (Weinberg, 1997; O'Connor, Sigman and Kasari, 1993). Children who live in alcoholic families are often at risk of physical and emotional neglect and may be exposed to greater rates of family violence and abuse (Weinberg, 1997; Kumpfer and Bays, 1995; Stratton, Howe et al., 1996). Alcohol-affected children living in these environments may suffer from increased behavioural problems, such as reactive attachment disorder, or the behavioural effects of stress, so that it can be difficult to differentiate one behavioural effect from another (Stratton, Howe et al., 1996). These children may also be at greater risk of suffering from injury, poisoning and medical hospitalization (Weinberg, 1997; Bijur, Kuzon, Overpeck and Scheidt, 1992). It should be pointed out, however, that these risk factors do not occur in every family where parental alcohol abuse is a factor and, when they do occur, they are most often linked to other psycho-social stressors, such as poverty, unemployment and mental illness.

Roberts and Nanson (2000) point out that early instability in the child's living situation may be the result of stress placed on care givers and the child due to medical complications and the need for repeated hospitalization and consequent separation from parents during infancy (Niccols, 1994). This may be particularly true for Aboriginal children who must travel to urban centres for medical treatment and, in some cases, may result in children being removed from the care of their mothers/care givers for extended periods of time over several years. This may also result in children being taken into foster care because the needed medical services are not readily available in home communities.

Children identified as having FAS/ARBEs are often children living in foster care homes. In a study in Saskatchewan, Habbick and colleagues (1996) found only 25.6% of FAS patients (n=53/207) were living with their biological parents. One-hundred and forty-nine (72%) had been in foster care at some time and many experienced multiple-placements throughout their childhood. An extreme example of multiple-placement, although not necessarily uncommon, was reported by Tait (2000a; 2003). In this example, a young Aboriginal woman, who had been diagnosed with FAS as a child, reported being placed in twenty different foster care homes before she reached the age of eighteen. This raises the issue of the impact of multiple-placement on affected persons and whether affected persons are more vulnerable to multiple-placement. Habbick and colleagues found that the mean length of time in care for the 112 cases they had detailed information on was approximately five years. They found that eighty-six per cent (178) of the sample group were Aboriginal. Because Aboriginal children are already over-represented in foster care systems in Canada, being Aboriginal and affected by in-utero alcohol exposure may be confounding risk factors for ending up in foster care, specifically in multiple-placements. Research suggests that when foster care or adoption is required, these alternative placements need to be prolonged rather than brief stays (Roberts and Nanson, 2000). Roberts and Nanson write:

> Adoptive and foster families can be greatly challenged by these children and they find support groups to be helpful for information exchange and dealing with emotions (Weiner and Morse, 1994). It would be beneficial to invest funds into in-home care for the child and respite care for families (LaDue et.al., 1992). Information and training for foster and adoptive families on how to promote the development of alcohol-affected children has been recommended as a source of support, as has training for adoption workers and attorneys on issues relating to parental substance abuse (Olson and Burgess, 1997). Unfortunately, none of these interventions has been empirically evaluated (2000:67).

Ernst and colleagues report similar findings in the *Seattle Birth to Three Program*. At a three-year follow-up, a significant number of the children were in some form of foster placement, either at the mother's request or because of child welfare concerns (Ernst et al., 1999 in Roberts and Nanson, 2000). Studies have found that some parents willingly place their children in foster care because they feel their substance abuse will have a negative impact on the child's development (Roberts and Nanson, 2000; Tait, 2003). Tait found that, in Manitoba, biological relatives who foster children in their extended family are given half the financial compensation given to non-relative foster families. This penalizes those families who are likely to be in the best position to offer family continuity and reinforcement of cultural identity for the child (Tait, 2003).

Roberts and Nanson (2000) report that specialized infant development or therapeutic child care programs may promote the desired stability. They write:

> In some cases these programs operate out of the home and work with at-risk parents and children or those who have experienced challenges generally. These programs may be adjusted to better handle the needs of children affected by prenatal substance use and their caregivers. Issues addressed by these programs include coming to terms with the diagnosis, making best use of services, increasing parental knowledge of pertinent factors in the overall growth and development of their child, and learning skills that promote the child's growth (Niccols 1994) (Roberts and Nanson, 2000:64).

Roberts and Nanson (2000) add that these programs often need to work with care givers on methods to calm the child and to address failure to thrive. Providing this type and range of service for Aboriginal people living in rural and remote areas is, however, met with several challenges, including developing programming that is culturally sensitive to the needs of the families and identifying and training local service providers to implement the goals of the program. Programming for Métis, Inuit and First Nations will not necessarily be the same, as the needs of their communities may differ and culturally sensitive programming should reflect local beliefs and customs. The needs of urban Aboriginal communities and communities with multiple Aboriginal groups will also require special consideration because of cultural and social diversity. The communities who face the biggest challenges are those where alcohol abuse and other health and social problems are endemic. Special consideration by Aboriginal leaders and their health and social service agencies and organizations (e.g., Aboriginal Nurses Association, Aboriginal Physician Association) on how best to assist and support these communities is needed. Financial resources to design programming that will improve the current and long-term situation of these communities in a culturally sensitive manner is central to this process. Provincial and federal governments must be willing to channel funding for Aboriginal groups, including those, such as Métis, non-status Indians and urban Aboriginal people, whose health care falls under mainstream umbrella funding.

Few studies, which examine the first two years of life of alcohol-affected children, exist and, in many cases, there has been no effect demonstrated, particularly in children without the full syndrome (Stratton, Howe et al., 1996; Streissguth, Barr, Martin and Harmon, 1980). During the pre-school period (2.5 to 6 years of age), there are relatively few studies of prospectively followed alcohol-exposed children. Stratton and colleagues (1996) point out that those that have been completed differ in their findings across most areas studied, including cognition (Greene, Ernhart, Ager, Sokol, Martier et al., 1991; Streissguth et al., 1989), attention (Boyd, Ernhart, Greene, Sokol and Martier, 1991; Brown, Coles, Smith, Plazman, Silverstein et al., 1991; Streissguth, Martin, Barr, Sandman, Kirchner et al., 1984) and behaviour (Brown, Coles, Smith, Plazman, Silverstein et al., 1991; Landesman-Dwyer and Ragozin, 1981; Morrow-Tlucak and Ernhart, 1987). Empirical studies on effective interventions in pre-school child care do not currently exist; however, experts commonly recommend that child care programs have a low staff-child ratio, follow structured routines and regulate the amount of stimulation received by the child (Roberts and Nanson, 2000). Experts also suggest that this type of training and extra support is beneficial for child care providers of children with FAS (Roberts and Nanson, 2000; Olson and Burgess, 1997).

During the pre-school period, cognitive deficits are observed frequently, as is attention-deficit hyper-activity disorder (ADHD) (Stratton, Howe et al., 1996; Conry, 1990; Nanson and Hiscock, 1990). Language dysfunction, perceptual problems and behavioural disturbance are also reported (Stratton, Howe et al., 1996; Morse, 1991). Roberts and Nanson (2000) suggest that program themes for older pre-school alcohol or drug-affected children could include attachment security, dealing with transitions, expressing feelings and needs, verbal self-regulation, nutritional, medical and developmental assessment and appropriate therapy.

Roberts and Nanson (2000) suggest that programs that focus on the family, particularly the mother and child, are important in addressing the needs of infants and young children. Substance abuse treatment is of particular importance for the biological mother, and father, if necessary. Currently in Canada, very few treatment centres are able to accommodate families and/or mothers with newborns. However, Roberts and Nanson argue that family-centred treatment can lead to increased stability in the home and more positive outcomes for the child. A model, which has been identified by experts as having great potential, is a comprehensive, one-stop model that addresses the treatment needs of the parent(s), as well as the developmental needs of the child. This model has been tried in Toronto since 1995. Robert and Nanson write:

> Breaking the Cycle (BTC) program in Toronto ... offer[s] comprehensive services through a single-access venue in which mothers and children can receive addiction, health, developmental and parenting services using an integrated, transdisciplinary approach. An evaluation of Breaking the Cycle's first 2½ years of operation indicated that participation in BTC had contributed to healthier birth outcomes, better maternal health ratings, fewer health concerns, fewer parenting breakdowns resulting in separation of children from their mothers, and fewer maternal developmental concerns. Because of their involvement at BTC, young children did not, at the point of evaluation, experience the developmental lags often reported in the literature for those who have been substance-exposed (Paquet, 1998) (2000:65).

Parenting education has been identified as an important area of support for biological mothers and fathers who are parenting an affected child (Leslie and Roberts, 2001; Van Bibber, 1997). Parents, for various reasons, can lack child care skills and parenting support to help them raise their children, particularly when caring for an affected child who has special needs. Parenting education can be combined with other programming, including substance abuse treatment; however, clinical reports suggest that combining substance abuse treatment with parenting information too early in treatment or in an unintegrated way may distract the mother from her own recovery (Roberts and Nanson, 2000; Olson and Burgess, 1997).

Some Aboriginal parents, because of disrupted childhoods in which they experienced a range of problems, often including physical, sexual and/or emotional abuse, may bring relatively few personal resources to a parenting role. If this is not addressed by these parents and by the services mandated to assist them, affected children may be at risk of neglect, abuse and failure to thrive (Streissguth and LaDue, 1985; Stratton, Howe et al., 1996). Olson and colleagues suggest a number of guidelines in working with substance-using or alcohol-affected parents of children with FAS or ARBEs. They include: understanding that parents may be less skilled than they appear; keeping parenting advice concrete; setting up structured parental support; having modest expectations about what the parents can do on their own; referring the parents for needed treatment; and assisting agencies being sensitive to their needs (Olson et al., 1992 in Roberts and Nanson, 2000).

Leslie and Roberts add that assisting parents in finding respite care through agencies or through parent support groups can help "reduce parental stress, and provides opportunities for the child to interact with other children and engage in new experiences in stable environments" (2001:43).

Programs that target Aboriginal parents should consider integrating local traditional care giving roles of extended family members and incorporate, where possible, these individuals into program development to support biological parents. This will be more difficult in urban communities, where parents may not have family members living near them. In this case, a single service provider who builds a trusting relationship with the family may play a central role and can assist in connecting the family to parent

Chapter 10

and community support groups. Some First Nations communities have developed traditional parenting programs, which work as prevention and support services for families at risk of having a child with FAS/ARBEs or who already are parenting an affected child (Van Bibber, 1997).

An advocacy model, originally developed in Seattle, Washington (Ernst et al., 1999), has been modified to several sites in Manitoba, including sites targeting Aboriginal women in both urban and rural settings. The *Stop-FAS* programs address the range of problems 'high risk' women and their offspring face by giving long-term (three-year) support to women who are at risk of having children affected by alcohol exposure during pregnancy (Tait, 2000a). Tait writes:

> The difference between this model and other prevention strategies is that it focuses on the well-being of the mother and her children, rather than just on that of the children. As a result, even if the children are removed from the care of their mother, she remains in the program. The program takes a hands-on approach to helping women access the services they need, and unlike other programs, the woman, rather than the service provider, determines what those needs are (2000a:19).

In the *Stop-FAS* programs, women are supported in their efforts to meet the needs of their children and, where possible, other family members are encouraged to participate in supporting the mother and her child. Although the programs are relatively new, positive outcomes have been reported by women who are enrolled and by service providers who provide front-line services to 'high risk' women (Tait, 2000a). The Aboriginal Health and Wellness Centre in Winnipeg, Manitoba, operates a *Stop-FAS* program, which is a modified version of the original model designed in Seattle. The program targets a diverse group of urban Aboriginal women who come from differing Nations and social backgrounds (e.g., from urban and rural communities) and who experience a wide range of health and social problems. The program is based on a holistic approach, which incorporates traditional knowledge and practices into service delivery, and provides a prevention/education component extended to the larger Aboriginal community in Winnipeg. An important aspect of this program is that it reinforces Aboriginal identity for the women in the program. Many of the women, for various reasons, including having attended residential schools, being raised in non-Aboriginal foster and adoptive homes and experiencing on-going racism, have very limited knowledge of their culture or have become alienated from their Aboriginal identity. Those who operate the *Stop-FAS* program have found that the reintroduction and reinforcement of Aboriginal identity has positively influenced women's desire to address their addiction needs, build healthy support networks and parent their children. Central to this process for the women is having the program located in an Aboriginal-run health and wellness centre and all of the staff are Aboriginal people.

Although there are no published studies demonstrating the benefits of either FAS-specific programming or general early educational intervention for young children with FAS and related conditions, early education has been shown to be beneficial for children with other developmental conditions, such as Down syndrome, as well as those living in poverty (Roberts and Nanson, 2000). American pre-school programs for children with known prenatal substance exposure have identified self-contained classrooms, careful teaching strategies, high staff-to-student ratios, frequent participation by speech and language specialists, adaptive physical educators, school social workers, psychologists, nurses and a physician as important components for these programs (Roberts and Nanson, 2000). A second support is the inclusion of affected preschool children in classes with non-exposed peers, using strong professional support and low staff-child ratios (Olson and Burgess, 1997 in Roberts and Nanson, 2000).

Some authors suggest that the use of clear expectations and reinforcement of appropriate responses guide the pre-school education learning process when dealing with impulsivity, which is common with affected children (Phelps and Grabowski, 1992 in Roberts and Nanson, 2000). The use of medication, such as Ritalin to treat hyper-activity of children with FAS, has proven effective in some cases and counter-productive in others (Streissguth and Giunta, 1988 in Roberts and Nanson, 2000).

'Revised best practices'

Multi-Disciplinary Teams

1. There is a consensus among experts to support the use of a professional, multi-disciplinary team to address the range of complex health needs of affected children. The multi-disciplinary team should be designed to work at the various levels of health care delivery, including team members, such as traditional Aboriginal practitioners and local health, education and social service providers, acting as front-line team members who coordinate their efforts with team members in hospital and clinical settings.

Environmental Supports

2. There is some evidence to suggest that a longer-term, stable living environment contributes to more positive outcomes for children affected by alcohol in-utero. This may be facilitated by family-centred substance abuse treatment, respite care, other support services and FAS-specific information and training for birth, foster and adoptive parents. Programs must be culturally-sensitive to the target group and specific attention must be given to the diversity of identities found among First Nations, Métis and Inuit populations. Biological relatives must be given the same financial support for fostering children in their extended family as non-relative foster parents and emphasis must be placed on fostering children within the community or in nearby locations where family and community members can maintain a relationship with the child.

3. There is a consensus among experts indicating that child care programs for children affected by prenatal alcohol exposure employing a low staff-child ratio, following structured routines and regulating the amount of stimulation received by the child may be more effective. Training of local child care workers to be knowledgeable and sensitive to the needs of children with FAS/ARBEs and to those of their family will greatly enhance this process. These workers should be included in the team of traditional, biomedical, education and social service professionals who are mandated to address the needs of affected children.

Developmental Needs

4. There is some evidence that services offering a single point of access, combining services for the mother with attention to the developmental needs of the child, improve outcomes for the child. These services could be incorporated into Aboriginal-run wellness and healing centres, Head

Chapter 10

Start Programs, Friendship Centres, outreach centres or expanded addiction treatment services. Coordination of various service providers, whether under one umbrella agency or within a local community context, is central to improving service access for mothers and their children.

5. There is some evidence from animal studies and studies of children experiencing developmental delay due to other causes suggesting that early educational interventions may contribute to improved outcomes for children affected by prenatal alcohol use, at least in the short term. Central to early educational interventions must be support of parents and their knowledge about the strengths and interests of their children and the empowerment of parents through culturally sensitive information on child development.

Later Childhood

Later childhood, the beginning of school age (usually 6 years of age) to early adolescence (13 years), has been the focus of a number of FAS/ARBEs research studies, which sought to identify age-related manifestations and appropriate interventions. Parent advocacy groups have also played a central role in the identification of gaps in service delivery and barriers that prevent adequate support for affected children and their families. Roberts and Nanson (2000), with the assistance of the National Steering Committee, identified four 'best practices' relating to later childhood:

'Best practices'

1. While there is no evidence to date, there is a consensus among experts that all persons parenting an affected child benefit from on-going support and advocacy for various medical, educational and psycho-social issues that arise with children prenatally exposed to alcohol and other substances.

2. There is no evidence to date, but there is a consensus among experts that children with FAS and related effects benefit from the development of an individualized education plan (IEP) tailored to meet the multiple cognitive, academic and psycho-social needs of these children, involving a range of collaborating professionals.

3. To date, there is no evidence on effective educational environments; however, there is a consensus among experts that the learning environment should be generally adjusted for children with FAS and related effects by establishing: a calm and quiet environment with structure, routine and few distractions; low-enrolment classrooms, resource rooms or self-contained classroom placement; defined specific work and play areas; and work spaces that are clear and routines that vary little from day to day. Other elements contributing to a suitable environment include: use of explicit instructions and visual aids to reinforce class rules and activities; repetition, hands-on learning; modelling of desired behaviours; and a caring teacher.

4. While there is no evidence on effective educational practices to date, there is a consensus among experts that considerations for school content should generally involve an individualized curriculum with a focus on functional skills for independent living (such as problem-solving, arithmetic,

social interacting and decision-making); developing realistic expectations of the child; behaviour management strategies that promise independence; adaptive living, social and communications skills; and role playing to teach logical consequences and appropriate behaviour.

Research Studies

A number of research studies examine the period of later childhood, including some of the first follow-up studies of diagnosed infants and young children. An early study by Streissguth and colleagues (1985) involved a ten-year follow-up of eleven patients who were the first to be diagnosed as having FAS. Two of the thirteen patients were deceased and one could not be located. Of the eight remaining, none had normal intellectual functioning (four mildly and four seriously handicapped). While the postnatal environment was difficult to assess, seven of the children during the first two years of their lives had several major disruptions in their home environments. Improvements in social and emotional development were noted in patients whose home environment eventually became stable. Three of the children had mothers who died of alcohol-related causes less than six years after their birth, which may suggest that biological factors associated with terminal stages of alcoholism contributed to the severe handicap (Streissguth et al., 1985).

A Saskatchewan study examined attention-deficits in sixty children aged five to twelve years of age who fell into three categories: normal, FAS/FAE and attention-deficit disorder (ADD). Equal numbers of children (n=20) in each category were recruited for the study and were divided into two age categories, younger and older, which were used as independent variables (Nanson and Hiscock, 1990). The majority of children with FAS/FAE had been diagnosed early in life, and all but two had lived in middle class adoptive or foster homes since early childhood. The other two subjects lived with biological parents who had recovered from alcoholism. The majority of the FAS/FAE children were Aboriginal. Ten were in regular classrooms, ranging from grades 1 to 6 and ten were in specialized classes. The authors do not state whether any of the children in the categories, normal and ADD, were Aboriginal. Nanson and Hiscock used several measures to assess the children's behaviour and parents were asked to fill out a questionnaire about their child.

Children with FAS/FAE were significantly more delayed in their intellectual development than children in either of the two other groups. Several of the FAS/FAE children also appeared to have experienced a decline in IQs significantly below their previous IQ of 75 or greater (Nanson and Hiscock, 1990). Characteristics, such as hyper-activity, inattention and social behaviour, were very similar in the FAS/FAE and ADD groups, a finding supported by parental rating. This suggests that, although children with FAS/FAE may be significantly more impaired intellectually than children with classical ADD, the attentional problems of both groups are similar. Nanson and Hiscock conclude:

> Two separate factors may interact to produce the problems with hyperactivity and attention in FAS/FAE. These are the CNS insult caused by the prenatal alcohol exposure, and the postnatal environmental disruptions resulting from the alcoholic parents' lifestyle. Although children who had experienced multiple caregiving arrangements were excluded from this study, the majority of subjects had experienced at least one move in

early childhood. Further research is needed to determine whether the treatment regimes designed to ameliorate attention problems and to facilitate learning in ADD children may also benefit children with FAS/FAE (1990:660).

Coles and colleagues (1997) examined behavioural deficits in four groups of low-income African-American children attending an inner city teaching hospital in Atlanta, Georgia. Prenatal alcohol-exposed children were classified as either dysmorphic (FAS/FAE) or nondysmorphic. Children whose mothers did not use alcohol in pregnancy were classified as controls and children diagnosed with attention deficit hyper-activity disorder (ADHD) made up the fourth group. Coles and colleagues found that, in general, ADHD children are best identified by behaviour checklists and measures of the ability to focus and sustain attention. Children with FAS appeared to have deficits in visual/spatial skills, encoding information, and flexibility in problem-solving. Coles and colleagues suggest that the fact that the majority of the FAS children in their study had not experienced highly disorganized environments or multiple custody arrangements may account somewhat for the lack of ADHD in this group. They write:

> This explanation would imply either that the behaviours attributed to ADHD in children with FAS result from environmental effects (e.g., attachment disorder, anxiety, posttraumatic stress disorder, socialization deficits associated with neglect), or that there is some differences in 'degree' of FAS with only the more 'severe' FAS cases exhibiting externalizing behaviours associated with ADHD. Both of these possibilities should be explored further (Coles, Platzman et al., 1997:159).

These findings have implications for pharmaceutical treatments, such as Ritalin. ADHD-diagnosed children, for example, were found to benefit from Ritalin in helping them to focus attention appropriately. When their attention was focused, they could perform relatively well on the encoding dimension on short-term memory and learning. Children with FAS/FAE were able to focus and maintain their attention quite well, but were unable to encode the information they attended to or to use new information meaningfully in problem solving (Coles, Platzman et al., 1997). Coles and colleagues suggest that this may indicate that ADHD and FAS/FAE children require different medication regimes and educational interventions to address their differing problems. Roberts and Nanson (2000) point out that, while many children with FAS are given stimulant medication to address ADHD, there are only a handful of studies that have assessed the efficacy of this type of treatment.

A study by Oesterheld and colleagues (1998) found that, after two groups of Aboriginal children, one with ADHD and one with FAS, had been treated with Ritalin, teachers recorded improved ratings of hyper-active behaviour. Other problems, such as daydreaming and inattention, continued unchanged for the four children with FAS while taking the medication (Oesterheld et al., 1998 in Roberts and Nanson, 2000). Studies looking at the benefits of stimulant medication have typically employed very small sample sizes and, therefore, it is difficult to glean any conclusive evidence from their findings (Roberts and Nanson, 2000).

A study of neuro-psychological deficits associated with FAS/FAE among a population of diagnosed children in an isolated, economically depressed, Aboriginal community was conducted by Conry (1990). Nineteen children, aged 6 to 18, participated in the study. Nine boys and four girls were diagnosed with

Chapter 10

FAS and three boys and three girls in the sample group were diagnosed with FAE. A control group was selected from children living in the community. A battery of tests were administered to the children, including some selected for their appropriateness to the "learning styles of Native Indian children" (Conry, 1990:651). Conry points out that the FAS/normal comparison was of particular importance in this community in gauging the extent of alcohol effects, because normative statistics for tests developed in the United States may have limited applicability in the Canadian and Aboriginal context. She adds:

> The concept of impaired functioning is complicated in this study, due to the cultural isolation of the native population examined and the effect that isolation might have on the development [of] cognitive, and particularly verbal, abilities. Some of the children had never left the reserve, even to visit the nearest town, a 20-minute drive away (Conry, 1990:652).

Conry (1990) found an 'unexpected' severity of intellectual deficit among FAS/FAE children. Thirteen of the nineteen affected children (68%) had IQs in the delayed intellectual development range (IQ<70) and four of these (21%) had IQs<55. The range of IQs for the FAS/FAE children was 40 to 101 and, for the case controls, 74 to 101. Conry notes that the mean for the normal controls was below 100, the average population value. She suggests that the low IQ range in affected children may reflect an interaction between brain damage and educational deprivation; however, she provides no details about the educational situation in the community.

Conry (1990) also points out that Aboriginal children, generally, have been shown to have an eight to nineteen point discrepancy between verbal and performance IQ scores, with performance scores in the average range and verbal scores in the low range. This has been attributed to differential exposure to and opportunity to learn the content of verbal measures, as well as, a culturally influenced learning style favouring the development of visual and perceptual abilities.

In conclusion, Conry suggests that children with FAE may go undetected in an environment where factors, such as isolation and deprived socio-economic circumstances, play a role. She writes:

> When a child's background is disadvantaged with respect to developing readiness for school learning, school difficulties are commonly attributed to that background. These results indicate that performance on standardized instruments conventionally used to assess school aptitude may not differentiate a group of FAE children from others for whom the cultural deprivation hypothesis also holds—in this case, the matched controls (Conry, 1990:655).

The problems here, Conry (1990) adds, are the neurological causes of learning problems caused by FAE may have different prognostic and remedial implications as the children develop and progress through school. While Conry's point is important, what is even more troublesome is that, in this context, all the Aboriginal children living in this environment are not receiving adequate education. It is difficult to imagine prioritizing a sub-group of these children for specialized educational services, when what appears to be needed are improved educational programs and social services for *all* children in the community, including specialized education services.

Chapter 10

Roberts and Nanson (2000) found no empirical studies that provided conclusive information on effective educational interventions. However, they did find that a number of researchers, parents and educators had "developed strategies for adjusting the learning environment and the content" (2000:72). Roberts and Nanson state that it is generally recommended that a range of professionals (e.g., educators, speech and language therapists, occupational therapists and educational psychologists) participate in developing and monitoring a thorough psycho-educational assessment leading to a tailored individualized education plan (IEP) that would address the multiple cognitive, academic and psycho-social needs of these children (2000; Phelps and Grabowski, 1992; Phelps, 1995; Stratton, Howe et al., 1996).

Roberts and Nanson (2000) point out that a diagnosis of FAS by itself would not qualify someone for IEP coverage in Canada; however, the benefit of such help in coordinating these various service providers, along with pediatricians, psychologists and social workers who may be involved, would be of great benefit for children and their families.

In relation to the learning environment, Roberts and Nanson (2000) found the following were recommended as being beneficial to affected children: a calm and quiet environment; maximizing structure and routine with low enrolment classrooms; resource rooms or self-contained classroom placement; defined specific work and play areas; clear work spaces free of distractions; the placement of materials not in use and out of sight; few distractions; the establishment of routines that vary little from day to day; the provision of explicit instructions; the use of visual aids to reinforce class rules and activities; repetition and modelling of desired behaviours; and a loving teacher.

Educational content recommendations to teach logical consequences and appropriate behaviour were: an individualized curriculum with a focus on functional skills for independent living (such as problem-solving, arithmetic, social interaction and decision-making); the development of realistic expectations of the child; behaviour management strategies that promote independence; adaptive living; social and communication skills; and the use of role-playing (Roberts and Nanson, 2000). Roberts and Nanson point out that the effectiveness of particular pedagogical strategies and practices is still unknown, as they have not been systematically studied with alcohol-effected children.

Resource Manuals for Care Givers and Educators

Several resource manuals and videos targeting families caring for children affected by FAS/ARBEs and educators and other service providers who are involved with children were reviewed for this report (Normand and Rutman, 1996; Rutman and Normand, 1996; Van Bibber, 1997; Yellowknife Association of Community Living, n.d.; Society of Special Needs Adoptive Parents, 1994; Lasser, 1999). These manuals identify a number of 'best practices' derived from the experience and wisdom of parents, educators and service providers who care for and work with affected children. With the exception of the resource community-based manual, *It Takes A Community* (Van Bibber, 1997), none of the parental and educator manuals reviewed for this report specifically target Aboriginal audiences, although Aboriginal children, mothers and families are clearly one of the targeted groups in the manuals.

In general, the manuals identify the following issues as being important for meeting the needs of affected children and their care givers. The first issue is early identification, which can greatly facilitate the creation of specialized programming and services for affected children. Without a diagnosis, affected children

Chapter 10

may be misdiagnosed and receive inappropriate treatment, or be labelled as 'problem children.' Parents can also be labelled as 'bad' parents because of their child's behavioural problems. Early identification allows for more effective medical and educational interventions. Also, problems within the family can be reduced through early education and altering of the environment in which the child lives (Leslie and Roberts, 2001). Leslie and Roberts point out that identification and diagnosis may not necessarily result in access to services, as services are generally tied to the developmental quotient (DQ) or IQ of the child. Some children affected by alcohol may be excluded from certain supports because their scores are above those that distinguish children in the 'normal' range from those who are 'disabled.'

In some instances, care givers, social workers and other service providers may feel that a child is alcohol-affected but there is not enough evidence (e.g., confirmation of maternal alcohol exposure cannot be made) for a physician to make a diagnosis (Rutman and Normand, 1996). This can cause a great deal of frustration for care givers:

> The school doesn't see (the child) as a serious problem. So trying to get an assessment, she's not a priority for them whatsoever. I believe that this child must be fetal alcohol-affected. We had her seen by a pediatrician. He'd like to say that, but he can't quite. We're going to go back to him again. The foster parents are totally frustrated. They're running out of ideas to help her ... (The foster mother) asks, "Why can't they give us a diagnosis? Then the school will help us." There's our frustration. I told her, "I doubt we'll ever get a diagnosis" ... So now what's happened to the child, she's diagnosed as "lazy" at school (cited in Rutman and Normand, 1996:14).

Specialized services for children may also be withheld if the child is not acting in disruptive ways that force social service providers and educators to intervene: "But it is frustrating. These children have a different kind of handicap—they're not going to get services. So they almost have to act out at school to notice them. Some kids don't have behaviour problems" (cited in Rutman and Normand, 1996:15).

Identification of children who are alcohol-affected and require specialized services involves a complex process that requires the input of various health care practitioners and, in many cases, the involvement of ministries of social services. With the high percentage of Aboriginal children in foster care systems across Canada and a commonly held association between alcohol abuse, Aboriginal people and FAS/ARBEs, it is likely many of these children, particularly if they have behavioural and/or academic problems, will be informally labelled as alcohol-affected prior to a medical assessment or, in some instances, even after diagnosticians have ruled out FAS/ARBEs. While some unassessed children may be alcohol-affected, a diagnosis should not be the determining factor as to whether a child, alcohol-affected or not, receives support and specialized programming to address their behavioural and/or academic problems. With the myriad of problems that can be experienced by children who eventually end up in foster care, such as family disruptions, multiple placement, physical and sexual abuse and neglect, behavioural and/or academic problems can be expected. Special consideration for these children within the school system, in general, is needed. Care givers, while right in pursuing assessments, should not be forced to have a diagnosis before services are offered to their children.

Chapter 10

Furthermore, FAS/ARBEs researchers have pointed out that a range of behavioural and academic problems can exist for affected children and, therefore, specialized services are best delivered according to the specific needs of the child (Streissguth and Kanter, 1997; Streissguth, 1997; Abel, 1998a). Rutman and Normand point out that care givers have a "unique and unsurpassed knowledge of that child's strengths, challenges and need" (1996:13) and are clearly in the best position to know what types of services will work or not work with their child. Teachers are also in a unique position to interact with and observe the child (Lasser, 1999) and may have years of experience dealing with children who have a range of behavioural, academic and medical problems, which places these teachers in a key position to work with care givers to design appropriate programming. However, this requires a financial and human resource commitment by governments to schools, so that they can work efficiently with care givers to best meet the needs of children with behavioural and academic problems, including alcohol-affected children.

Respite care for parents was an important concern expressed in the manuals, as children affected by in-utero alcohol exposure require constant supervision. However, respite care may not be available for biological and adoptive families, if other family members and friends are unavailable or unwilling to assist in caring for the child, and if the family cannot afford or find care givers who are willing to look after the child. Generally, biological and adoptive parents do not qualify for government subsidies to cover the costs of respite care. However, even though foster families may be able to access some financial support for respite care, finding appropriate care givers may be very difficult. Some adoptive parents are able to access government support for respite care; however, usually by the time this happens, the stress already placed on the family by having to care for an affected child and insufficient support from social service agencies, in general, results in adoptive parents placing their affected children in foster care (Rutman and Normand, 1996). Normand and Rutman point out that there is a need for a 'pool' of respite workers to be trained to assist families in caring for alcohol-affected children.

The financial costs of raising a child with FAS/ARBEs can place significant burden on the family in relation to medical and dental bills, cost of assessments, tutoring, respite and psycho-therapy. These are just some of the associated costs for the family. A particular problem for birth and adoptive families is that they do not receive the same level of financial assistance from the ministries of social services that foster parents receive for their children with FAS/ARBEs. For example, orthodontic bills and support for respite care are paid for by the ministries when children are in foster care; however, if the children live with their biological or adoptive parents, these costs are the responsibility of the family. This may result in poor families placing their affected child into care because they cannot carry the extra financial burden required to meet the needs of their child, despite their ability to provide a stable and loving home environment.

Children with FAS/ARBEs may be at increased risk of remaining in foster care for their entire childhood. Their chances for adoption are decreased, partially by foster parents being reluctant to adopt affected children they foster because they will lose government financial support after the adoption is finalized (Tait, 2003). Even though foster parents may want to make an alcohol-affected child a permanent member of their family, the increased financial burden of adoption can dissuade some care givers. This effectively makes a child with FAS/ARBEs vulnerable to being removed at any time by social services from the homes of care givers, which they have grown attached to and who have grown attached to them.

Chapter 10

Furthermore, foster parents have no legal rights in preventing the children from being removed from their custody by social services; therefore, by not adopting the child, the foster parents are vulnerable to having the child taken from their care.

Rutman and Normand (1996) found that the number of parents willing to adopt alcohol-affected children has dropped in British Columbia over the past few years. They attribute this to the efforts of the Ministry of Social Services to convey the 'realities' of parenting children with FAS/ARBEs. What this means in relation to Aboriginal children in foster care is unknown, but several questions are raised by this decrease. First, are fewer alcohol-affected Aboriginal children being adopted because of their illness? If so, what are the reasons for this decrease? For example, are some Aboriginal families refusing to adopt alcohol-affected children and/or is the Ministry of Social Services preventing adoption of alcohol-affected children by some Aboriginal families because they feel these families are ill-equipped to parent an affected child? Are alcohol-affected Aboriginal children more vulnerable to multiple foster placements and to being placed in foster care by adoptive parents than other fostered children? Are Aboriginal families, who want to adopt an alcohol-affected Aboriginal child, disadvantaged in their efforts because of issues such as poverty, because they live in an isolated community and/or because they are a single parent?

Foster parents may feel vulnerable to the power of social services on a number of levels, as expressed by one community-based social worker who works closely with foster families:

> Ninety percent of foster parents are petrified of MSS [Ministry of Social Services]. They're afraid if they ask for help they are going to be seen as bad foster parents; they're afraid if they ask for respite they are going to be seen as inefficient. If the child suffers an accident, (they're afraid) they're going to be seen as not able to supervise. If they ask for more resources, that they're greedy. They share things with me that they wouldn't dream of sharing with social workers. They're afraid. I find that extremely sad (Rutman and Normand, 1996:12).

This vulnerability may be even more exaggerated for Aboriginal foster families who could also be confronted with racism and misunderstanding of their cultural beliefs and practices (e.g., traditional parenting styles) by social workers, teachers, and health care practitioners. These families may also be under greater surveillance and scrutiny than non-Aboriginal families, simply because they are Aboriginal.

Rutman and Normand (1996) found that in British Columbia, a chronic shortage of appropriate foster care resources was reported by social service workers. This shortage could potentially have devastating consequences for children, including children with FAS/ARBEs, which was expressed by a social worker in their study:

> (W)e have so many children who are desperately waiting for a home. And it really affects the children. So when you have behaviour problems, you don't know whether it's because of FAS/E, or because they're so upset that they don't have a family ... It must be a terrible feeling to be waiting and waiting for a home (Rutman and Normand, 1996:23).

Chapter 10

In Manitoba, Tait (2003) found that a shortage of foster homes meant that some children were being cared for in hotel rooms, with different care givers coming in to supervise the children at various times of the day. This greatly contrasts with the stable home environment with consistent care giving recommended for alcohol-affected children. Rutman and Normand (1996) point out that shortages of foster homes can result in alcohol-affected children being placed with new foster families who are uninformed about the illness, and ill-prepared to deal with challenges of parenting an affected child.

The resource manuals, reviewed for this report, stressed the importance of care givers advocating for their children. For example, a guide for parents developed by the Society of Special Needs Adoptive Parents (SNAP) includes the following advice for parents:

> The ability to work effectively with schools, doctors, and support workers may be challenging but is critical. As a parent, you are likely the best advocate for your own child. Expand your advocacy skills. Look for advocacy resources and workshops in your own community, and check your local library for books on self-advocacy (1999:25).

Advocacy involves care givers educating human service professionals who may be unfamiliar with FAS/ARBEs. Normand and Rutman (1996) found that advocacy seems to begin or to be most concerned with the school system and, depending on the awareness of the school and teachers about FAS/ARBEs, parents could be faced with several challenges in having the special needs of their child met. Teaching and supervising FAS/ARBE children at school can place a great deal of burden on teachers and teacher's aides in schools where there are inadequate financial and human resources to provide the extra supervision and attention required. Therefore, in some instances, advocacy by parents, teachers and school officials for increased government resources for children with FAS/ARBEs may be needed.

Parent support groups were identified as important for care givers of alcohol-affected children. Support groups can be FAS/ARBE-specific or can be more generalized support groups for care givers of disabled children. The sharing of information is an important component of the group, as is the general support of having contact with others who are living in similar situations (Normand and Rutman, 1996). Parent support can also be found at different internet sites and some provinces have telephone support services for care givers of alcohol-affected children (Society of Special Needs Adoptive Parents, 1994).

The resource manuals identify several areas of importance for parenting and educating alcohol-affected children. These generally include: effective communication, described as offering simple direction to the child, tasks being broken down into small steps and the teaching of each step being accomplished through repetition and concrete reward; consequence and positive feedback, described as creating structure in expectations and consequences through recognition of the child's unique strengths and weaknesses, and abilities and interests; transitions, described as developing rituals and routines that assist the child in daily activities and, when major changes occur, the establishment of a routine and means by which to lessen the child's anxiety and fears; structure and routine, described as building security into the child's day by maintaining consistency through the creation of a structured environment with a clear and predictable routine; and supervision, described as careful supervision so that the child does not get into trouble or place themselves in dangerous situations (Society of Special Needs Adoptive Parents, 1994; Kleinfeld and Wescott, 1993). These recommendations clearly indicate that a great deal of organization and stability is required within home and school environments to maintain this level of support on a daily basis.

Two issues not covered sufficiently or, in some cases not at all, in the resource manuals are those specifically concerning biological parents who are parenting their affected children and parenting issues related to poverty. Van Bibber (1997) points out that biological parents have the added trauma of guilt, shame, depression and anger as they work through their grief concerning their child's illness. This suggests that biological families, particularly mothers, may need counselling and greater support for an extended period of time. Biological parents may have greater difficulty advocating for services for their children, as service providers may blame them for their child's problems and treat them with a certain level of contempt. For biological parents, who are Aboriginal, this may be more difficult because of racist attitudes held by some service providers. The experience of biological parents, however, may be different in various communities, with some communities, including their service providers, being more supportive of biological parents than others. The size and cohesion of the community may play an important role in how biological parents with alcohol-affected children are treated, as well as the level of awareness service providers have of alcohol abuse and addiction and of FAS/ARBEs. More research is needed to understand the challenges faced by biological families in relation to acquiring services for their child and in maintaining a stable home environment.

An influential book, *Fantastic Antone Succeeds!*, attempts to address the negative stereotypes commonly held about alcohol-affected children (Kleinfeld and Wescott, 1993). The book illustrates that FAS/FAE is not a condition with little hope for the affected person and includes accounts by care givers, affected children and health and social service providers conveying a strong message that positive advances are being made in the lives of alcohol-affected children and that stable home environments with supportive care givers are key to this process. Although they do not address the question of poverty, it is clear from the chapters in this book, as well as the information given in the resource manuals, that parenting an alcohol-affected child is very difficult, if not impossible, if the care giver is living in poverty. Although no studies have examined this issue, when raised with a group of middle-class foster and adoptive parents of alcohol-affected children, Tait (2003) found a general consensus among the group that a certain degree of financial security was needed in order to parent the children, particularly for biological and adoptive parents who were not eligible for financial support from government to offset costs associated with their child's illness.

The group agreed that a single mother on social assistance would require a great deal of support to successfully parent her child, including extra financial support for medical bills, respite care and affordable stable housing. Added to the financial considerations for poor families are the difficulties they may face in advocating for their child, especially if they have low levels of education and feel intimidated by teachers, social workers and health care practitioners. Because many Aboriginal families live below the poverty line, these concerns are of particular importance for Aboriginal people, as they could result in Aboriginal children not being fostered or adopted by members of their extended family, but rather with non-Aboriginal families who have more financial resources. Furthermore, if the social services ministry in the province or territory where the family lives gives less money to foster families who are related to the child, this bias could further penalize biological relatives from being care givers of alcohol-affected children (Tait, 2003).

Chapter 10

Childhood has been identified as an important period in which the special needs of alcohol-affected children must be addressed, in order to prevent or decrease behavioural, academic and social problems during adolescence and adulthood. While this report only covers some of the myriad of issues that can influence what will, or will not, assist alcohol-affected children and their families, it is clear that more needs to be known about the impact of environmental influences, including multiple foster placements, family dysfunction and poverty.

'Revised best practices'

Support and Advocacy

1. While there is no evidence to date, there is a consensus among experts that all persons parenting an affected child benefit from on-going support and advocacy for various medical, educational and psycho-social issues that arise with children prenatally exposed to alcohol and other substances. This is particularly important for biological parents who may face several challenges not faced by adoptive and foster parents, including issues of stigma, poverty and racism.

2. There is no evidence to date, but there is a consensus among experts that children with FAS and related effects benefit from the development of an individualized education plan (IEP), tailored to meet the multiple cognitive, academic and psycho-social needs of these children, involving a range of collaborating professionals. Care givers of the child must be given a central role in this process and schools should be given the needed financial and human resources to meet the requirements of the plan.

3. To date, there is no evidence on effective educational environments; however, there is a consensus among experts that the learning environment should be generally adjusted for children with FAS and related effects by establishing: a calm and quiet environment with structure, routine and few distractions; low enrolment classrooms, resource rooms or self-contained classroom placement; defined specific work and play areas; and work spaces that are clear and routines that vary little from day to day. Other elements contributing to a suitable environment include: use of explicit instructions and visual aids to reinforce class rules and activities; repetition and hands-on learning; modelling of desired behaviours; and a caring teacher. Schools should be given the needed financial and human resources to meet these requirements for alcohol-affected children.

4. While there is no evidence on effective educational practices to date, there is a consensus among experts that consideration for school content should generally involve: an individualized curriculum with a focus on functional skills for independent living (such as problem-solving, arithmetic, social interacting and decision-making); developing realistic expectations of the child; behaviour management strategies that promise independence; adaptive living, social and communications skills; and role playing to teach logical consequences and appropriate behaviour. Schools should be given the needed financial and human resources to meet the requirements of these strategies.

Chapter 10

Adolescence

There are almost no published studies of the effectiveness of interventions for adolescents with FAS/ARBEs. As a result, Roberts and Nanson (2000) suggest that only tentative conclusions can be made about the positive impacts of the various intervention options presently being used. Roberts and Nanson, with the assistance of the National Steering Committee, identified four 'best practices' relating to adolescence:

'Best practice'

1. While there is no evidence to date, there is a consensus among experts that adolescents with FAS and related effects benefit from assistance with basic socialization and communication skills, as well as tailored vocational counselling and employment supervision, money management training, sexuality and birth control education and drug education.

2. There is no evidence to date, but there is a consensus among experts that adolescents with FAS or related effects who become involved with substance abuse treatment, mental health or the correctional system, may benefit from tailored programming.

3. There is no evidence to date, but there is a consensus among experts that families, caring for those with FAS and related effects, benefit from appropriate professional services and mutual support groups that extend over the life span of the person.

4. Although those with intellectual deficits due to prenatal alcohol exposure have not been studied specifically, there is some evidence that cognitive-behavioural family therapies are effective in helping those with intellectual deficits to learn and maintain various basic living skills.

Streissguth and colleagues (1991) examined sixty-one patients (38 males and 23 females), ranging in ages from twelve to forty years, to determine the life-long trajectory of FAS/FAE. Seventy per cent of participants had a FAS diagnosis and thirty per cent were classified as FAE. All participants received a diagnosis/classification of FAS/FAE somewhere between five and twelve years prior to the study and most received their diagnosis from one of the study's authors. Most participants were diagnosed in infancy and forty-three were adolescents (12 to 17 years old) at the time of the study. Seventy-four per cent of the sample were American Indians, twenty-one per cent were Caucasian and five per cent were Black. Forty-seven per cent lived on reservations of the southwest and northwest United States, while the remainder lived in urban areas (39%) and rural, non-reservation areas (14%).

Streissguth and colleagues (1991) found that the average academic functioning of the study sample was at the early grade school level and most had required some remedial help in school. The average IQ score for the combined FAS/FAE group was 68, technically just into the mentally retarded range, representing "significantly sub-average intellectual function" (1991:1964). IQ scores ranged from 20 (severely retarded) to 105 (normal). The forty-two per cent who had an IQ level above seventy would not readily qualify for special community services upon leaving school. Arithmetic skills were particularly low in this group, which Streissguth and colleagues suggest are reflected in their extreme difficulty with abstractions like time and space, cause and effect, and generalizing from one situation to another. This deficit extended into independent living issues, as it contributed to poor judgement and dysfunction in everyday living.

Maladaptive behaviours were common in all patients and sixty-two per cent were at 'significant' levels, based on testing scores. Common maladaptive behaviours found among the group were: poor concentration and attention; dependency, stubbornness or sullenness; social withdrawal; teasing or bullying; crying or laughing too easily; impulsivity; and periods of high anxiety. Many patients were also reported to lie, cheat or steal, to show a lack of consideration and to exhibit excessive unhappiness. Streissguth and colleagues (1991) point out that, at the time of the study, none of the patients were receiving help with mental health problems.

A second study by the same group of authors (Olson, Feldman et al., 1998) revealed that a cohort of non-retarded teenagers with FAS (n=9) had a spectrum of behavioural problems leading to secondary disabilities, such as mental health, school and job problems that went beyond their primary CNS dysfunction. These problems increased with a higher dose (levels of mother's drinking)-response (infant response) association.

Streissguth and colleagues (1991; Olson, Feldman et al., 1998) caution that, despite these groups experiencing a spectrum of behavioural problems, it is difficult to determine the primary origin of the problems. For both group of patients, postnatal environments were marked by "remarkably unstable family environments" (Streissguth, Aase et al., 1991:1965). In the earlier study, patients, aged twelve to seventeen, lived in an average of 3.5 different principal homes in their lifetime, excluding receiving homes or temporary shelters. Nine per cent were living with a biological parent (3% with a biological mother) and those patients where accurate data could be obtained, sixty-nine per cent of the biological mothers were known to be dead. These deaths were due to alcohol-related illnesses, suicide, homicide, falls and automobile accidents (Streissguth, Aase et al., 1991).

Streissguth and colleagues ask the questions: "Have children with FAS been put in multiple placements *because* they are difficult to manage? Or have their multiple placements *made* them difficult to manage?" (1991:1966). The data presented in the two studies do not provide evidence that can answer these questions and, since they originally posed the questions in 1991, very limited research has attempted to explore this issue (Tait, 2003) despite high rates of children diagnosed with FAS/ARBEs being involved in the foster care system and generally experiencing multiple placements throughout their childhood. Research has tended to focus overwhelmingly on identifying neuro-psychological anomalies, while paying only limited attention to postnatal environments. Streissguth and colleagues (1994) did not use a control group in their study, which may have shed some light on the influence of multiple foster placements, socio-economic status, geographical location and ethnic/cultural factors.

A population-based, longitudinal, prospective study of adolescent attention/memory performance and its relationship with prenatal alcohol exposure was conducted by Streissguth and colleagues (1994). Mothers of the children were predominantly non-Aboriginal (88%), married (87%), middle class (81%) and had 13.7 years of education. This group of mothers was considered 'low risk' by conventional pregnancy outcome criteria. At seven years of age, ninety-five of the children still lived with their biological mother and seventy per cent with their biological father. This meant the cohort included a large number of offspring who were simultaneously at relatively *high* risk for alcohol effects and at relatively *low* risk for other competing causes of poor developmental outcome.

Streissguth and colleagues (1994) argue that, because the mothers of the children were basically a low-risk group (primarily married, well-educated women, all in prenatal care by mid-pregnancy and with very low rates of other prenatal risk indicators), their high-risk drinking behaviour (drinking during pregnancy) could be directly associated with adverse developmental outcomes. Furthermore, they argue, because batteries of neuro-behavioural and attentional tests at various ages were given to the sample, it was possible to demonstrate which outcomes at what age were primarily associated with prenatal alcohol exposure.

The 464 participants represented eighty-two per cent of the original birth cohort. Participants underwent a battery of tests to determine attention and short-term memory problems. Streissguth and colleagues (1994) found prenatal alcohol exposure continued to affect the neuro-behavioural functioning of young adolescents. Participants had difficulties with complex problem-solving, poorer learning from experience in short-term recall of complex information and fluctuating attentional states. The likelihood of poor performance on attention/memory tasks was clearly linked to increased prenatal alcohol exposure. Increased prenatal alcohol exposure was also linked to increased problems in the classroom, such as problems with arithmetic and spelling and behavioural problems, such as inattention.

Secondary disabilities are a central focus of clinicians and researchers who deal with adolescents. In a study by Griesler and Kandel (1998), they attempt to examine the impact of prenatal alcohol exposure on the subsequent substance use of offspring, particularly alcohol consumption in adolescence. They conducted a longitudinal prospective study of 185 mother and first-born child pairs in New York City. At the time of follow-up in 1990, the children varied in ages from nine to seventeen years of age. Griesler and Kandal found that a dose-response relationship existed in relation to the female offspring. Daughters, whose mothers were moderate to heavy drinkers during pregnancy, were almost three times as likely to have drunk alcohol in their lifetime and six times as likely to have drunk alcohol in the previous year, as compared to the daughters not exposed to alcohol prenatally. This occurred despite controlling for other potentially important familial predictors of adolescent drinking, including current maternal drinking, maternal delinquency in early adulthood, maternal closeness, monitoring, a rule against drinking and childhood behaviour problems. However, while Griesler and Kandal hypothesize about the biological mechanisms linking prenatal alcohol exposure to alcohol use in female adolescents, they only briefly mention that they found a *slight* negative effect of maternal drinking during pregnancy on reducing lifetime drinking of the sons. Also, their study did not explore other factors, such as paternal drinking, the availability of and opportunity for using alcohol, or the adolescents' pre-drinking alcohol knowledge, beliefs, expectations and intentions. Socio-economic and cultural influences were also excluded from the study.

A Canadian study by Fast and colleagues (1999) examined the percentage of FAS/FAE found among a cohort of youth (n=287) remanded to the In-patient Assessment Unit (IAU) of the Youth Forensic Psychiatric Services in Burnaby, British Columbia. All youth who were remanded to the IAU between July 1, 1995 and June 30, 1996 were evaluated for FAS and FAE. This group represented approximately 2.5% of youth in custody in British Columbia and the Yukon during this time. Sixty-seven (23.3%)

had an alcohol-related diagnosis. All had a history of significant prenatal exposure to alcohol. The youth ranged in ages from twelve to eighteen years; fifty-four were males and thirteen were females. Thirty-eight were non-Aboriginal, eighteen Aboriginal, seven non-Aboriginal/Aboriginal and four were from other ethnic groups. IQs ranged from 55 to 129, with an average of approximately 87. Three were diagnosed as having the full FAS and 64 were diagnosed as having FAE. Only three had been diagnosed prior to the study's assessment.

Fast and colleagues (1999) argue that, because of the high percentage of FAS/FAE youth found in this study (10 to 40 times the accepted worldwide incidence rates), this group is disproportionately represented in the juvenile justice system. They write:

> There is a paucity of clinical expertise to identify and provide for the needs of incarcerated youth with FAS/FAE. There needs to be education of health professionals and corrections workers around this high-risk population to develop skills in recognition and referral for diagnosis when warranted. Early identification and treatment of these youth is essential to improve services for this population before, during, and after incarceration (Fast, Conry et al., 1999:371).

They add that individuals with FAS/FAE, like offenders with other disabilities, require special consideration regarding diversion, sentencing, disposition, intervention and treatment (1999).

The study by Fast and colleagues fails to give information about postnatal environments in which the sixty-seven diagnosed individuals grew up. While they suggest that alcohol-affected youth are at risk for getting in trouble with the law, the limited information given in their study does not allow for consideration of factors such as foster placement (including multiple placements), past traumas (such as child physical and sexual abuse, family dysfunction, including parental alcohol abuse other than maternal alcohol exposure) and socio-economic status. Furthermore, while these individuals are now diagnosed as having brain damage, it is not clear in the article if this diagnosis led to some type of intervention program or service. Also of great importance, although beyond the scope of the article, is whether these individuals accepted or rejected the diagnosis and interventions offered to them.

Aboriginal communities across Canada have been very concerned about their youth population and have sought various ways to reduce problems among youth and to ensure a positive future for the next generation. Included in this concern has been the prevention of FAS/ARBEs and the development of interventions and services to assist affected individuals and their families. Unfortunately, there is limited research, including other grey literature, that specifically discusses Aboriginal adolescence with FAS/ARBEs and, therefore, limited information about the specific needs of this population, their families and communities is included in this review. However, the research literature does indicate that Aboriginal adolescents are experiencing problems, as is indicated by 18 of the 67 diagnosed youth in the study by Fast and colleagues (1999) being Aboriginal and a further 7 of the 67 being non-Aboriginal/Aboriginal. This over-representation of remanded Aboriginal youth in the forensic psychiatric services is troublesome and points to further information needed to be gathered about this group and other high-risk Aboriginal youth. This also indicates the need for appropriate services to be developed in which the needs of high-risk Aboriginal youth are targeted. Aboriginal communities, in both urban and rural settings, have begun this process and further financial and human resources must be directed toward assisting these initiatives.

Chapter 10

Adolescence can be a difficult period for many individuals and this appears to be particularly true for alcohol-affected persons. While experiencing the same major life transitions as other adolescents, such as "adjusting to sexual maturity, becoming less reliant on parents and family, establishing areas of independence, and planning for a fulfilling role in society as an adult" (Society of Special Needs Adoptive Parents, 1999:41), alcohol-affected adolescents face these in relation to their disability. This can place a great deal of stress and strain on the person, as well as on their family members, particularly if appropriate structure, supervision and supports are not in place for the family. Adolescence may also be a time when some Aboriginal persons who are alcohol-affected and living with non-Aboriginal foster or adoptive families may want to find out more about their Aboriginal heritage and biological family. This can further add stress and strain on the family, particularly between the adolescent person and the parents. The facilitation of this process by Aboriginal organizations and communities, in conjunction with foster and adoptive families, should be considered, in order for these individuals to have the option to choose if they want to be integrated back into their biological family or Aboriginal nation.

'Revised best practices'

1. While there is no evidence to date, there is a consensus among experts that adolescents with FAS and related effects benefit from assistance with basic socialization and communication skills, as well as tailored vocational counselling and employment supervision, money management training, sexuality and birth control education and drug education. These services must consider local traditional beliefs and practices and involve extended family members, Elders, traditional practitioners and other local health and social service providers.

2. There is no evidence to date, but there is a consensus among experts that adolescents with FAS or related effects, who become involved with substance abuse treatment, mental health or the correctional system, may benefit from tailored programming. Aboriginal adolescents with FAS may benefit from culturally sensitive programming, which helps to reinforce their Aboriginal identity and assists them in building support networks in the Aboriginal community after the program is completed.

3. There is no evidence to date, but there is a consensus among experts that families caring for those with FAS and related effects benefit from appropriate professional services and mutual support groups that extend over the life span of the person. Aboriginal care givers may benefit from local support groups that involve the participation of Elders and include traditional community supports.

4. Although those with intellectual deficits due to prenatal alcohol exposure have not been studied specifically, there is some evidence that cognitive-behavioural family therapies are effective in helping those with intellectual deficits to learn and maintain various basic living skills. Therapies involving Aboriginal families need to be sensitized to their cultural beliefs and may be more effective if they combine western and traditional therapeutic strategies.

Chapter 10

Adulthood

Research literature concerning interventions for affected adults are few in number and Streissguth and colleagues (1996) in Seattle, Washington have published the majority of studies (Roberts and Nanson, 2000). Because of this, only tentative conclusions can be drawn about 'best practices' for adults. Roberts and Nanson, with the assistance of the National Steering Committee, identified two 'best practices' in relation to adulthood:

'Best practices'

1. While there is no evidence to date, there is a consensus among experts supporting the continuation of advocacy or case management to help the adult, affected by prenatal alcohol exposure, to adequately deal with the many challenges of adult life.

2. While there is no evidence to date, there is a consensus among experts that frequently required programs, such as substance abuse treatment, employment training, mental health therapy and correctional services, need to be modified to be of benefit.

In most of the studies by Streissguth and colleagues involving adults, small patient populations have been used without the use of a comparative control group, which makes it "difficult to assess the relative contribution of prenatal alcohol exposure and various postnatal social factors such as lack of support services, late diagnosis, poverty and family dysfunction to the development of problems" (Roberts and Nanson, 2000:78). Behavioural problems, such as those found among adolescents with FAS/ARBEs, were found among affected adults. Streissguth and colleagues found that, although mental retardation was not necessarily predictable from the diagnosis alone, "major psychosocial problems and life-long adjustment problems were characteristic of most of these patients" (1991:1965-1966). However, a study by Tishler and colleagues (1998) found that adult offspring of women who drank during pregnancy showed only two differences in psycho-social parameters from non-exposed controls: a history of longer alcohol drinking and a greater likelihood of never being married.

Tishler and colleagues (1998) studied a group of male veterans who were chosen because of both their accepted level of function within society (e.g., honourable discharge from the military) and their admission to an alcohol treatment unit (thus, a greater likelihood of parental alcoholism, because of familial aggregation). A smooth philtrum was a highly significant predictor of exposed offspring, as was low birth weight and length, although this factor was only marginally significantly associated with case status. Apart from this, the men who had a maternal history of prenatal alcohol exposure were remarkably similar to the controls, who were selected only by virtue of their admission to treatment at a time proximate to the study sample. No significant differences between cases and controls in general characteristics, such as age, father's age at birth, ethnicity, parental educational levels and whether their parents were deceased or not, were found. In relation to comparisons more directly associated with alcohol exposure, such as level of education, other developmental/educational indices (e.g., subject was thought to be learning disabled, had a speech problem or attended special educations classes, occupation score, Alcohol Severity Index; history of incarceration) and somatic parameters (e.g., facial features, growth variables), only low birth weight/height, a smooth philtrum and a long history of alcohol abuse were found to distinguish the case population from controls.

Chapter 10

The study by Tishler and colleagues (1998) indicates that further research involving low-risk groups is needed to fully understand FAS/ARBEs. Their study contradicts common understandings held about affected individuals. For example, Streissguth and colleagues (1991) argue that poor outcome is found, even among patients with normal intellectual functioning, which suggests that subtle manifestations of prenatal brain damage are involved. Although none of the case population studied by Tishler and colleagues had the full blown syndrome, there was sufficient evidence to suggest a rough estimate of 11 to 13% of their case population had FAE. They conclude that this indicates "at least certain adult offspring of alcoholic mothers are not different or minimally different in physical appearance, intellectual achievement, or psychosocial development from individuals without drinking mothers" (Tishler, Henschel, Ngo, Walters and Worobec, 1998:1828). This supports research findings that only a portion of women who abuse alcohol when pregnant give birth to affected children and that environmental factors are important considerations in understanding the life span trajectory of the illness.

Examining 'Secondary Disabilities:' The Example of Aboriginal Inmates

A great deal of concern by medical researchers, clinicians and community and parent advocacy groups has been given to 'secondary disabilities,' which are believed to be the result of the interaction between primary disabilities, particularly neuro-developmental anomalies and the environment in which the person lives. Because the biological markers of FAS/FAE and ARBEs (e.g., facial features, growth retardation) in some individuals, particularly during adolescence and adulthood, may change and become indistinguishable from normal standards, and because there are no brain imaging tests to identify brain damage caused by in-utero alcohol exposure, behaviour is relied upon as a marker of in-utero alcohol damage. Secondary disabilities are believed to arise after birth and presumably could be ameliorated through better understanding and appropriate interventions (Streissguth et al., 1997). Experts contend that certain health and social problems, 'secondary disabilities,' such as mental health problems, disrupted school experience (suspended, expelled or dropped out), trouble with the law, confinement (in-patient treatment for mental health or addiction problems or incarceration), inappropriate sexual behaviour, and alcohol/drug problems may be suggestive of FAS/ARBEs, if there is known or suspected alcohol exposure in-utero.

All of the 'secondary disabilities' have been documented as occurring disproportionately among the general Aboriginal population of Canada (Tait, 2000b; Royal Commission on Aboriginal Peoples, 1993; 1996b; Waldram, Herring and Kue Young, 1995). Generally, the disproportionate representation of these problems has been attributed to long-term colonialist oppression, which continues to impact daily upon Aboriginal communities and their constituents (Royal Commission on Aboriginal Peoples, 1996a) and FAS/ARBEs have recently been included by some Aboriginal authors as a further outcome of colonialist acculturation strategies, such as residential schooling (Fournier and Crey, 1997).

However, the danger with using this group of health and social problems as markers for FAS/ARBEs, in the absence of any distinguishable biological markers, even when maternal alcohol exposure is confirmed, is that individuals may be incorrectly labelled as suffering from permanent brain damage. While authors, such as Fournier and Crey (1997), link the impact of colonialist oppression with FAS/ARBEs, this is the exception rather than the rule. For example, intergenerational problems that are prevalent among some Aboriginal groups, such as mental health problems, high rates of incarceration and school drop-out, sexual dysfunction and alcohol and drug problems, once reconceptualized as 'secondary disabilities' of in-utero alcohol damage, end up being dealt with as medical conditions rather than social and health outcomes of colonialist oppression. Interventions typically target affected individuals rather than focusing on strategies, such as community development.

Within this framework, populations become labelled as having high rates of FAS/ARBEs, even when very few individuals are actually assessed or diagnosed (Tait, 2003). A recent example involving Aboriginal men is found in the significant attention FAS/ARBEs have been given by Correctional Services of Canada. Presently, there is only one preliminary study in Canada determining prevalence rates among incarcerated populations (Fast, Conry et al., 1999); virtually no adult inmates and only a limited number of young offenders have been assessed or diagnosed. Despite this, Correctional Services of Canada has released a research report (Boland, Burrill et al., 1998) and article (Boland, Duwyn et al., 2000) indicating that high prevalence rates of FAS/ARBEs exist among Aboriginal inmates. Boland and colleagues write: "Given that Aboriginal offenders are considerably over-represented in the federal justice system, the question arises as to whether one of the contributing factors is the high rate of FAS/FAE experienced by our Aboriginal population (2000:18).

In this account, social marginalization, colonialist acculturation strategies, including the residential school system, and systemic racism are replaced with substance abusing mothers and brain damaged offspring as central contributing factors to high incarceration rates of Aboriginal men. However, Aboriginal inmates, in general, experience all of the 'secondary disabilities' attributed to FAS/FAE (Tait, 2003). For example, in a synthesis of two surveys of the Aboriginal federal offender population in Canada, Johnston (2000) found that Aboriginal inmates shared similar childhood histories, including poverty, alcohol and drug abuse, parental absence and behavioural problems.

Physical and sexual abuse was common in the childhood background of the study populations (Johnston, 2000) that, according to research discussed in chapter four, could lead to various problems in adulthood, including substance abuse, impulsivity, dissociation, personality disorders, sexual dysfunction, low self-steem, depression and behavioural re-enactments (Green, 1993). A significant percentage of the inmates in Johnston's study were not raised by their families, but in foster and adoptive homes, raised as wards of the community or attended residential schools (Johnston, 2000). Twenty-one per cent had attempted suicide and/or self-injury, suggesting high rates of mental distress and/or illness.[53]

The findings of Johnston's study indicate that caution should be taken when discussing prevalence rates of FAS/ARBEs among Aboriginal inmates (Tait, 2003). While some Aboriginal inmates will be affected by in-utero alcohol exposure, the impact of compounding traumas found among the general Aboriginal population indicates that in-utero alcohol damage may be very difficult to distinguish from other factors, such as childhood disruptions and traumas. Furthermore, scientific research suggests that even if all the mothers of Aboriginal inmates abused alcohol, only a minor percentage would be alcohol-effected (Abel, 1998a).

---

[53]   Mental distress has been identified as a 'secondary disability;' however, there are no studies found that persons with FAS/ARBEs are at risk for suicide. Follow-up studies of diagnosed persons found no correlation between suicide or self-injury and FAS/ARBEs.

Chapter 10

However, an important reaction to this type of analysis is given by FAS/ARBES experts, including advocacy groups, who argue that FAS/ARBEs are distinguishable and deserve special attention with regard to the sentencing and incarceration of inmates (Conry and Fast, 2000). These are clearly important considerations for any person influenced by a mental deficit who commits a crime; however, when situated within a broader context, several considerations are raised. These considerations are best illustrated by a specific example of a young Aboriginal man diagnosed with FAS who recounted his experience with the criminal justice system.

Tait writes:

> When I met James[54] he was in his late twenties, and had just completed a six-month prison term. James is First Nations and as a child was diagnosed with FAS. He currently lacks any of the physical phenotypic [facial features, growth retardation] features, and does not remember ever accessing specialized services or taking medication because of his diagnosis. James' childhood was very tumultuous and he spent most of it being moved in and out of different group and foster homes. He dropped out of school in the ninth grade after being placed in a special education class. By this time he was already using drugs and alcohol on a daily basis. As with most foster children, once he reached legal age he was not allowed to stay with his foster family. James had no transitional support out of foster care and basically was left to fend for himself. He started getting in trouble with the law before leaving foster care and since then has been in and out of jail for minor offences. This he links to a number of factors: "When you're locked up I guess you become a better criminal because you're surrounded by it, you get ideas, you hear other people talk about how they did their stuff and that … but I guess for a lot of people like us Indians it becomes, like part of our lives because you have uncles, aunts, cousins locked up in there, and then you go and you have family among you, it becomes part of your life…like my younger brother, before I got sentenced he said "well, its about time you went back to jail". For them it is kind of like respectable to go to jail. James was living with his girlfriend in a run-down hotel room in a region of the city known for drugs, prostitution, violence, and poverty. Neither could conceive of how their situation would improve in the near future. When I asked James about what he planned to do now that he was out of prison, he explained: "When I got released they said, "here's your money. There'll always be a place when you decide to come back". That was it. Getting a job because I have a criminal record is pretty hard. Getting welfare is hard because I've been incarcerated … They expect I won't be out too long and I'll be back in". James was supporting himself by 'scheming', which basically meant stealing money and other things he could pawn or sell on the street. He had no other income, and felt his best strategy was to stay out of the vision of police. However, he fully expected to end up back in jail in the next year or two. Outside of his relationship with his girlfriend, all his friends and relatives were heavily involved in drinking alcohol or sniffing inhalants. Even though he had been to a number of addiction treatment programs, once back in his neighbourhood he quickly fell back into using (Tait, 2003:338-339).

---

[54]   James is a pseudonym to protect the person's identity.

Chapter 10

What is illustrated by James' situation is that, apart from his illness, there are many factors that contributed to him ending up in jail. While some would argue that he is in jail because of being alcohol-affected and having a difficult childhood, the fact remains that he may very well have ended up in jail even if his mother did not drink during pregnancy. Too often, attention is paid only to alcohol-affects so that the rest of the lives of people, such as James, become mute. James clearly expresses that going to jail is not just a matter of getting caught for committing a crime, but is surrounded by a number of environmental and relationship factors that are very important in understanding his recidivism (Tait, 2003). Kleinman and colleagues argue: "what we represent and how we represent it prefigures what we will, or will not, do to intervene. What is not pictured is not real. Much of routinized misery is invisible; much that is made visible is not ordinary or routine" (1997:xiii).

'Revised best practices'

1. While there is no evidence to date, there is a consensus among experts supporting the continuation of advocacy or case management to help the adult, affected by prenatal alcohol exposure, to adequately deal with the many challenges of adult life. Involvement of Aboriginal adults who are alcohol-affected in community activities, which reinforce their Aboriginal identity and teaching of traditional skills and knowledge, may assist in the continued integration of affected individuals.

2. While there is no evidence to date, there is a consensus among experts that frequently required programs, such as substance abuse treatment, employment training, mental health therapy and correctional services, need to be modified to be of benefit. Caution needs to be taken so that individuals in these programs are not labelled as having FAS/ARBEs without a medical assessment. Aboriginal adults, affected by in-utero alcohol exposure, may benefit from programs that reinforce their Aboriginal identity and help them build strong links to the Aboriginal community. Traditional practitioners and Elders could play a central role in working with affected individuals while they attend these programs or are incarcerated. This could greatly facilitate the reintegration of affected persons back into the community.

Children Affected by Other Drug Use During Pregnancy[55]

Roberts and Nanson (2000), with the assistance of the National Steering Committee, identified three 'best practices' for children affected by other drug use during pregnancy.

'Best practices'

1. There is some evidence that comfort measures (i.e., swaddling and holding) are effective interventions for mild cases of neonatal abstinence syndrome, while pharmacological treatments, such as phenobarbital and paregoric, can support withdrawal management in more severe cases.

---

[55]   The literature regarding fetal drug exposure has been briefly touched upon in this report. For further review of the literature and discussion of 'best practices,' see Roberts and Nanson, 2000.

2. There is some evidence and a consensus among experts indicating that support of the mother immediately following birth, with a comprehensive range of services (such as mental health, substance abuse treatment, family counselling, parenting education, schooling, job training and housing assistance), leads to improved outcomes for mother and child.

3. There is some evidence and a consensus among experts pointing to intensive case management, mentoring, home visits and single points of access as effective vehicles for the delivery of services.

Intergenerational Links with Residential Schools

> [There is an] epidemic of substance abuse and hopelessness that envelops our young people and results in the highest suicide rates among [youth] in the nation today. Of the 200 to 275 deaths by injury and poisoning that have occurred among First Nations in the last decade, fully three-quarters were in the 10-year to 20-year age group. Those deaths compare to the 65 to 70 deaths that occurred in the same category nationally ...

> Fetal and infant death among First Nations babies was nearly twice the national average reported since 1987. Once again the social and economic factors of poor housing, lack of sewage disposal and potable water, and poor access to health services were considered factors in the higher rates. As well, the poor health of the mother, inadequate nutrition and lack of pre-natal care, as well as the adverse effects of drugs and alcohol, also contributed (cited in Royal Commission on Aboriginal Peoples, 1996b: Vol. 3, ch. 3, s. 2).

Based on discussions within this report, intergenerational links between the residential school system and current health and social problems among Aboriginal groups in Canada are apparent. Included within this context is substance abuse by pregnant women and FAS/ARBEs. The Royal Commission on Aboriginal Peoples (1996b) wrote that prevention of FAS/ARBEs among Aboriginal people depended on one thing: the reduction of alcohol consumption during pregnancy. And, while the Commission was right in its assertion, they also illustrate in their report that this 'one thing' exists within a complex history of indigenous people, most specifically in the history of indigenous and non-indigenous relations in which colonialist forces waged a brutal assault on Aboriginal culture and identity. At the centre of this assault were the minds and bodies of Aboriginal children and, as has been illustrated in previous chapters, although this assault was met with resistance by Aboriginal children, parents and communities, it nevertheless has long-term implications for Aboriginal people, including a range of serious health and social problems.

Fetal alcohol syndrome and alcohol-related birth effects have been identified by Aboriginal leaders and by many communities as a recently recognized and particularly insidious manifestation of colonialist oppression, in that it permanently damages the health of children, the seventh generation and future of Aboriginal people. The logic behind this threat appears to be straightforward, as alcohol abuse is a recognized problem within the general Aboriginal population and, therefore, so must FAS/ARBEs. Links to the residential school system are also relatively straightforward, given the level of trauma experienced by former students, particularly sexual and physical abuse, and when combined with other social and cultural upheavals being experienced by Aboriginal people during this period and afterwards has, without doubt, influenced the abuse of alcohol by many individuals, including pregnant women.

Chapter 10

This report, however, takes a cautionary approach to the issues of FAS/ARBEs. As pointed out above, risk for Aboriginal people is not just located in a pregnant woman's use of alcohol, but is also situated in the present day context in which most Aboriginal people live. Poverty, whether it be in the form of poor housing, lack of sewage disposal and potable water, poor access to health services, a lack of adequate nutritious food or the emotional, mental, physical and spiritual *poverty* experienced and witnessed by individuals and communities, it stands as the most significant risk factor currently confronting Aboriginal communities in relation to FAS/ARBEs. An individual from Sioux Lookout, Ontario, reported to the Royal Commission on Aboriginal Peoples that: "Any disease category related to the First Nations is two to three times higher than the national figures" (1996b:203). These figures are directly influenced by colonialist oppression, which left many Aboriginal communities with an overall health status among its members equivalent to that found in some of the poorest countries in the world. As has been described in this report, chronic poverty exacerbates the damage caused by in-utero alcohol exposure and, when poverty is absent, affected individuals show a significant decrease in behavioural and cognitive problems (Abel, 1998a).

Conclusion

Underfunded First Nations health care systems, both on reserve and in the inner city, have difficulty getting and allocating funding to take care of their own fetal-alcohol-damaged children and adults. Yet when a native child is taken into care, it appears that funding suddenly kicks in to take him or her on the round of medical appointments that the child will need for the rest of his or her life. Diagnosis and visits to a psychologist can be more readily organized and reimbursed when a child is in government care. Birth parents struggling to take care of their own alcohol-affected children may feel discouraged and ultimately be defeated by the lack of diagnosis, counselling, tutoring, respite care, and by the need for ceaseless advocacy to achieve services for their child and to keep the family intact. On an isolated reserve, access to good health care and diagnosis is a challenge, unless the First Nation has specifically developed programs for alcohol-affected children. Frustrated [A]boriginal parents may surrender a child to government care so that he or she can get the medical and social help needed. Rather than stimulating a flow of funding to help First Nations take care of their own, FAS/FAE is too frequently used as another justification for separating [A]boriginal children from their parents and extended family (Fournier and Crey, 1997:179-180).

Even though [he] did not benefit from a mother able to turn away from drinking, he benefited as a young adult from the Native American community attitude. After graduating from high school, he was too old to remain in residential care and was released, choosing to live with a relative in one of the reservation communities. Instead of drifting through life without connections, however, [he] joined community life through employment, continuing education, and improved ties with his family and Native American culture. He lives independently, but members of the community subtly guide his social interaction through a sense of obligation and interdependence (Hornby, 2000:275).

251

Chapter 10

This chapter reviewed the research literature and 'best practices' concerning alcohol-affected persons. As illustrated in this discussion, there is a great deal of information that is lacking about the life trajectory of affected individuals, the role of environmental influences and how best to address the needs of alcohol-affected persons at various stages of their lives. This review found alcohol-affected persons, who are Aboriginal, may be at risk of multiple environmental insults, which could further exaggerate their illness, such as multiple foster placements, poverty, family dysfunction and long-term separation from family members. Aboriginal communities may also lack the range of services needed to address the needs of alcohol-affected children and, as indicated above by Fournier and Crey, this may result in the children being removed from the community, despite having care givers who could provide a stable and loving home environment.

There is limited written information about the response of Aboriginal communities to alcohol-affected persons. Hart (1999) suggests that recognition of the diversity of cultures and histories found among and between First Nations, Métis and Inuit communities is important in understanding how communities respond to FAS/ARBEs. Hornby (2000) found that Native American communities he worked with showed more acceptance of persons who were alcohol-affected than that found in mainstream society and used gentle guidance with family and tribal members who had FAS/ARBEs. Aboriginal people, as they have done with treatment for alcohol, are at the forefront of designing culturally appropriate services for their people. In this process, they work with non-Aboriginal health and social service professionals in implementing 'best practices' that are locally determined and 'best practices' based on scientific research and professional biomedical opinions that are modified to local context to meet the needs of alcohol-affected persons.

As Aboriginal communities address substance abuse by pregnant women and FAS/ARBEs, the *Guide for Health Professionals Working with Aboriginal Peoples* (Smylie, 2000) provides important direction and guidance for Aboriginal communities and health and social service providers who work in these communities. The guidelines, which received input from a number of Aboriginal contributors and supporting organizations, give the following recommendations:

1. health professionals should have a basic understanding of the appropriate names with which to refer to the various groups of Aboriginal people in Canada;

2. health professionals should have a basic understanding of the current socio-demographics of Aboriginal people in Canada;

3. health professionals should familiarize themselves with the traditional geographic territories and language groups of Aboriginal people;

4. health professionals should have a basic understanding of the disruptive impact of colonization on the health and well-being of Aboriginal people;

5. health professionals should recognize that the current socio-demographic challenges facing many Aboriginal individuals and communities have a significant impact on health status;

6. health professionals should recognize the need to provide health services for Aboriginal people as close to home as possible;

7. health professionals should have a basic understanding of governmental obligations and policies regarding the health of Aboriginal people in Canada; and

8. health professionals should recognize the need to support Aboriginal individuals and communities in the process of self-determination (Smylie, 2000).

The guidelines put forth by Smylie can be extended to other services providers, such as social workers, teachers and outreach workers, and can serve as a basis for the identification and implementation of 'best practices' for Aboriginal people in Canada.

Chapter 11

Epilogue

As an adult, Jane told me of being sexually abused by her foster parent's son, who was never charged and is now a Christian missionary in Africa. In her late teens, Jane gave birth to a son who was adopted by the same parents and continues to live there. It hurts me to see my nieces and nephews repeat our history as foster kids in white, ultra-Christian homes. Jane now spends most of her time on Vancouver's meanest streets, on a methadone-maintenance program but receiving no psychiatric care or counselling to help her cope with the immense losses in her life ... The troubles my siblings and I have suffered can only truly be understood in a cultural context, not just as a series of traumatic life events but as a deep spiritual estrangement from the complex of Sto:lo beliefs. As Sto:lo, we believe that our ancestors continue to play a role in our daily lives. In our society, when you are ill or feeling discomfort, you are described as being "Indian sick", which means that spiritual forces are a work in you life. In order to understand these forces, you must return to spiritual teachers. The elders believe the voices and spirits that non-native medical experts might diagnose as a profound mental illness are in fact an expression of the cultural estrangement so many of us have suffered (Fournier and Crey, 1997:43-44).

... FAS is implicated in most adoptions that go bad. Virtually every native child adopted over the past 20 years has some degree of alcohol damage. It is that, and not the pain of alienation from white society, that accounts for their frequent estrangement from their adoptive families and their terrible problems in life.

The failure of cross-cultural adoptions is one of the most tragically misunderstood stories of recent years. It has wreaked havoc in some of Canada's most prominent families ... And yet adoptive families everywhere are still being told their children were ruined by a cultural identity crisis (Wente, 2000:A17).

Indigenous attempts to reclaim land, language, knowledge and sovereignty have usually involved contested accounts of the past by colonizers and colonized. These have occurred in the courts, before various commissions, tribunals and official enquiries, in the media, in Parliament, in bars and on talkback radio. In these situations contested histories do not exist in the same cultural framework as they do when tribal or clan histories, for example, are being debated within indigenous community itself. They are not simply struggles over 'facts' and 'truth'; the rules by which these struggles take place are never clear (other than that we as the indigenous community know they are going to be stacked against us); and we are not the final arbiters of what really counts as the truth (Smith, 1999:33-34).

Fetal alcohol syndrome (FAS) has emerged in recent decades as a serious health and social concern for Aboriginal people in Canada. Its appearance, first recognized among infants and children, and then among adolescents and adults, has a significant impact upon Aboriginal people, who already face a myriad of devastating illnesses, injuries and health risks within their communities. FAS, however, is particularly devastating, as it is a chronic illness that effects newborns and is seen by most people, Aboriginal and non-Aboriginal, as one-hundred per cent preventable. In previous chapters, FAS and alcohol-related birth effects (ARBEs) have been discussed in relation to residential schools and intergenerational links between the experiences of former students, their families and communities and current rates of FAS/ARBEs found among Aboriginal people in Canada.

This report has set out to examine these links by looking at historical and scientific research covering issues, such as the colonization of indigenous people in Canada, most specifically the impact of the residential school system; the use of alcohol by Aboriginal groups in North America; child abuse; and contemporary health and social issues affecting Aboriginal people, specifically substance abuse among women and the occurrence of FAS/ARBEs. As presented in previous chapters, the intergenerational links between the residential school system and current rates of FAS/ARBEs are influenced by a number of inter-related factors, for example: economic and social marginalization of Aboriginal people; loss of traditional land bases; the removal of generations of Aboriginal children from their families and communities by child welfare services; loss of community control and autonomy over various aspects of daily living, including education and health care; and colonialist assaults on Aboriginal cultures and identity, specifically indigenous languages, ceremonies and political and social structures.

This report has also argued that the intergenerational links between the residential school system and current rates of FAS/ARBEs are contested in various arenas. First, as indicated in the statements at the beginning of this chapter, the history of Aboriginal and non-Aboriginal relations and, specifically, the impact of colonization on the lives of Aboriginal people is contested, with FAS being a recent 'bone of contention' that is generally understood differently by Aboriginal and non-Aboriginal people. Secondly, the scientific literature written about FAS/ARBEs illustrates the 'facts' and 'truth' surrounding these diagnostic categories are under debate within scientific circles. Debates over the current prevalence of FAS/ARBEs continues and, as illustrated in chapter seven, the epidemiological data concerning Aboriginal people is inconclusive and not representative of the overall Aboriginal population in Canada.

Controversy still exists over the precision of the diagnostic criteria for FAS/ARBEs and medical researchers are actively seeking to improve diagnostic validity and reliability through the development of standardized diagnostic tools and measurements, including the sensitization of these instruments to account for ethnic diversity. Also, researchers have not yet determined a 'safe level' of alcohol use for pregnant women and methodological problems, such as under-reporting of alcohol use by women, and the use of research methods, such as 'average drinks per day,' which may mask risk behaviours, such as binge drinking, have resulted in controversy among medical researchers about safe levels. Debate also exists as to whether alcohol alone is sufficient to cause FAS/ARBEs or whether effects only occur when alcohol abuse happens in conjunction with other variables, such as poor nutrition, alcohol related illnesses, poverty, increased maternal age, binge drinking, genetic factors related to the mother and the fetus and other health risks related to substance abuse, such as violence, smoking, drug use and overall poor health.

Interestingly, the controversy around FAS/ARBEs that occurs in the realm of scientific research is minimized greatly outside this arena. Public health messages increasingly present a message that any alcohol use by a pregnant woman is dangerous to the developing fetus. Most messages imply that a pregnant woman's use or non-use of alcohol is an uncomplicated choice. Outcries that 'epidemic' numbers of children with FAS/ARBEs are being born, specifically in Aboriginal communities, are commonly found in media reports, government documents and from health, education and social service providers. In efforts to acknowledge and to take steps to address the problem in their communities, Aboriginal people have taken on a leadership role in front-line FAS prevention and intervention strategies that, while yielding positive outcomes at the community level, has reinforced the perception that this is mainly a health problem of Aboriginal people and that the level of attention it is receiving is indicative of the vastness of the problem among the overall Aboriginal population (Tait, 2003).

This report argues that a level of caution should be adopted by Aboriginal leaders and their constituents in relation to FAS/ARBEs, as the labelling of individuals and populations of people as 'brain-damaged' is very serious and will have long-term consequences for those who are labelled. However, this is not to argue that the concern expressed by Aboriginal people about FAS/ARBEs is misplaced. In fact, the complete opposite is true, as certain communities are currently dealing with endemic poverty and related health issues, such as substance abuse, alcohol-related illnesses, mental illness, poor nutrition, high rates of smoking and general poor health among adults and children. These communities are also dealing with high rates of family dysfunction, including child abuse, domestic violence and family breakdown, chronic unemployment and poor education, health and social services, all of which can contribute to substance abuse by pregnant women and the occurrence of FAS/ARBEs.

Outrage, Silence and the Trickster

As the conclusion for this report is being written, the Canadian public watches the Vancouver police search for bodies of missing women from Vancouver's downtown eastside on a pig farm on the outskirts of a nearby suburb of Port Coquitlam. Sadly, one of the women being looked for is the sister of one of the co-authors of *Stolen From Our Embrace: The Abduction of First Nations Children and the Restoration of Aboriginal Communities* (Fournier and Crey, 1997). In their account, Fournier and Crey combine numerous archival, scientific and historical texts with personal accounts from Aboriginal people to discuss the links between colonialist acculturation strategies, specifically the residential school and child welfare systems and intergenerational problems experienced by some Aboriginal people, such as sexual abuse, family and relationship dysfunction, alcohol abuse and FAS. Their analysis is the first in Canada to look at the intergenerational links between residential schools and FAS/ARBEs and they point to a legacy of child physical and sexual abuse in residential schools, in foster and adoption homes and, most recently, experienced within Aboriginal families and communities that has been tied to alcohol abuse by Aboriginal women and to FAS among their children.

One of the most striking personal narratives in *Stolen From our Embrace* is Crey's recounting of his growing up in British Columbia during the 1950s and 1960s. Crey tells of four generations of his Sto: lo family, beginning with the lives of his great-grandparents who lived "amid a thriving [A]boriginal populace, at the peak of the Fraser River civilization" (1997:21). His life story is moving and powerful, illustrating first hand the experience of many Aboriginal families in Canada. Crey writes:

> As a child, I was forcibly removed from Sto:lo culture by social welfare authorities. Our family life was shattered after seven of my eight siblings and I were split apart into separate foster homes. We were never again to reunite as a family. My grandparents were proud, independent people who had lived through the deliberate dismantling of Sto:lo culture by priests who probed and pried into every corner of our lives. I had seen my

Chapter 11

father's spirit dimmed by the residential school where his culture was choked out of him, so that all his life he held his Halq'emeylem language and spiritual knowledge in check, depriving us, his children, of our most precious birthright (Fournier and Crey, 1997:20).

Crey's story is not just one of loss and trauma, but also tells of resistance, resilience and his rediscovery of his Sto:lo culture: strengths that one assumes he is drawing upon as he watches police search the property of the farm in Port Coquitlam for his sister's body.

The fifty women gone missing from Vancouver's downtown eastside have disappeared from one of Canada's poorest and most dangerous neighbourhoods. The women have been collectively described as 'street involved,' 'prostitutes' and 'drug addicts' and many of them are Aboriginal. What is shocking about this story is that fifty women from one neighbourhood disappeared over a number of years without anyone ever being implicated in their disappearance. This, despite families and friends giving police several leads, including identifying the farm in Port Coquitlam. Lingering questions are: Had these women disappeared from an upscale neighbourhood in West Vancouver, would it have taken so long to make an arrest and would the number of missing women ever have been allowed to reach as many as fifty before public outcry demanded something be done? Had these women been the wives, mothers and daughters of some of Vancouver's most prominent families, would the police have waited so long to create a special task force to investigate the disappearances and commit the resources needed to investigate the farm in Port Coquitlam?

The lack of public outcry and the silence around the disappearance of fifty women from a poor inner-city neighbourhood are indicative of other issues related to women who are street-involved and who have substance addictions. These women are what some have referred to as the 'undeserving poor,' unlike their children, who are part of Canada's 'deserving poor,' as reflected in government programs to address 'child poverty' rather than 'poverty' in general. When a street-involved woman becomes pregnant, she challenges this distinction and hence becomes the 'trickster' (Tait, 2003). The 'trickster' is a common character found in some indigenous oral traditions. The vulgar but sacred trickster assumes many forms, and alternately scandalizes, disgusts, amuses, disrupts and humiliates. However, the trickster is also a creative force, ultimately transforming the world around her in outrageous and shocking ways. The pregnant addict is the perfect trickster as she simultaneously conjures up outrage and anxiety, indignation and concern. She is both vulgar and sacred, disgusting and hallowed. The trickster's power lies within her ability to be pregnant and in her ability to disrupt the ideas of who others believe her to be and, instead, to redefine herself as a mother and deserving. No longer invisible, she demands our attention and forces us to see her. The trickster's power, her new visibility, rallies those around her; she suddenly is worthy of care, support and concern, as we become self-consciously aware that somehow, as a society, we are implicated in her being addicted.

This report, however, points out that while a pregnant woman who abuses substances may be a powerful trickster, her power is gone the moment she gives birth. Research has shown that women with substance abuse problems who give birth to an affected child are at high risk of dying within a few years if they continue to abuse substances. Whereas, the pregnant trickster conjures up outrage. The outrage quickly turns to silence and indifference, as her baby is apprehended and she returns to the streets. The deterioration of her health, the acts of violence committed against her and the pain she feels from experiencing multiple losses are met with further silence, as is her disappearance and death. Whether we will come to understand the lesson of the trickster is yet to be seen, but increasing attention is broadening to address the needs of women with substance abuse problems, along with, rather than apart from, the needs of their children — a reassuring sign for certain.

'Best Practices'

The 'best practices' put forth by Health Canada (Roberts and Nanson, 2000) for FAS prevention, identification and intervention have been re-examined in this report in relation to Aboriginal people. A small but significant part of the re-examination was a discussion of the role of traditional Aboriginal knowledge and practices in relation to a 'best practice' model for prevention and intervention. While the report stressed the importance of traditional teachings and the role of traditional practitioners and Elders, it was beyond the scope of this report to go further than to point out areas of prevention and intervention where traditional knowledge, practitioners and Elders could play a key role. A further step in the development of 'best practices' could be a re-examination of this report, as well as other 'best practice' documents, in relation to traditional Aboriginal knowledge and practices. This would further expand the scope and possibilities of the 'best practice' model in important and culturally relevant ways for Aboriginal people.

The 'best practices' reviewed in this report stress that equal emphasis be placed on improving the health of both the mother and her child. Aboriginal communities have already taken steps in this direction and are current leaders in FAS/ARBE prevention and intervention services. However, this report points out that Aboriginal people face a number of unique challenges when addressing substance abuse by pregnant women and the problem of FAS/ARBEs more generally. These include providing appropriate services to remote communities, addressing the needs of high risk communities where alcohol abuse and other health and social problems are endemic, providing culturally appropriate services in the urban milieu to a culturally and socially diverse Aboriginal population and securing adequate, long-term funding for program delivery. As indicated in previous chapters, the demands are significant. However, much has been accomplished to date that can be built upon to further meet these challenges.

Appendix A

'Best Practices'

I: Prevention

Primary Prevention

1. There is some evidence that measures to limit the availability of alcohol, such as bans on sales and importation that are broadly supported by the community, or price increase, can reduce heavy alcohol use by pregnant women at least in the short-term. These measures should be undertaken along with added measures to address the problem of 'bootlegging' of alcohol, which may contribute to increased binge drinking among pregnant women, and include measures that would address the use of replacement substances, such as solvents. Bans on sales of alcohol will be more effective if they are combined with a multi-component strategy that builds upon individual and community strengths. Research is needed to examine the impact of alcohol bans and price increases in Aboriginal communities with high, moderate and low levels of alcohol abuse among their members to better determine the effectiveness of these prevention strategies in local settings.

2. There is some evidence to support warning labels and posters as a means of increasing awareness and effecting short-term behaviour change among low-risk women. However, women who drink heavily during pregnancy do not appear to be affected by warning labels. Public health prevention messages in Aboriginal communities need to be culturally sensitive to local communities, and their success may be enhanced by community involvement, investment and control of the creation and dissemination of the public health message.

3. There is some evidence to support multi-component community-wide initiatives as a means of increasing awareness generally, reducing consumption for pregnant women and promoting referrals. These initiatives must be driven by a combination of community readiness, sufficient human and financial resources to sustain the initiative, and must be characterized by sensitivity to local beliefs and customs.

4. There is moderate evidence to support the use of life-skills-based and multi-component school-community substance use prevention programs as a means of preventing or delaying substance use among youth and, in turn, reducing substance use problems among adults. An important component of these initiatives should be Aboriginal youth groups and outreach programs, specifically those that target high risk youth who have dropped out of school and are accessing few services. Special attention should be given in these programs to reducing the possibility of informal diagnosing of individuals in the community as alcohol-effected once a discussion of FAS/ARBE prevention begins.

Secondary Prevention

1. There is a consensus among experts to support routine screening of pregnant women for use of alcohol and other substances in various settings, including justice, housing and health settings. However, routine screening is only beneficial if follow-up evaluation and appropriate intervention services exist that pregnant women are willing to participate in and can easily access.

Appendix A

2. There is moderate evidence to support the use of the T-ACE and TWEAK, and some evidence to support the use of CAGE and AUDIT alcohol dependence instruments in a supportive milieu to identify women who would benefit from intervention for their alcohol use during pregnancy. In all settings using such instruments, measures must be taken to ensure that the women being screened are: 1) properly informed about the reasons behind the screen; 2) clearly ensured that the information obtained will remain strictly confidential; and 3) properly informed what follow-up evaluations or interventions (e.g., addiction treatment programs) may be recommended to them and that participation in these services is voluntary on their part. Screening instruments should be tested locally to gauge their sensitivity and cultural appropriateness.

3. There is some evidence and a consensus among experts to support selective use of bio-markers by physicians, with the informed consent of the client, as a follow-up to a written screen. Obtaining informed consent must be preceded by a very clear explanation given to women about the purpose of the tests, the confidentiality of the information and what follow-up evaluations or interventions (e.g., addiction treatment programs) may be recommended to them, and that participation in these services, as well as the screening interview, is strictly voluntary on their part. Special attention must be given to ways in which informed consent is obtained, including consideration of how best to fully inform women of what they are agreeing to (e.g., information given in Aboriginal languages) and the role that Aboriginal customs or historical influences of Aboriginal and non-Aboriginal relations may play in this process.

4. There is good evidence that brief interventions in prenatal settings, based on cognitive-behavioural principles, are an effective low-cost means of helping pregnant women with early-stage alcohol problems to reduce or eliminate alcohol use during pregnancy. These interventions must be developed in ways that are sensitive to both the individual and collective experiences of Aboriginal women and include, where possible, the integration of traditional Aboriginal knowledge and practices, as well as Aboriginal practitioners, such as midwives and community Elders.

5. There is some evidence to support the effectiveness of drug education programs in reducing substance use among pregnant adolescents attending prenatal clinics. Before these programs are adopted, they must be culturally sensitized to the needs of the local community. A community assessment should be undertaken to determine if these programs are the proper strategy, given the local level of substance abuse in the community. Research examining risk and protective factors in high, moderate and low risk communities that compare and contrast variables, such as social integration, community control and autonomy, could yield important information on adolescent behaviour and attitudes, thus better informing prevention and intervention strategies for this group and their communities.

6. There is some evidence and a consensus among experts that training can be effective in helping physicians and other professionals work with women who have substance use problems. Training must seek to address questions of racism and discrimination and aim at making biomedical health care practitioners sensitive to the specific needs of Aboriginal women. Support for traditional Aboriginal practitioners in rural and urban Aboriginal communities, along with traditional child-birth and rearing practices, can be important factors in assisting pregnant Aboriginal women who have substance use problems.

Appendix A

Tertiary Prevention

1. There is no evidence to support the use of punitive measures, such as mandated treatment, as being effective in improving maternal and fetal health. A consensus among experts suggests that such measures deter pregnant women from seeking needed services. Poor Aboriginal women may be particularly vulnerable to forms of coercion and measures should be taken to ensure that more positive and meaningful supports are given to those women who are struggling with substance abuse. These could include: assisting women in preparing to enter treatment by emphasizing the benefits to her health and the health of her unborn baby; listening and assisting her to address the concerns she has about entering treatment; and identifying a treatment program that will best meet her needs.

2. There is moderate evidence and a consensus among experts that combining prenatal care with other services, including substance abuse treatment, show positive outcomes for women with substance use problems and their newborn child. For smaller, isolated communities where services are limited, efforts should be made to modify this strategy at the local level to prevent women from having to travel outside the community for support services. Elders and midwives could play a central role in building and implementing local strategies.

3. There is some moderate evidence and a consensus among experts that gender-specific substance abuse treatment is more effective for women than programs serving both men and women. Gender-specific treatment targeting Aboriginal women should be sensitive to specific intergenerational experiences of Aboriginal women, particularly with regard to past sexual and physical abuse and the removal of children from their care. While Aboriginal women and men share similar intergenerational experiences, acknowledgement of experiences specific to women because of their gender and incorporation of this into mainstream and traditional addiction treatment and mental health/wellness services are essential.

4. There is some evidence and a consensus among experts that treatment services employing a respectful, flexible, culturally appropriate and women-centred approach that is open to intermediary harm reduction goals, based on client circumstances, are effective in engaging and retaining women in supportive programming and in improving the quality of their lives. However, little is known about how effective harm reduction approaches are among members of urban and rural Aboriginal communities, particularly in communities where alcohol abuse is endemic. Further research and evaluation is needed in this area.

5. There is some evidence and a consensus among experts that services with a single point of access addressing the range of social and health needs of pregnant women with substance use problems (e.g., assistance with transportation and child care, education, vocational training, job placement, housing, getting food, income support and help in accessing health care and mental health services), through collaboration between relevant service providers, are effective in engaging and retaining women in treatment. These initiatives should be based on local community priorities and traditions (including the involvement of local traditional practitioners and Elders), which should be reflected in their efforts to support women and their children.

Appendix A

6. There is strong evidence that intensive case management or coordination services that advocate for women can be effective in promoting family planning, access to substance abuse treatment, retention in treatment, reduced consumption and connections to community services for high-risk pregnant women. Organizations, such as Friendship Centres, Aboriginal Health and Wellness Centres, Aboriginal Head Start Programs and other wellness and healing services, can play an important role in providing this support for women. This service must be provided in a non-judgmental context where women feel safe accessing the service.

II. Identification

1. There is some evidence that prenatal screening for FAS is most effective when initiated by routine, collaborative screening of mothers during prenatal care. The inclusion of traditional practitioners, along with service providers being familiar with the local cultural beliefs and practices and the history of Aboriginal communities, are key in screening and identification strategies. The involvement of mentors and outreach workers, who can assist and advocate for high risk women when accessing prenatal care, will help to build trusting relationships between pregnant women and health care practitioners.

2. There is a consensus among experts that the availability of diagnostic services can be enhanced through mechanisms such as specialized training, consultation and support, telemedicine, and travelling clinics. Included in this process should be the sensitization of diagnostic tools to the local community context (e.g., psychological testing, standard measurements). Prior to the commencement of assessments diagnostic initiatives must develop intervention and support strategies, driven by the priorities of the community that will be put in place for affected individuals and their families. A collaborative effort between diagnosticians and local traditional practitioners, Elders and health and social service providers, in conjunction with community leaders and their constituents, should be prioritized in any assessment and intervention initiative, even when time and financial constraints would suggest otherwise.

3. There is a consensus among experts that, in the presence of particular maternal characteristics (including lack of prenatal care, previous unexplained fetal demise, repeated spontaneous abortion, severe mood swings and precipitous labour) or infant attributes (including prematurity, unexplained intra-uterine growth retardation, neuro-behavioural abnormalities, urogenital anomalies, myocardial infarction and blood flow restriction), selective screening for maternal substance use by taking a detailed maternal history in a supportive atmosphere can be effective in identifying children affected by prenatal use of substances other than alcohol. Support for the mother must also be prioritized, including referral and follow-up, to culturally sensitive addiction treatment and after care services.

III. Intervention

Infant and Early Childhood

1. There is a consensus among experts to support the use of a professional, multi-disciplinary team to address the range of complex health needs of affected children. The multi-disciplinary team should

be designed to work at the various levels of health care delivery, including team members, such as traditional Aboriginal practitioners and local health, education and social service providers, acting as front-line team members who coordinate their efforts with team members in hospital and clinical settings.

2. There is some evidence to suggest that a longer-term, stable living environment contributes to more positive outcomes for children affected by alcohol in-utero. This may be facilitated by family-centred substance abuse treatment, respite care, other support services and FAS-specific information and training for birth, foster and adoptive parents. Programs must be culturally-sensitive to the target group and specific attention must be given to the diversity of identities found among First Nations, Métis and Inuit populations. Biological relatives must be given the same financial support for fostering children in their extended family as non-relative foster parents and emphasis must be placed on fostering children within the community or in nearby locations where family and community members can maintain a relationship with the child.

3. There is a consensus among experts indicating that child care programs for children affected by prenatal alcohol exposure employing a low staff-child ratio, following structured routines and regulating the amount of stimulation received by the child may be more effective. Training of local child care workers to be knowledgeable and sensitive to the needs of children with FAS/ARBEs and to those of their family will greatly enhance this process. These workers should be included in the team of traditional, biomedical, education and social service professionals who are mandated to address the needs of affected children.

4. There is some evidence that services offering a single point of access, combining services for the mother with attention to the developmental needs of the child, improve outcomes for the child. These services could be incorporated into Aboriginal-run wellness and healing centres, Head Start Programs, Friendship Centres, outreach centres or expanded addiction treatment services. Coordination of various service providers, whether under one umbrella agency or within a local community context, is central to improving service access for mothers and their children.

5. There is some evidence from animal studies and studies of children experiencing developmental delay due to other causes suggesting that early educational interventions may contribute to improved outcomes for children affected by prenatal alcohol use, at least in the short term. Central to early educational interventions must be support of parents and their knowledge about the strengths and interests of their children and the empowerment of parents through culturally sensitive information on child development.

Later Childhood

1. While there is no evidence to date, there is a consensus among experts that all persons parenting an affected child benefit from on-going support and advocacy for various medical, educational and psycho-social issues that arise with children prenatally exposed to alcohol and other substances. This is particularly important for biological parents who may face several challenges not faced by adoptive and foster parents, including issues of stigma, poverty and racism.

2. There is no evidence to date, but there is a consensus among experts that children with FAS and related effects benefit from the development of an individualized education plan (IEP), tailored to meet the multiple cognitive, academic and psycho-social needs of these children, involving a range of collaborating professionals. Care givers of the child must be given a central role in this process and schools should be given the needed financial and human resources to meet the requirements of the plan.

3. To date, there is no evidence on effective educational environments; however, there is a consensus among experts that the learning environment should be generally adjusted for children with FAS and related effects by establishing: a calm and quiet environment with structure, routine and few distractions; low enrolment classrooms, resource rooms or self-contained classroom placement; defined specific work and play areas; and work spaces that are clear and routines that vary little from day to day. Other elements contributing to a suitable environment include: use of explicit instructions and visual aids to reinforce class rules and activities; repetition and hands-on learning; modelling of desired behaviours; and a caring teacher. Schools should be given the needed financial and human resources to meet these requirements for alcohol-affected children.

4. While there is no evidence on effective educational practices to date, there is a consensus among experts that consideration for school content should generally involve: an individualized curriculum with a focus on functional skills for independent living (such as problem-solving, arithmetic, social interacting and decision-making); developing realistic expectations of the child; behaviour management strategies that promise independence; adaptive living, social and communications skills; and role playing to teach logical consequences and appropriate behaviour. Schools should be given the needed financial and human resources to meet the requirements of these strategies.

Adolescence

1. While there is no evidence to date, there is a consensus among experts that adolescents with FAS and related effects benefit from assistance with basic socialization and communication skills, as well as tailored vocational counselling and employment supervision, money management training, sexuality and birth control education and drug education. These services must consider local traditional beliefs and practices and involve extended family members, Elders, traditional practitioners and other local health and social service providers.

2. There is no evidence to date, but there is a consensus among experts that adolescents with FAS or related effects, who become involved with substance abuse treatment, mental health or the correctional system, may benefit from tailored programming. Aboriginal adolescents with FAS may benefit from culturally sensitive programming, which helps to reinforce their Aboriginal identity and assists them in building support networks in the Aboriginal community after the program is completed.

3. There is no evidence to date, but there is a consensus among experts that families caring for those with FAS and related effects benefit from appropriate professional services and mutual support groups that extend over the life span of the person. Aboriginal care givers may benefit from local support groups that involve the participation of Elders and include traditional community supports.

Appendix A

4. Although those with intellectual deficits due to prenatal alcohol exposure have not been studied specifically, there is some evidence that cognitive-behavioural family therapies are effective in helping those with intellectual deficits to learn and maintain various basic living skills. Therapies involving Aboriginal families need to be sensitized to their cultural beliefs and may be more effective if they combine western and traditional therapeutic strategies.

Adulthood

1. While there is no evidence to date, there is a consensus among experts supporting the continuation of advocacy or case management to help the adult, affected by prenatal alcohol exposure, to adequately deal with the many challenges of adult life. Involvement of Aboriginal adults who are alcohol-affected in community activities, which reinforce their Aboriginal identity and teaching of traditional skills and knowledge, may assist in the continued integration of affected individuals.

2. While there is no evidence to date, there is a consensus among experts that frequently required programs, such as substance abuse treatment, employment training, mental health therapy and correctional services, need to be modified to be of benefit. Caution needs to be taken so that individuals in these programs are not labelled as having FAS/ARBEs without a medical assessment. Aboriginal adults, affected by in-utero alcohol exposure, may benefit from programs that reinforce their Aboriginal identity and help them build strong links to the Aboriginal community. Traditional practitioners and Elders could play a central role in working with affected individuals while they attend these programs or are incarcerated. This could greatly facilitate the reintegration of affected persons back into the community.

Appendix B

Diagnostic Criteria for Fetal Alcohol Syndrome (FAS) and Alcohol-Related Birth Effects (ARBE) Adopted by the American Institute of Medicine [56]

Fetal Alcohol Syndrome

1. **FAS with confirmed maternal alcohol exposure**

   A. Confirmed maternal alcohol exposure.

   B. Evidence of a characteristic pattern of facial anomalies that include features such as short palpebral fissures and abnormalities in the premaxillary zone (e.g., flat upper lip, flattened philturm and flat midface).

   C. Evidence of growth retardation, as in at least one of the following:

   - low birth weight for gestational age;

   - decelerating weight over time not due to nutrition; and

   - disproportional low weight to height.

   D. Evidence of CNS neuro-developmental abnormalities, as in at least one of the following:

   - decreased cranial size at birth;

   - structural brain abnormalities (e.g., microcephaly, partial or complete agenesis of the corpus callosum, cerebellar hypoplasia); and

   - neurological hard or soft signs (as age appropriate), such as impaired fine motor skills, neuro-sensory hearing loss, poor tandem gait, poor eye-hand coordination.

2. **FAS without confirmed maternal alcohol exposure**

   B, C, and D as above.

3. **Partial FAS with confirmed maternal alcohol exposure**

   A. Confirmed maternal alcohol exposure.

   B. Evidence of some components of the pattern of characteristic facial anomalies.

   Either C or D or E.

---

[56] From *Fetal Alcohol Syndrome: Diagnosis, Epidemiology, Prevention and Treatment* (Stratton, Howe et al., 1996).

C. Evidence of growth retardation, as in at least one of the following:

- low birth weight for gestational age;

- decelerating weight over time not due to nutrition; and

- disproportional low weight to height.

D. Evidence of CNS neuro-developmental abnormalities, as in:

- decreased cranial size at birth;

- structural brain abnormalities (e.g., microcephaly, partial or complete agenesis of the corpus callosum, cerebellar hypoplasia); and

- neurological hard or soft signs (as age appropriate), such as impaired fine motor skills, neuro-sensory hearing loss, poor tandem gait, poor eye-hand coordination.

E. Evidence of a complex pattern of behaviour or cognitive abnormalities that are inconsistent with developmental level and cannot be explained by familial background or environment alone, such as: learning difficulties; deficits in school performance; poor impulse control; problems in social perception; deficits in higher level receptive and expressive language; poor capacity for abstraction or metacognition; specific deficits in mathematical skills; or problems in memory, attention or judgment.

Alcohol-Related Effects

Clinical conditions in which there is a history of maternal alcohol exposure, and where clinical or animal research has linked maternal alcohol ingestion to an observed outcome. There are two categories that may co-occur. If both diagnoses are present, then both diagnoses should be rendered.

4. Alcohol-related birth defects (ARBD)

List of congenital anomalies, including malformations and dysplasias:

Cardiac	Atrial septal defects	Aberrant great vessels
	Ventricular septal defects	Tetralogy of Fallot
Skeletal	Hypoplasic nails	Clinodactyly
	Shortened fifth digits	Pectus excavatum and carinatum
	Radioulnar synostosis	Klippel-Feil syndrome
	Flexion contractures	Hemivertebrae
	Camptodactyly	Scoliosis

Renal	Aplastic, dysplastic	Ureteral duplications
	Hypoplastic kidneys	Hydronephrosis
	Horseshoe kidneys	
Ocular	Strabismus	Refractive problems secondary to small globes
	Retinal vascular anomalies	
Auditory	Conductive hearing loss	Neuro-sensory hearing loss
Other	Virtually every malformation has been described in some patient with FAS. The etiologic specificity of most of these anomalies to alcohol teratogenesis remains uncertain.	

5. Alcohol-related neuro-developmental disorder (ARND)

Presence of:

A. Evidence of CNS neuro-developmental abnormalities, as in any one of the following:

-   decreased cranial size at birth;

-   structural brain abnormalities (e.g., microcephaly, partial or complete agenesis of the corpus callosum, cerebellar hypoplasia); and

-   neurological hard or soft signs (as age appropriate), such as impaired fine motor skills, neuro-sensory hearing loss, poor tandem gain, poor eye-hand coordination;

and/or

B. Evidence of a complex pattern of behaviour or cognitive abnormalities that are inconsistent with developmental level and cannot be explained by familial background or environment alone, such as: learning difficulties; deficits in school performance; poor impulse control; problems in social perception; deficits in higher level receptive and expressive language; poor capacity for abstraction or metacognition; specific deficits in mathematical skills; or problems in memory, attention or judgment.

Appendix C

Screening Tools for Alcohol Use[57]

The CAGE

The CAGE is one of the oldest brief screening instruments. It is a simple 4-item yes/no alcohol screen that focuses on the consequence of drinking, rather than the quantity of frequency of alcohol consumption.

The Questions of the CAGE are:

C Have you ever tried to CUT DOWN on your drinking?

A Have people ever ANNOYED you by criticizing your drinking?

G Have you ever felt GUILTY because of something you did when you have been drinking?

E Have you ever had a morning EYE-OPENER? (Taken a drink first thing in the morning)?

One positive answer is considered an overall positive screen.

The possible advantages of the CAGE:

1. It is brief and has good validity, sensitivity and specificity.

2. It is easy to administer.

3. It can be modified to include drug use and for differing circumstances and clinical styles.

The possible disadvantages of the CAGE:

1. It does not assess quantity or frequency of use, nor consequences related to use of other drugs.

2. It is not time bound, so it can be unclear if the problem is current or historical.

T-ACE

The T-Ace is a widely used screening tool. There is a space for recording the results of the T-Ace on the antenatal record form used by physicians in British Columbia.

---

[57]   From *Community Action Guide: Working Together for the Prevention of Fetal Alcohol Syndrome* (BC FAS Resource Society, 1998:68-74).

Appendix C

The T-ACE questions are:

Tolerance

How many drinks does it take to make you feel high/feel the effects of alcohol? Record the number of drinks_____

Annoyed

Have people annoyed you by criticizing your drinking? Yes_____ No_____

Cut down

Have you felt that you ought to cut down on your drinking? Yes_____ No_____

Eye opener

Do you ever have an eye-opener – a drink first thing in the morning – to steady your nerves or get rid of a hangover? Yes_____ No_____

T question: ___score 2 points if the woman indicates 3 drinks or more.

A, C and E.

___score 1 point for a positive (yes) response.

Two or more points equal risk of a drinking problem, which may pose a risk to the fetus/offspring.

TWEAK

The TWEAK questions are:

Tolerance

How many drinks does it take to make you feel high? Record the number of drinks_____

How many drinks can you "hold"? Record the number of drinks_____

Worried

Have close friends or relatives worried or complained about your drinking in the past year? Yes_____ No_____

Appendix C

Eye Opener

Do you ever need a drink or medication of some kind first thing in the morning to steady your nerves or get over a hangover? Yes_____ No_____

Amnesia

Has a friend or family member ever told you things you said or did while you were drinking that you could not remember? Yes_____ No_____

K(C)ut Down

Have you felt that you ought to cut down on your drinking? Yes_____ No _____

T question: _____score 2 points if the woman indicates 3 drinks or more for "high" or 6 or more drinks for "hold".

W question: _____score 2 points for a positive (yes) response.

E, A and K questions: _____score 1 point for a positive (yes) response.

Two or more points equals risk of a drinking problem.

AUDIT Questionnaire

During the past 12 months

1. How often do you have a drink containing alcohol?
   (0) Never
   (1) Monthly or less
   (2) Two to Four Times a Month
   (3) Two to Three Times a Week
   (4) Four or More Times a Week

2. How many drinks containing alcohol do you have on a typical day when you are drinking?
   (0) 1 or 2
   (1) 3 or 4
   (2) 5 or 6
   (3) 7 to 9
   (4) 10 or more

Appendix C

3. How often do you have six or more drinks on one occasion?
   (0) Never
   (1) Less than monthly
   (2) monthly
   (3) weekly
   (4) daily or almost daily

4. How often during the past year have you found you were not able to stop drinking once you had started?
   (0) Never
   (1) Less than monthly
   (2) monthly
   (3) weekly
   (4) daily or almost daily

5. How often during the past year have you failed to do what was normally expected from you because of drinking?
   (0) Never
   (1) Less than monthly
   (2) monthly
   (3) weekly
   (4) daily or almost daily

6. How often during the past year have you needed a drink in the morning to get yourself going after a heavy drinking session?
   (0) Never
   (1) Less than monthly
   (2) monthly
   (3) weekly
   (4) daily or almost daily

7. How often during the past year have you had a feeling of guilt or remorse after drinking?
   (0) Never
   (1) Less than monthly
   (2) monthly
   (3) weekly
   (4) daily or almost daily

8. How often during the past year have you been unable to remember what happened the night before because you had been drinking?
   (0) Never
   (1) Less than monthly
   (2) monthly
   (3) weekly
   (4) daily or almost daily

9. Have you or someone else been injured as a result of your drinking?
    (0) No
    (2) Yes but not in the last year
    (4) Yes during the last year

10. Has a relative or friend or doctor or other health worker been concerned about your drinking or suggested you cut down?
    (0) No
    (2) Yes but not in the last year
    (4) Yes during the last year

Audit Scoring

Question 1
0=Never
1=Monthly or less
2=2 to 4 times per month
3=2 to 3 times per week
4=4 or more times per week

Question 2
0=1 or 2
1=3 or 4
2=5 or 6
3=7 to 9
4=10 or more

Question 3-8
0=Never
1=Less than monthly
2=Monthly
3=Weekly
4=Daily or almost daily

Question 9-10
0=No
2=Yes, but not in the last year
4=Yes, during the last year

The lowest score possible is 0 and the highest is 40. A score of 8 or more suggests the individual's use of alcohol may be causing her problems and indicates the need for a more in-depth assessment of her alcohol use and related issues.

References

Aase, J.M. (1981). The Fetal Alcohol Syndrome in American Indians: A High Risk Group Neurobehavioral Toxicology and Teratology 3(2): 153-156.

Aase, J.M. (1990). Diagnostic Dysmorphology. New York: Plenum Publishing.

Aase, J.M. (1994). Clinical Recognition of FAS: Difficulties of Detection and Diagnosis. Alcohol Health and Research World 18(1): 5-9.

Aase, J.M., K.L. Jones and S.K. Clarren (1995). Do We Need the Term "FAE"? Pediatrics 95(3): 428-430.

Abel, E.L. (1982). Characteristics of Mothers of Fetal Alcohol Syndrome Children. Neurobehavioral Toxicology 4: 3-4.

Abel, E.L. (1984). Fetal Alcohol Syndrome and Fetal Alcohol Effects. New York: Plenum Press.

Abel, E.L. (1988). Fetal Alcohol Syndrome in Families. Neurotoxicology and Teratology 10: 12.

Abel, E.L. (1990). Fetal Alcohol Syndrome. Oradell, NJ: Medical Economics.

Abel, E.L. (1995). An Update on Incidence of FAS: FAS Is Not an Equal Opportunity Birth Defect. Neurotoxicology and Teratology 17(4): 427-443.

Abel, E.L. (1997a). Maternal Alcohol Consumption and Spontaneous Abortion. Alcohol and Alcoholism 32(3): 211-219.

Abel, E.L. (1997b). Was the Fetal Alcohol Syndrome Recognized in the Ancient Near East? Alcohol and Alcoholism 32(1): 3-7.

Abel, E.L. (1998a). Fetal Alcohol Syndrome: The 'American Paradox'. Alcohol and Alcoholism 33(3): 195-201.

Abel, E.L. (1998b). Fetal Alcohol Abuse Syndrome. New York: Plenum Press.

Abel, E.L. (1998c). Prevention of Alcohol Abuse-Related Birth Effects - I. Public Education Efforts. Alcohol and Alcoholism 33(4): 411-416.

Abel, E.L. (1998d). Prevention of Alcohol Abuse-Related Birth Effects - II. Targeting and Pricing. Alcohol and Alcoholism 33(4): 417-420.

Abel, E.L. (1999a). What Really Causes FAS: from the sublime to the ridiculous. Teratology 60(5): 250.

Abel, E.L. (1999b). Was Fetal Alcohol Syndrome Recognized by the Greeks and Romans? Alcohol and Alcoholism 34(6): 868-872.

References

Abel, E.L. (2001). Gin Lane: Did Hogarth Know About Fetal Alcohol Syndrome? Alcohol and Alcoholism 36(2): 131-134.

Abel, E.L. and B.A. Dintcheff (1984). Factors Affecting the Outcome of Maternal Alcohol Exposure: I Parity. Neurobehavioral Toxicology and Teratology 6(5): 373-377.

Abel, E.L. and B.A. Dintcheff (1985). Factors Affecting the Outcome of Maternal Alcohol Exposure: II Maternal Age. Neurobehavioral Toxicology and Teratology 7(3): 263-266.

Abel, E.L. and J.H. Hannigan (1995). Maternal Risk Factors in Fetal Alcohol Syndrome: Provocative and Permissive Influences. Neurotoxicology and Teratology 17(4): 445-462.

Abel, E.L. and M.L. Kruger (1995). Hon Stroh Brewery Co.: What do we mean by "moderate" and "heavy" drinking? Alcoholism: Clinical and Experimental Research 19: 1024-1031.

Abel, E.L. and M.L. Kruger (1998). What do physicians know and say about fetal alcohol syndrome: a survey of obstetricians, pediatricians, and family medicine physicians. Alcoholism: Clinical and Experimental Research 22(9): 1951-1954.

Abel, E.L., S. Martier, M. Kruger, J. Ager and R.J. Sokol (1993). Ratings of Fetal Alcohol Syndrome Facial Features by Medical Providers and Biomedical Scientists. Alcoholism: Clinical and Experimental Research 17(3): 717-721.

Abel, E.L. and R.J. Sokol (1986). Fetal Alcohol Syndrome is now Leading Cause of Mental Retardation. The Lancet 2(8517): 1222.

Abel, E.L. and R.J. Sokol (1991). A Revised Conservative Estimate of the Incidence of FAS and its Economic Impact. Alcoholism: Clinical and Experimental Research 15(3): 514-524.

Abele, F., Carolyn Dittburner and Katherine A. Graham (2000). Towards a Shared Understanding in the Policy Discussion about Aboriginal Education. In Castellano, M. Brant, L. Davis and L. Lahache (eds.) (1974). Aboriginal Education: Fulfilling the Promise. Vancouver: UBC Press.

Abkarian, G.G. (1992). Communication Effects of Prenatal Exposure. Journal of Communication Disorders 25(4): 97-124.

Adams, D.W. (1995). Education for extinction: American Indians and the Boarding School Experience. Lawrence: University of Kansas Press.

Addiction Research Foundation of Ontario (1996). The Hidden Majority, a guidebook on alcohol and other drug issues for counsellors who work with women. Toronto.

Adelson, N. (2000). 'Being Alive Well': Health and the Politics of Cree Well-Being. Toronto: University of Toronto Press.

References

Adrian, M., N. Layne and R.T. Williams (1990-91). Estimating the Effect of Native Indian Population on County Alcohol Consumption: The Example of Ontario. The International Journal of the Addictions 25(5A and 6A): 731-765.

Adrian, S.R.F. (1997). An Evaluation of The Alvin Buckwold Child Development Program's Big Travelling Clinics. Saskatoon, Saskatchewan. Unpublished Report.

Albrecht, P.G.E. (1974). The Social and Psychological Reasons for the Alcohol Problems among Aborigines. In Hetzel, B.S., L. Lippmann and E. Eggleston (eds.) (1974). Better Health for Aborigines?: Report of a national seminar at Monash University. St. Lucia: University of Queensland Press.

Allen, B., L. Anglin and N. Giesbrecht (1998). Effects of Others' Drinking as Perceived by Community Members. Canadian Journal of Public Health 89(5): 337-341.

Amaro, H., L.E. Fried, H. Cabral and B. Zuckerman (1990). Violence During Pregnancy and Substance Abuse. American Journal of Public Health 80(5): 575-579.

American Academy of Pediatrics Committee on Drugs (1998). Neonatal Drug Withdrawal. Pediatrics 101(6): 1079-1088.

American Psychiatric Association (1987). Diagnostic and Statistical Manual of Mental Disorders (DSMIII-R). Washington, D.C.

American Psychiatric Association Task Force on Nomenclature and Statistics (1980). Diagnostic and Statistical Manual of Mental Disorders (DSM-III). Washington, D.C.

Ames, G.M. and L.A. Rebhun (1996). Women, Alcohol and Work: Interactions of Gender, Ethnicity and Occupational Culture. Social Science & Medicine. 43(11): 1649-1663.

Ammendola, A., D. Gemini, S. Iannaccone, F. Argenzio, G. Ciccone, E. Ammendola, L. Serio, G. Ugolini and F. Bravaccio (2000). Gender and Peripheral Neuropathy in Chronic Alcoholism: A Clinical-Electroneurographic Study. Alcohol and Alcoholism 35(4): 368-371.

Anada, R.F., D.F. Williamson and P.L. Remington (1988). Alcohol and Fatal Injuries Among US Adults. The Journal of the American Medical Association (JAMA) 260(17): 2529-2532.

Armitage, A. (1995). Comparing the policy of Aboriginal Assimilation: Australia, Canada, New Zealand. Vancouver: University of British Columbia Press.

Armor, D.J., J.M. Polich and H.B. Stambul (1976). Alcoholism and Treatment. Santa Monica, CA: Rand.

Armstrong, E.M. (1998). Diagnosing Moral Disorder: The Discovery and Evolution of Fetal Alcohol Syndrome. Social Science & Medicine, 47(12): 2025-2042.

References

Armstrong, E.M. and E.L. Abel (2000). Fetal Alcohol Syndrome: The Origins of a Moral Panic. Alcohol and Alcoholism 35(3): 276-282.

Aronson, J.E. (2000). Alcohol-Related Disorders and Children Adopted from Abroad. In Barth, R.P., M. Freundlich, and D. Brodzinsky (eds.) (2000). Adoption & Prenatal Alcohol and Drug Exposure: Research, Policy, and Practice. Washington, D.C.: Child Welfare League of America: 147-169.

Aronson, M. (1997). Children of Alcoholic Mothers: Results from Goteborg, Sweden. In Streissguth, A.P. and J. Kanter (eds.) (1997). The Challenge of Fetal Alcohol Syndrome: Overcoming Secondary Disabilities. Seattle: University of Washington Press.

Asante, K.O. (1981). FAS in northwest BC and the Yukon. BC Medical Journal 23(7): 331-335.

Asante, K.O. and J. Nelms-Matzke (1985). Survey of Children with Chronic Handicaps and Fetal Alcohol Syndrome in Yukon and British Columbia. Ottawa: National Native Advisory Council on Alcohol and Drug Abuse, Health and Welfare Canada.

Asante, K.O. and G. Robinson (1990). Pregnancy Outreach Program in British Columbia: The Prevention of Alcohol-Related Birth Defects. Canadian Journal of Public Health 81(1): 76-77.

Ashley, M.J., J.S. Olin, W.H. le Richie, A. Kornaczewski, W. Schmidt and J.G. Rankin (1977). Morbidity in Alcoholics: Evidence for Accelerated Development of Physical Disease in Women. Archives of Internal Medicine 137(7): 883-887.

Astley, S.J., D. Bailey, T. Talbot and S.K. Clarren (2000a). Fetal Alcohol Syndrome (FAS) Primary Prevention Through FAS Diagnosis: II. A Comprehensive Profile of 80 Birth Mothers of Children With FAS. Alcohol and Alcoholism 35(5): 509-519.

Astley, S.J., D. Bailey, T. Talbot and S.K. Clarren (2000b). Fetal Alcohol Syndrome (FAS) Primary Prevention Through FAS Diagnosis: I. Identification of High-Risk Birth Mothers Through the Diagnosis of Their Children. Alcohol and Alcoholism 35(5): 499-508.

Astley, S.J. and S.K. Clarren (1995). A Fetal Alcohol Syndrome Screening Tool. Alcoholism: Clinical and Experimental Research 19(6): 1565-1571.

Astley, S.J. and S.K. Clarren (2000). Diagnosing The Full Spectrum of Fetal Alcohol-Exposed Individuals: Introducing the 4-Digit Diagnostic Code. Alcohol and Alcoholism 35(4): 400-410.

Astley, S.J. and S.K. Clarren (2001). Measuring the Facial Phenotype of Individuals with Prenatal Alcohol Exposure: Correlation with Brain Dysfunction. Alcohol and Alcoholism 36(2): 147-159.

Astley, S.J., S.K. Clarren, R.E. Little, P.D. Sampson and J.R. Daling (1992). Analysis of Facial Shape in Children Gestationally Exposed to Marijuana, Alcohol, and/or Cocaine. Pediatrics 89(1): 67-77.

References

Astley, S.J., S.I. Magnuson, L.M. Omnell, S.K. Clarren (1999). Fetal Alcohol Syndrome: Changes in Craniofacial Form With Age, Cognition, and Timing of Ethanol Exposure in the Macaque. Teratology 59: 163-172.

Astley, S.J. and S.K. Clarren (1999). Diagnostic Guide for Fetal Alcohol Syndrome (FAS) and Related Conditions: The 4-digit diagnostic code. Seattle, WA: University of Washington.

Bagley, C. and R. Ramsay (1986). Sexual Abuse in Childhood: Psychosocial Outcomes and Implications for Social Work Practice. Journal of Social Work and Human Sexuality 4(1-2): 33-47.

Balicki, A. (1963). Shamanistic Behavior Among the Netsilik Eskimos. Southwestern Journal of Anthropology 19: 380-396.

Barbour, B.G. (1990). Alcohol and Pregnancy. Journal of Nurse-Midwifery 35(2): 78-85.

Barden, T.P. (1975). Prenatal Care. In Romney, S. (1975). Gynaecology and Obstetrics: the health care of women. New York: McGraw-Hill: 223.

Barker-Collo, S. (1999). Reported Symptomatology of Native Canadian and Caucasian Females Sexually Abused In Childhood: A Comparison. Journal of Interpersonal Violence 14(7): 747-760.

Barkley, R.A. (1997). Attention-Deficit/Hyperactivity Disorder, Self-Regulation, and Time: Toward a More Comprehensive Theory. Journal of Developmental and Behavioral Pediatrics 18(4): 271-279.

Barnett, C.C. (1997). A Judicial Perspective on FAS: Memories of the Making of Nanook of the Norm. In Streissguth, A. P. and J. Kanter (eds.) (1997). The Challenge of Fetal Alcohol Syndrome: Overcoming Secondary Disabilities. Seattle: University of Washington Press.

Barr, H.M. and A.P. Streissguth (2001). Identifying Maternal Self-Reported Alcohol Use Associated With Fetal Alcohol Spectrum Disorders. Alcoholism: Clinical and Experimental Research 25(2): 283-287.

Bayer, S.A. (1989). Cellular Aspects of Brain Development. Neurotoxicology 10: 307-320.

BC FAS Resource Society (1998). Community Action Guide: Working together for the prevention of Fetal Alcohol Syndrome. Victoria: British Columbia Ministry for Children and Families BC FAS Resource Society.

Beals, J., J. Piasecki, S. Nelson, M. Jones, E. Keane, P. Dauphinais, R. Red Shirt, W. Sack and S. M. Manson (1997). Psychiatric Disorder Among American Indian Adolescents: Prevalence in Northern Plains Youth. Journal of the American Academy of Child & Adolescent Psychiatry 36(9): 1252-1259.

Beauvais, F., E.R. Oetting and R.W. Edwards (1985). Trends in Drug Use of Indian Adolescents Living on Reservations: 1975-1983. The American Journal of Drug Alcohol Abuse 11(3-4): 209-229.

References

Beauvais, F., E.R. Oetting, F. Wolf and R.W. Edwards (1989). American Indian Youth and Drugs: a continuing problem. American Journal of Public Health 79(5): 634-636.

Bechtold, D.W. (1994). Indian Adolescent Suicide: Clinical and Developmental Considerations. American Indian and Alaska Native Mental Health Research: The Journal of the National Center (Monograph) 4: 71-80.

Beckett, J. (1964). Aborigines, Alcohol and Assimilation. IN Reay, M. (ed.) (1964). Aborigines Now. Sydney: Angus and Robertson.

Behrman, R.E. (1978). The effects of moderate alcohol consumption during pregnancy on fetal growth and morphogenesis. The Journal of Pediatrics 92(3): 457-460.

Beiser, M. and C.L. Attneave (1982). Mental Disorder Among Native American Children: Rates and Risks Periods Entering Treatment. American Journal of Psychiatry 139(2): 193-198.

Beitchman, J. H., K.J. Zucker, J.E. Hood, G.A. DaCosta, D. Akman and E. Cassavia (1992). A Review of the Long-term Effects of Child Sexual Abuse. Child Abuse and Neglect 16: 101-118.

Bennion, L. and T.K. Li (1976). Alcohol Metabolism in American Indians and Whites. New England Journal of Medicine 294(1): 9-13.

Benoit, C. and D. Carroll (2001). Marginalized Voices From the Downtown Eastside: Aboriginal Women Speak About Their Health Experiences. Vancouver: The National Network on Environments and Women's Health.

Berenson, A.B., N.J. Stiglich, G.S. Wilkinson and A.D. Anderson (1991). Drug Abuse and Other Risk Factors for Physical Abuse in Pregnancy Among White Non-Hispanic, Black and Hispanic Women. American Journal of Obstetrics and Gynaecology 164(6): 1491-1499.

Best Practice Network (2000). Project Guide and Application Kit. Best Practice Network established by American Association of Critical-Care Nurses, Aliso Viejo, CA.

Bijur, P.E., M. Kuzon, M.D. Overpeck and P.C. Scheidt (1992). Parental Alcohol Use, Problem Drinking and Children's Injuries. The Journal of the American Medical Association (JAMA) 267(3): 3166-3171.

Billson, J.M. and M. Stapleton (1994). Accidental Motherhood: Reproductive Control and Access to Opportunity Among Women in Canada. Women's Studies International Forum 17(4): 357-372.

Blum, K., E. Noble, P. Sheridan, T. Ritchie, P. Jagadeeswaran, H. Norgami, A. Briggs and J. Cohen (1990). Allelic Association of Human Dopamine D2 Receptor Gene in Alcoholism. The Journal of the American Medical Association 263(15): 2055-2060.

Blume, S.B. (1990). Chemical Dependency in women: important issues. American Journal of Drug and Alcohol Abuse 16(3-4): 297-307.

References

Blume, S.B. (1996). Preventing fetal alcohol syndrome: where are we now? Addiction 91(4): 473-475.

Boe, R. (2000). Aboriginal Inmates: Demographic Trends and Projections. Forum on Correctional Research 12(1): 7-9.

Boland, F.J., R. Burrill, M. Duwyn and J. Karp (1998). Fetal Alcohol Syndrome: Implications for Correctional Service (R-71). Ottawa: Correctional Service Canada.

Boland, F.J., M. Duwyn and R. Serin (2000). Fetal Alcohol Syndrome: Understanding its impact. Forum on Corrections Research 12(1): 16-18.

Boney-McCoy, S. and D. Finkelhor (1995). Prior Victimization: A Risk Factor for Child Sexual Abuse and for PTSD-related Symptomatology Among Sexually Abused Youth. Child Abuse and Neglect 19 (12): 1401-1421.

Bonthius, D.J., N.E. Bonthius, R.M.A. Napper, S.J. Astley, S.K. Clarren and J.R. West (1996). Purkinje Cell Deficits in Nonhuman Primates Following Weekly Exposure to Ethanol During Gestation. Teratology 53: 230-236.

Bookstein, F.L. (1997). Rapporteur's Report: A Summary of the Conference. In Streissguth, A.P. and J. Kanter (eds.) (1997). The Challenge of Fetal Alcohol Syndrome: Overcoming Secondary Disabilities. Seattle: University of Washington Press.

Botvin, G.J., E. Baker, L. Dusenbury, E.M. Botvin and T. Diaz (1995). Long-Term Follow-Up Results of a Randomized Drug Abuse Prevention Trial in a White Middle Class Population. Journal of the American Medical Association 273(14): 1106-1112.

Bourgois, P. and J. Bruneau (2000). Needle Exchange, HIV Infection, and the Politics of Science: Confronting Canada's Cocaine Injection Epidemic with Participant Observation. Medical Anthropology 18: 325-350.

Bowerman, R.J. (1997). The Effect of a Community-Supported Alcohol Ban on Prenatal Alcohol and Other Substance Abuse. American Journal of Public Health 87(8): 1378-1379.

Boyd, S.C. (1999). Mothers and Illicit Drugs: Transcending the Myths. Toronto: University of Toronto Press.

Boyd, T.A., C.B. Ernhart, T.H. Greene, R.J. Sokol and S. Martier (1991). Prenatal Alcohol Exposure and Sustained Attention in the Preschool Years. Neurotoxicology and Teratology 13(1): 49-55.

Brady, M. (1995). Culture in Treatment, Culture as Treatment. A Critical Appraisal of Developments in Addictions Programs for Indigenous North Americans and Australians. Social Science & Medicine 41(11): 1487-1498.

References

Brady, M. (2000). Alcohol Policy Issues for Indigenous People in the United States, Canada, Australia and New Zealand. Contemporary Drug Problems 27(Fall): 435-509.

Brady, M. and K. Palmer (1984). Alcohol in the Outback: A Study of Drinking in an Aboriginal Community. Darwin, Australian National University, North Australia Research Unit.

Brady, M. and K. Palmer (1991). Drug and Alcohol Use Among Aboriginal People. In Reid, J. and P. Trompf (eds.) (1991). The Health of Aboriginal Australia. Sydney: Harcourt Brace Jovanovich.

Brant-Castellano M., L. Davis, L. Lahache, eds. (2000). Aboriginal Education: Fulfilling the Promise. Vancouver: University of British Columbia Press.

Bray, D.L. and P.D. Anderson (1989). Appraisal of the Epidemiology of Fetal Alcohol Syndrome Among Canadian Native Peoples. Canadian Journal of Public Health 80(1): 42-45.

Bresnahan, K., B. Zuckerman and H. Cabral (1992). Psychosocial Correlates of Drug and Heavy Alcohol Use Among Pregnant Women at Risk for Drug Use. Obstetrics and Gynaecology 80(6): 976-980.

Briere, J. and M. Runtz (1987). Post Sexual Abuse Trauma: Data and Implications for Clinical Practice. Journal of Interpersonal Violence 2(4): 367-379.

Brill, H. (1970). Drugs and Aggression. Mental Health Digest 2: 11-19.

Brindis, C.D., Z. Clayson and G. Berkowitz (1997). Options for Recovery: California's Perinatal Project. Journal of Psychoactive Drugs 29(1): 89-98.

Brody, H. (1977). Alcohol, Change and the Industrial Frontier. Etudes/Inuit/Studies 1(2): 31-47.

Brody, H. (1988). Maps and Dreams: Indians and the British Columbia Frontier. Vancouver: Douglas and McIntyre.

Brown, R.T., C.D. Coles, I.E. Smith, K.A. Plazman, J. Silverstein, S. Erikson and A. Falek (1991). Effects of Prenatal Alcohol Exposure at School Age: II. Attention and Behavior. Neurotoxicology and Teratology 13(4): 369-376.

Browne, A. and D. Finkelhor (1986). Impact of Child Sexual Abuse: A Review of the Research. Psychological Bulletin 99(1): 66-77.

Browne, A. J. and J. Fiske (2001). First Nations Women's Encounters With Mainstream Health Care Services. Western Journal of Nursing Research 23(2): 126-147.

Bryce, P.H. (1907). Report on the Indian Schools of Manitoba and the Northwest Territories. Ottawa, Government Printing Bureau.

References

Bucholz, K.K., V.M. Hesselbrock, A.C. Heath, J.R. Kramar and M.A. Schuckit (2000). A latent class analysis of antisocial personality disorder symptom data from a multi-centre family study of alcoholism. Addiction 95(4): 553-567.

Bull, L. (1991). Native Residential Schooling: The Native Perspective. Canadian Journal of Native Education 18(Supplement): 3-63.

Bullock, L.F. and J. McFarlane (1989). The Birth-Weight/Battering Connection. American Journal of Nursing September: 1153-1155.

Burd, L. and M.E.K. Moffatt (1994). Epidemiology of Fetal Alcohol Syndrome in American Indians, Alaskan Natives, and Canadian Aboriginal Peoples: a Review of the Literature. Public Health Reports 109(5): 688-693.

Bushnell, J.A., J.E. Wells and M.A. Oakley-Browne (1992). Long-term Effects of Intrafamilial Sexual Abuse in Childhood. Acta Psychiatrica Scandinavica 85(2): 136-142.

Caldwell, S. (1993). Nurturing the Delicate Rose. In Kleinfeld, J. and S. Wescott (eds.) (1993). Fantastic Antone Succeeds! Experiences in Educating Children with Fetal Alcohol Syndrome. Fairbanks: University of Alaska Press.

Cariboo Tribal Council (1990). Faith Misplaced: Lasting Effects of Abuse in a First Nations Community. Canadian Journal of Native Education 18(2): 161-197.

Cariboo Tribal Council (1991). Faith Misplaced: Lasting Effects of Abuse in a First Nations Community. Williams Lake, BC: Cariboo Tribal Council.

Carr, R.A. (1995). Field-Test of a Peer Educator Workbook for the Prevention of Fetal Alcohol Syndrome and Fetal Alcohol Effects. Victoria, BC: Peer Systems Consulting Group.

Carroll, J.T. (2000). Seeds of faith: Catholic Indian Boarding Schools. New York: Garland Publishing Ltd.

Celentano, D.D. and D.V. McQueen (1984). Multiple Substance Abuse Among Women with Alcohol-Related Problems. In Wilsnack, S.C. and L.J. Beckman (eds.) (1984). Alcohol Problems in Women: antecedents, consequences and intervention. New York: Guilford: 97-116.

Centers for Disease Control (CDC) (1993). Fetal Alcohol Syndrome - United States, 1979-1992. Morbidity and Mortality Weekly Report 42(17): 339-341.

Centers For Disease Control (CDC) (1994). Alcohol Consumption and Fetal Alcohol Syndrome Awareness - Alaska, 1991 and 1993. The Journal of the American Medical Association (JAMA) 271(6): 422-423.

Centers for Disease Control (CDC) (1995). Update: Trends in Fetal Alcohol Syndrome - United States, 1979-1993. Morbidity and Mortality Weekly Report 44(13): 249-251.

References

Centers For Disease Control (CDC) (1997). Surveillance for Fetal Alcohol Syndrome Using Multiple Sources - Atlanta, Georgia, 1981-1989. Morbidity and Mortality Weekly Report 46(47): 1118-1120. Chandler, M.J. and C. Lalonde (1998). Cultural Continuity as a Hedge Against Suicide in Canada's First Nations. Transcultural Psychiatry 35(2): 191-219.

Chandy, J.M., R.W. Blum and M.D. Resnick (1996). History of Sexual Abuse and Parental Alcohol Misuse: Risk, Outcomes and Protective Factors in Adolescents. Child and Adolescent Social Work Journal 13(5): 411-431.

Chappell, M. (1996). Relief...At What Cost? Women with Disabilities and Substance Use/Misuse: Tobacco, Alcohol and Other Drugs. Ottawa: Disabled Women's Network Canada.

Chasnoff, I.J. (1992). Cocaine, Pregnancy, and the Growing Child. Current Problems in Pediatrics 22(7): 302-320.

Chavez, G. F., J.F. Cordero and J.E. Becerrant (1988). Leading Major Congenital Malformations Among Minority Groups in the United States 1981-1986. Morbidity and Mortality Weekly Report 37(SS-3): 17-25.

Chiu, A.Y., P.E. Perex and R.N. Parker (1997). Impact of Banning Alcohol on Outpatient Visits in Barrow, Alaska. Journal of the American Medical Association 278(21): 1775-1777.

Chrisjohn, R.D. and S. Young (1997). The Circle Game: Shadows and Substance in the Indian Residential School Experience in Canada. British Columbia: Theytus Books Ltd.

Chudley, A.E., D.L. Kowlessar, M. Moffatt and J.A. Evans (1999). Pitfalls in Diagnosis of FAS in a Manitoba Native School-Aged Population, Concurrent Session 4A. Prairie Province Conference on Fetal Alcohol Syndrome, Together let's find a solution, Calgary, Alberta: University of Calgary.

Church, M.W., W.L. Abel, B.A. Dintcheff and C. Matyjasik (1990). Maternal Age and Blood Alcohol Concentration in the Pregnant Long-Evans Rat. Journal of Pharmacology and Experimental Therapeutics 253(1): 192-199.

Church, M.W., W.L. Abel, B.A. Dintcheff and C. Matyjasik (1997). Hearing, Language, Speech, Vestibular, and Dentofacial Disorders in Fetal Alcohol Syndrome. Alcoholism: Clinical and Experimental Research 21(2): 227-237.

Church, M.W. and K.P. Gerkin (1988). Hearing Disorders in Children with Fetal Alcohol Syndrome: Findings from Case Reports. Pediatrics 82(2): 147-154.

Cicchetti, D. and V. Carlson (eds.) (1989). Child Maltreatment: Theory and Research on the Causes and Consequences of Child Abuse and Neglect. New York, Cambridge University Press.

References

Clark, D.B., N. Pollock, O.G. Bukstiein, A.C. Mezzich, J.T. Bromberger and J.E. Donovan (1997). Gender and Comorbid Psychopathology in Adolescents With Alcohol Dependence. Journal of the American Academy of Child & Adolescent Psychiatry 36(9): 1195-1203.

Clarren, S.K. (1978). The Fetal Alcohol Syndrome. The New England Journal of Medicine 298(19): 1063-1067.

Clarren, S.K. (1981). Recognition of Fetal Alcohol Syndrome. The Journal of the American Medical Association (JAMA) 245(23): 2436-2439.

Clarren, S.K., P.D. Sampson, J. Larsen, D.J. Donnell, H.M. Barr, F.L. Bookstein, D.C. Martin and A.P. Streissguth (1987). Facial Effects of Fetal Alcohol Exposure: Assessment by Photographs and Morphometric Analysis. American Journal of Medical Genetics 26(3): 651-666.

Clarren, S.K. (1998). FAS: A Diagnosis for Two. Finding common ground: Working together for the future. Vancouver, B.C.: Continuing Education in the Health Sciences, UBC.

Clarren, S.K. (1999). The Development of the FAS-Diagnostic and Prevention network: A practical approach to FAS identification, treatment and primary prevention. In Forum on Fetal Alcohol Syndrome, Government Conference Centre, May 25, 1999, Ottawa, Ontario. 8-20.

Clarren, S.K. and S.J. Astley (1997). Development of the FAS Diagnostic and Prevention Network in Washington State. In Streissguth, A.P. and J. Kanter (eds.) (1997). The Challenge of Fetal Alcohol Syndrome: Overcoming Secondary Disabilities. Seattle, University of Washington Press.

Clarren, S.K., S.J. Astley and D.M. Bowden (1988). Physical Anomalies and Developmental Delays in Non-human Primate Infants Exposed to Weekly Doses of Ethanol During Gestation. Teratology 37(6): 561-569.

Clarren, S.K., S.J. Astley, D.M. Bowden, H. Lai, A.H. Milan, P.K. Rudeen and W.J. Shoemaker (1990). Neuroanatomic and Neurochemical Abnormalities in Nonhuman Primate Infants Exposed to Weekly Doses of Ethanol during Gestation. Alcoholism: Clinical and Experimental Research 14(5): 674-683.

Clarren, S.K. and D.W. Smith (1978). The Fetal Alcohol Syndrome. The New England Journal of Medicine 298(19): 1063-1067.

Clarren, S.K. and D.W. Smith (1999). The Development of the FAS-Diagnostic and Prevention Network: A Practical Approach to FAS Identification, Treatment and Primary Prevention. Forum on Fetal Alcohol Syndrome, Government Conference Centre, Ottawa, Ontario.

Claxton-Oldfield, S. and S.M. Keefe (1999). Assessing Stereotypes about the Innu of Davis Inlet, Labrador. Canadian Journal of Behavioural Science 31(2): 86-91.

Clayson, Z., G. Berkowitz and C. Brindis (1995). Themes and Variations among Seven Comprehensive Perinatal Drug and Alcohol Abuse Treatment Models. Health and Social Work 20(3): 234-238.

References

Coles, C.D., R.T. Brown, I.E. Smith, K.A. Platzman, S. Erickson and A. Falek (1991). Effects of Prenatal Alcohol Exposure at School Age: I. Physical and Cognitive Development. Neurotoxicology and Teratology 13(4): 357-367.

Coles, C.D. and K.A. Platzman (1992). Fetal Alcohol Effects in Preschool Children: Research, Prevention, and Intervention. OSAP Monograph 11, Identifying the Needs of Drug-Affected Children: Public Policy Issues. Rockville, MD, U.S. Department of Health and Human Services: 59-86.

Coles, C.D., K.A. Platzman, C.L. Raskind-Hood, R.T. Brown, A. Falek and I.E. Smith (1997). A Comparison of Children Affected by Prenatal Alcohol Exposure and Attention Deficit, Hyperactivity Disorder. Alcoholism: Clinical and Experimental Research 21(1): 150-161.

Coles, C.D., I.E. Smith, P.M. Fernhoff and A. Falek (1985). Neonatal neurobehavioral characteristics as correlates of maternal alcohol use during gestation. Alcoholism: Clinical and Experimental Research 9(5): 454-460.

Collmann, J. (1979). Social Order and the Exchange of Liquor: A Theory of Drinking Among Australian Aborigines. Journal of Anthropological Research 32(2): 208-224.

Colmant, S.A. (2000). United States and Canadian Boarding Schools: A Review, Past and Present. Native American Hemispheric Journal of Indigenous Issues 17(4): 24-32.

Connors, G.J. and K.S. Walitzer (1997). Harm Reduction Interventions with Women Who are Heavy Drinkers. In Erickson, P.G., D.M. Riley, Y.W. Cheung and P.A. O'Hare (eds.) (1997). Harm Reduction: A new direction for drug policies and programs. Toronto, University of Toronto Press: 290-302.

Conry, J. (1990). Neuropsychological Deficits in Fetal Alcohol Syndrome and Fetal Alcohol Effects. Alcoholism: Clinical and Experimental Research 14(5): 650-655.

Conry, J. and D.K. Fast (2000). Fetal Alcohol Syndrome and the Criminal Justice System. Vancouver: B.C. Fetal Alcohol Syndrome Resource Society Law Foundation of British Columbia.

Copway, George (1972). The traditional history and characteristic sketches of the Ojibway nation. Toronto: Coles Publishing Co.

Couture, J.E. (1994). Aboriginal Behavioural Trauma: Towards a Taxonomy. Saskatoon, Corrections Canada.

Creamer, S. and C. McMurtrie (1998). Special Needs of Pregnant and Parenting Women in Recovery: A Move Towards a More Women-Centred Approached. Women's Health Issues 8(4): 239-245.

Dagher-Margosian, J. (1997). Representing the FAS Client in Criminal Case. In Streissguth, A.P. and J. Kanter (eds.) (1997). The Challenge of Fetal Alcohol Syndrome: Overcoming Secondary Disabilities. Seattle: University of Washington Press.

References

Davis, P.J., J.W. Partridge and C.N. Storrs (1982). Alcohol Consumption in Pregnancy. How Much is Safe? Archives of Disease in Childhood 57(12): 940-943.

Day, N.L., D. Jasperse, G. Richardson, N. Robles, U. Sambamoorthi, P. Taylor, M. Scher, D. Stoffer and M. Cornelius (1989). Prenatal Exposure to Alcohol: Effect on Infant Growth and Morphologic Characteristics. Pediatrics 84(3): 536-541.

Day, N.L., M. Cornelius, L. Goldschmidt, G. Richardson, N. Robles and P. Taylor (1992). The Effect of Prenatal Tobacco and Marijuana Use on Offspring Growth From Birth Through 3 Years of Age. Neurotoxicology and Teratology 14(6): 407-414.

Day, N.L., C.M. Cottreau and G.A. Richardson (1993). The Epidemiology of Alcohol, Marijuana, and Cocaine Use Among Women of Childbearing Age and Pregnant Women. Clinical Obstetrics and Gynecology 36(2): 232-245.

Day, N.L., N. Robles, G. Richardson, D. Geva, P. Taylor, M. Scher, D. Stoffer, M. Corenelius and L. Goldschmidt (1991). The Effects of Prenatal Alcohol Use in the Growth of Children at Three Years of Age. Alcoholism: Clinical and Experimental Research 15(1): 67-71.

Day, N.L., G.A. Richardson, N. Robles, U. Sambamoorthi, P. Taylor, M. Scher, D. Stoffer, D. Jasperse and M. Cornelius (1990). Effect of Prenatal Alcohol Exposure on Growth and Morphology of Offspring at 8 Months of Age. Pediatrics 85(5): 748-752.

Dedam, R., C. McFarlane and K. Hennessy (1993). A Dangerous Lack of Understanding. The Canadian Nurse 89(6): 29-31.

Dehaene, P., G. Crepin, F. Delahousse, D. Querleu, R. Walbaum and M. Titian (1981). Aspects épidémiologiques du syndrome d'alcoolisme foetal. La Nouvelle Presse Medicale 10(3): 2639-2643.

Deiter, C. (1999). From Our Mothers' Arms: The Intergenerational Impact of Residential Schools in Saskatchewan. Toronto: United Church Publishing House.

Deveaux, M. (1994). Feminism and Empowerment: A Critical Reading of Foucault. Feminist Studies 20(2): 223-247.

DeVries, J. and A. Waller (1997). Parent Advocacy in FAS Public Policy Change. In Streissguth, A.P. and J. Kanter (eds.) (1997). The Challenge of Fetal Alcohol Syndrome: Overcoming Secondary Disabilities. Seattle: University of Washington Press.

Dick, R.W., S.M. Manson and J. Beals (1993). Alcohol Use among Male and Female Native American Adolescents: Patterns and Correlates of Student Drinking in a Boarding School. Journal of Studies on Alcohol 54(2): 172-177.

Dickson, S. (1993). Hey Monias! The Story of Raphael Ironstand. Vancouver: Arsenal Pulp Press Limited.

References

DiLillo, D., L. Peterson and G.C. Tremblay (2000). Linking Childhood Sexual Abuse and Abusive Parenting: the mediating role of maternal anger. Child Abuse and Neglect 24(6): 767-779.

Dion Stout, M.D. (1996). Aboriginal Canada: Women and Health. Ottawa, Paper prepared for the Canada-U.S.A. Forum on Women's Health. Retrieved from: http://www.hc-sc.gc.ca/canusa/papers/canada/english/indigen.htm.

Dorris, M. (1989). The Broken Cord. New York: Harper Collins.

Dozier, E.P. (1966). Problem Drinking among American Indians: The Role of Sociocultural Deprivation. Quarterly Journal of Studies on Alcohol 27(1): 72-87.

Driscoll, C.D., A.P. Streissguth and E.P. Riley (1990). Prenatal Alcohol Exposure: Comparability of Effects in Humans and Animal Models. Neurotoxicology and Teratology 12(3): 231-237.

Duimstra, C., D. Johnson, C. Kutch, B. Wang, M. Zenter, S. Kellerman and T. Welty (1993). A Fetal Alcohol Syndrome Surveillance Pilot Project in American Indian Communities in the Northern Plains. Public Health Reports 108(2): 225-229.

Durkheim, E. (1951). Suicide: A Study in Sociology. Glencoe, Ill.: The Free Press.

Dyer, K., G. Alberts and G. Nieman (1997). Assessment and Treatment of an Adult with FAS: Neuropsychological and Behavioural Considerations. In Streissguth, A.P. and J. Kanter (eds.) (1997). The Challenge of Fetal Alcohol Syndrome: Overcoming Secondary Disabilities. Seattle: University of Washington Press.

Dzakpasu, S., L.S. Mery and K. Trouton (1998). Canadian Perinatal Surveillance System: Alcohol and Pregnancy. Ottawa: Health Canada.

Eckermann, A.K. (1977). The Binge': Some Aboriginal Views. Aboriginal Health Worker 1(4): 49-55.

Edelstein, S.B. (1995). Children with Prenatal Alcohol and/or Other Drug Exposure: Weighing the Risks of Adoption. Washington, D.C.: CWLA Press.

Edwards, C.H., O.J. Cole, J. Oyemade, E.M. Knight, A.A. Johnson, O.E. Westney, H. Laryea, W. West, S. Jones and L.S. Westney (1994). Maternal Stress and Pregnancy Outcome in a Prenatal Clinic Population. The Journal of Nutrition 124(6 supplement): 1006s-1021s.

Egeland, G.M., K.A. Perham-Hester, B.D. Gessner, D. Ingle, J.E. Berner and J.P. Middaugh (1998). Fetal Alcohol Syndrome in Alaska, 1977 through 1992: An Administrative Prevalence Derived from Multiple Data Sources. American Journal of Public Health 88(5): 781-786.

Egelko, S., M. Galanter, H. Dematis and C. DeMaio (1998). Evaluation of Multisystems Model for Treating Perinatal Cocaine Addiction. Journal of Substance Abuse Treatment 15(3): 251-259.

References

Eliany, M., S. Wortley and E. Adlaf (1991). Alcohol and other drugs used by Canadian youth: a National Alcohol and Other Drugs Survey (1989) report. Ottawa: Health Canada.

Enloe, C.F. (1980). How Alcohol Affects the Developing Fetus. Nutrition Today 15(5): 1215.

Erickson, P.G. (ed.) (1997). Harm Reduction: A new direction for drug policies and programs. Toronto: University of Toronto Press.

Ernhart, C.B., A. Wolf, R.J. Sokol, G.M. Brittenham and P. Erhard (1985). Fetal Lead Exposure: Antenatal Factors. Environmental Research 38: 54-66.

Ernhart, C.B., T. Greene, R.J. Sokol, S. Martier, T.A. Boyed and J. Ager (1995). Neonatal Diagnosis of Fetal Alcohol Syndrome: Not Necessarily a Hopeless Prognosis. Alcoholism: Clinical and Experimental Research 19(6): 1550-1557.

Ernhart, C.B., M. Morrow-Tlucak, R.J. Sokol and S. Martier (1988). Under reporting of Alcohol Use in Pregnancy. Alcoholism: Clinical and Experimental Research 12(4): 506-511.

Ernhart, C.B., R.J. Sokol, J.W. Ager, M. Morrow-Tlucak and S. Martier (1989). Alcohol-Related Birth Defects: Assessing the Risk. Annals New York Academy of Sciences 562: 159-172.

Ernst, C.C., T.M. Grant and A.P. Streissguth (1999). Intervention with High-Risk Alcohol and Drug-Abusing Mothers: II. Three year findings from Seattle Model of Paraprofessional Advocacy. Journal of Community Psychology 27(1): 19-38.

Farris, J.J. and B.M. Jones (1978b). Ethanol Metabolism in Male American Indian and Whites. Alcoholism: Clinical and Experimental Research 2(1): 77-81.

Farris, J.J. and B.M. Jones (1978a). Ethanol Metabolism and Memory Impairment in American Indian and White Women Social Drinkers. Journal of Studies on Alcohol 39: 1975-1978.

Fast, D.K., J. Conry and C.A. Loock (1999). Identifying Fetal Alcohol Syndrome Among Youth in the Criminal Justice System. Developmental and Behavioural Pediatrics 20(5): 370-372.

Federal Provincial and Territorial Advisory Committee on Population Health (1999). Statistical Report on the Health of Canadians, Meeting of Ministers of Health. Charlottetown, PEI: Minister of Public Works and Government Services Canada.

Feehan, T.M. (1996). Stories of Healing from a First Nations Perspective. M.A. Thesis. Victoria: University of Victoria.

Fenna, D., L. Mix, O. Schaefer and J.A. Gilbert (1971). Ethanol Metabolism in Various Racial Groups. Canadian Medical Association Journal 105: 472-475.

References

Fink, L.A., D. Bernstein, M.D. Handelsman, J. Foote and M. Lovejoy (1995). Initial Reliability and Validity of the Childhood Trauma Interview: A New Multidimensional Measure of Childhood Interpersonal Trauma. American Journal of Psychiatry 152(9): 1329-1335.

Finkelstein, N. (1994). Treatment Issues for Alcohol and Drug Dependent Pregnant and Parenting Women. Health and Social Work 19(1): 7-15.

Finkelstein, N., C. Kennedy, K. Thomas, M. Kearns (1997). Gender-Specific Substance Abuse Treatment. M. Kearns for the National Women's Resource Centre for the Prevention and Treatment of Alcohol, Tobacco and Other Drug Abuse and Mental Illness. Alexandria: The Centre for Substance Abuse Prevention.

Fischer, G. (2000). Treatment of opioid dependence in pregnant women. Addiction 95(8): 1141-1144.

Fischer, G., R.E. Johnson, H. Eder, R. Jagsch, A. Peternell, M. Weninger, M. Langer and H.N. Aschauer (2000). Treatment of opioid-dependent pregnant women with buprenorphine. Addiction 95(2): 239-244.

Fisher, A.D. (1987). Alcoholism and race: the misapplication of both concepts to North American Indians. The Canadian Review of Sociology and Anthropology 24(1): 81-98.

Fiske, J. (1981). And Then We Prayed Again: Carrier Women, Colonialism, and Mission Schools. Vancouver: University of British Columbia.

Fiske, J. (1996). Gender and the Paradox of Residential Education in Carrier Society. In Miller, C. and P. Chuchryk (eds.) (1996). Women of the First Nations: Power, Wisdom, and Strength. Winnipeg: University of Manitoba Press.

Fitzpatrick, J.P. (1974). Drugs, Alcohol, and Violent Crime. Addictive Diseases 1: 353-367.

Fleming, J., P.E. Mullen, B. Sibthorpe, R. Attewell and G. Bammer (1998). The Relationship Between Childhood Sexual Abuse and Alcohol Abuse in Women - A Case Control Study. Addiction 93(12): 1787-1798.

Flood, J. (1995). Archaeology of the Dreamtime: The Story of Prehistoric Australia and its People. Pymble, New South Wales: Angus and Robertson.

Fournier, S. and E. Crey (1997). Stolen From Our Embrace: The Abduction of First Nations Children and the Restoration of Aboriginal Communities. Toronto: Douglas and McIntyre.

Frank, E., B. Anderson, D.G. West and J. Lando (1988). Depressive Symptoms and Adolescent Rape Victims. In Stiffman A.R. and R.A. Feldman (eds.) (1988). Advances in Adolescent Mental Health. Greenwich, CT: JAI Press.

References

Frank, J.W., R.S. Moore and G.M. Ames (2000). Historical and Cultural Roots of Drinking Problems Among American Indians. American Journal of Public Health 90(3): 344-351.

Freud, S. (1890). The Etiology of Hysteria. In Stroskey, J. (ed.) (1968). The Standard Edition of the Complete Psychological Works of Sigmund Freud 3: 191-221. London: Hogarth.

Fried, P.A., B. Watkinson, A. Grant and R.M. Knights (1980). Changing Patterns of Soft Drug Use Prior to and During Pregnancy: A Prospective Study. Drug and Alcohol Dependence 6: 323-343.

Funkhouser, J.E. and R.W. Denniston (1985). Preventing Alcohol-Related Birth Defects. Alcohol Health and Research World 10(1): 54-59.

Furniss, E. (1992). Victims of Benevolence: The Dark Legacy of The Williams Lake Residential School. Vancouver: Arsenal Pulp Press Limited.

Gale, T.C., J.A. White and T.K. Welty (1998). Differences in Detection of Alcohol Use in a Prenatal Population (On a Northern Plains Indian Reservation) Using Various Methods of Ascertainment. South Dakota Journal of Medicine 51(7): 235-240.

Garm, A. (1999). The Sheway Project. The Canadian Nurse November: 22-25.

Gere, A.R. (1993). Cindy's Story: FAE and College. In Kleinfeld, J. and S. Wescott (eds.) (1993). Fantastic Antone Succeeds! Experiences in Educating Children with Fetal Alcohol Syndrome. Fairbanks: University of Alaska Press.

Gfellner, B.M. and J.D. Hundelby (1995). Patterns of Drug Use Among Native and White Adolescents: 1990-1993. Canadian Journal of Public Health 86: 95-97.

Gibson, G.T., P.A. Baghurst and D.P. Colley (1983). Maternal Alcohol, Tobacco and Cannabis Consumption and the Outcome of Pregnancy. The Australian and New Zealand journal of obstetrics and gynaecology 23(15): 15-19.

Gill, J. (2000). The Effects of Moderate Alcohol Consumption on Female Hormone Levels and Reproductive Function. Alcohol and Alcoholism 35(5): 417-423.

Gill, K. (1997). Overview of Research on Substance Abuse and Native Communities. Widening the Circle: Collaborative Research for Mental Health Promotion in Native Communities, Montreal, Quebec, Institute of Community and Family Psychiatry, Sir Mortimer B. Davis-Jewish General Hospital.

Gill, L. (1995). From the reserve to the city: Amerindian women in Quebec urban centers. Ottawa: Canadian Advisory Council on the Status of Women.

Giso, J.A., E. Roman, H. Inskip, V. Beral and J. Donovan (1984). Alcohol Consumption and Outcome of Pregnancy. Journal of Epidemiology and Community Health 38(3): 232-235.

References

Gladstone, J., M. Levy, I. Nulman and G. Koren (1997). Characteristics of pregnant women who engage in binge alcohol consumption. Canadian Medical Association Journal 156(6): 789-794.

Glasgow, G. (1996). The incidence of fetal alcohol syndrome in New Zealand. New Zealand Medical Journal 109(1014): 18.

Godel, J.C., B.E. Lee, D.E. McCallum, S. Lee, C. MacNeil, G. Liddell and R. Shea (2000). Exposure to Alcohol in utero: Influence on Cognitive Function and Learning in a Northern Elementary School Population. Paediatric Child Health 5(2): 93-100.

Godel, J.C., H.F. Pabst, P.E. Hodges, K.E. Johnson, G.J. Froese and M.R. Joffres (1992). Smoking and caffeine and alcohol intake during pregnancy in a northern population: effect on fetal growth. Canadian Medical Association Journal 147(2): 181-188.

Godfrey, C. (1997). Can tax be used to minimize harm? a health economist's perspective. In Plant, M., E. Single and T. Stockwell (eds.) (1997). Alcohol: Minimizing the Harm. What Works? New York: Free Association Books.

Golden, J. (1999). "An Argument That Goes Back to the Womb": The Demedicalization of Fetal Alcohol Syndrome, 1973-1992. Journal of Social History 33(2): 269-298.

Goodlett, C.R., D.M. Gilliam, J.M. Nichols and J.R. West (1989). Genetic Influence on Brain Growth Restriction Induced by Development Exposure to Alcohol. Neurotoxicology 10(3): 321-334.

Gordon, L. (1988). Heroes in Their Own Lives. New York, Penguin.

Gotowiec, A. and M. Beiser (1994). Aboriginal Children's Mental Health: Unique Challenges. Canada's Mental Health 41(4): 7-11.

Gould, S. J. (1981). The Mismeasure of Man. New York: W.W. Norton and Company.

Graefe, S. (1999). Parenting Children Affected by Fetal Alcohol Syndrome: A Guide for Daily Living. Victoria: British Columbia Ministry for Children and Families and Society of Special Needs Adoptive Parents.

Graham, E. (1997). The Mush Hole Life at Two Indian Residential Schools. Waterloo: Heffle Publishing.

Grant, A. (1996). No End of Grief: Indian Residential Schools in Canada. Winnipeg, Pemmican Publishing Inc.

Grant, B.F. and D.A. Dawson (1997). Age of Onset of Alcohol Use and its Association with DSM-IV Alcohol Abuse and Dependence: Results from the National Longitudinal Alcohol Epidemiological Survey. Journal of Substance Abuse 9: 103-110.

References

Grant, T., C. Ernst, S. McAuliff, A.P. Streissguth and Porter (1997). An Advocacy Program for Mothers with FAS/FAE. In Streissguth, A.P. and J. Kanter (eds.) (1997). The Challenge of Fetal Alcohol Syndrome: Overcoming Secondary Disabilities. Seattle: University of Washington Press.

Graves, K.L. (1993). An evaluation of the alcohol warning label: a comparison of the United States and Ontario, Canada in 1990 and 1991. Journal of Public Policy and Marketing 12(1): 19-29.

Graves, T. (1967). Acculturation, Access and Alcohol in a Tri-ethnic Community. American Anthropologist 69(3): 306-321.

Gray, D., B. Morfitt, S. Williams, K. Ryan and L. Coyne (1996). Drug Use and Related Issues Among Young Aboriginal People in Albany. Perth: National Centre for Research into the Prevention of Drug Abuse, Curtin University of Technology and Albany Aboriginal Corporation.

Grayson, H., J. Hutchins and G. Silver (eds.) (1996). Charting a Course for the Future of Women's and Perinatal Health. Baltimore, MD: Women's and Children's Health Policy Centre, John Hopkins School of Public Health.

Greene, A.H. (1993). Child Sexual Abuse: Immediate and Long-Term Effects and Intervention. Journal of the American Academy of Child & Adolescent Psychiatry 32(5): 890-902.

Greene, T., C.B. Ernhart, J. Ager, R.J. Sokol, S. Martier and T. Boyd (1991). Prenatal alcohol exposure and cognitive development in the preschool years. Neurotoxicology and Teratology 13:57-68.

Greenspan, S.I. and S. Wieder (2000). Clinical Practice Guidelines: Overview and Recommendations. Bethesda: The Interdisciplinary Council on Developmental and Learning Disorders.

Grella, C. (1996). Background and Over View of Mental Health and Substance Abuse Systems: Meeting the Needs of Women who are Pregnant or Parenting. Journal of Psychoactive Drugs 28(4): 319-343.

Gresko, J. (1986). Creating Little Dominions within the Dominion: Early Catholic Indian Schools in Saskatchewan and British Columbia: Indian Education in Canada. In Barman, J., Y. Hébert and D. McCaskill (eds.) (1986). Indian Education in Canada. Vol. I: The Legacy, Vancouver: UBC Press.

Griesler, P.C. and D.B. Kandel (1998). The Impact of Maternal Drinking during and after Pregnancy on the Drinking of Adolescent Offspring. Journal of Studies on Alcohol 59(3): 292-304.

Grisco, J.A., E. Roman, H. Inskip, V. Beral and J. Donovan (1984). Alcohol Consumption and Outcome of Pregnancy. Journal of Epidemiology and Community Health 38: 232-235.

Groenveld, J. and M. Shain (1989). Drug Use Among Victims of Physical and Sexual Abuse: A Preliminary Report. Toronto: Addiction Research Foundation.

References

Groves, P.G. (1993). Growing with FAS: Parent to Parent Advice. In Kleinfeld, J. and S. Wescott (eds.) (1993). Fantastic Antone Succeeds! Experiences in Educating Children with Fetal Alcohol Syndrome. Fairbanks: University of Alaska Press.

Gurstein, M. (1977). Urbanization and Indian People: An Analytical Literature Review. Ottawa: Indian and Northern Affairs Canada.

Habbick, B.F., J.L. Nanson and R.E. Snyder (1997). Mortality in Foetal Alcohol Syndrome. Canadian Journal of Public Health 88(3): 181-183.

Habbick, B.F., J.L. Nanson, R.E. Snyder, R.E. Casey and A.L. Schulman (1996). Foetal Alcohol Syndrome in Saskatchewan: Unchanged Incidence in a 20-year Period. Canadian Journal of Public Health 87(3): 204-207.

Habbick, B.F., W.A. Zaleski, R. Casey and F. Murphy (1979). Liver Abnormalities in Three Patients with Fetal Alcohol Syndrome. The Lancet 1(8116): 580-581.

Hacking, I. (1983). Representing and intervening: Introductory topics in the philosophy of natural science. New York: Cambridge University Press.

Hacking, I. (1986). Making Up People. In Heller, T., M. Sosna and D.E. Wellberry (eds.) (1986). Reconstructing Individualism. Stanford: Stanford University Press.

Haig-Brown, C. (1988). Resistance and Renewal: Surviving the Indian Residential School. Vancouver: Tillicum Library.

Hallowell, A. J. (1955). Culture and Experience. Philadelphia: University of Pennsylvania Press.

Halmesmaki, E. (1988). Alcohol counselling of 85 pregnant problem drinkers: effect on drinking and fetal outcome. The British Journal of Obstetrics Gynaecolgy 95: 243-247.

Halmesmaki, E., K.A. Teramo, J.A. Widness, G.K. Clemons and O. Ulikorkala (1990). Maternal Alcohol Abuse is Associated With Elevated Fetal Erythropoietin Levels. Alcohol 76(2): August 1990.

Hamer, J. (1980). Acculturation Stress and the Functions of Alcohol Among the Forest Potawatomi. In Hamer, J. and J. Steinbring (eds.) (1980). Alcohol and Native Peoples of the North. Washington, D.C.: University Press of America: 107-153.

Hamer, J. and J. Steinbring (1980). Alcohol and the North American Indian: Examples from the Subartic. Hamer, J. and J. Steinbring (eds.) (1980). Alcohol and Native Peoples of the North. Washington, D.C.: University Press of America: 1-29.

Hampton, M., E. Hampton, G. Kinunwa and L. Kinunwa (1995). Alaska Recovery and Spirit Camps: First Nations Community Development. Community Development Journal 30(3): 257-264.

References

Han, Y.H. (1969). Why do Chronic Alcoholics Require More Anesthesia? Anesthesiology 30: 341-342.

Handwerker, L. (1994). Medical Risk: Implicating Poor Pregnant Women. Social Science & Medicine 38(5): 665-675.

Hankin, B.F., J.J. Sloan, I.J. Firestone, J.W. Ager, R.J. Sokol, S.S. Martier and J. Townsend (1993a). The alcohol beverage warning label: when did knowledge increase? Alcoholism: Clinical and Experimental Research 17(2): 4328-430.

Hankin, B., I. Firestone, J. Sloan, J. Ager, R. Sokol and S. Martier. (1993b). A time series analysis of the impact of the alcohol warning label on antenatal drinking. Alcoholism: Clinical and Experimental Research 17(3): 284-289.

Hankin, B.F., J.J. Sloan, I.J. Firestone, J.W. Ager, R.J. Sokol and S.S. Martier (1996). Has awareness of the alcohol warning label reached its upper limit? Alcoholism: Clinical and Experimental Research 20(3): 440-444.

Hanna, J.M. (1978). Metabolic Responses of Chinese, Japanese and Europeans to Alcohol. Alcoholism: Clinical and Experimental Research 2(1): 89-92.

Hanson, J.W., A.P. Streissguth and D.W. Smith (1978). The effects of moderate alcohol consumption during pregnancy on fetal growth and morphogenesis. The Journal of Pediatrics 92(3): 457-460.

Harlap, S. and P.H. Shiono (1980). Alcohol, smoking, and incidence of spontaneous abortion in first and second trimester. The Lancet ii: 173-176.

Hart, M.A. (1999). Support for First Nations to Address Fetal Alcohol Syndrome. In Turpin, J. and G. Schmidt (eds.) (1999). Fetal Alcohol Syndrome/Effect: Developing A Community Response. Halifax: Fernwood Publishing: 73-79.

Hay, M., S. Olech and J. Turpin (1998). FAS/E Children in Northern BC: A Study of 148 Children in one Pediatrician's Practice. Finding common ground: Working together for the future, UBC, Vancouver, B.C.: Continuing Education in the Health Sciences.

Health and Welfare Canada (1989). Health Promotion in the Northwest Territories. Ottawa: Ministry of National Health and Welfare.

Health and Welfare Canada (1989). The Health of the Registered Indian Population in Saskatchewan. Regina: Health and Welfare Canada, Medical Services Branch.

Health Canada (1996). Rural Women and Substance Use Current Issues and Implications for Programming. Ottawa: Office of Alcohol, Drugs and Dependency Issues, Population Health Directorate.

Health Canada (1997). Canadian Perinatal Surveillance System: Progress Report 1997-1998. Ottawa: Health Canada.

References

Herman, J.L. (1992). Trauma and Recovery. New York: Basic Books, Inc.

Hess, J.J. and G. Niemann (1997). Residential Programs for Persons With FAS: Programming and Economics. In Streissguth, A.P. and J. Kanter (eds.) (1997). The Challenge of Fetal Alcohol Syndrome: Overcoming Secondary Disabilities. Seattle: University of Washington.

Higgins, S.D. and T.J. Garite (1984). Late Abruptio Placentae in Trauma Patients: Implications for Monitoring. Obstetrics Gynecology 63(3 supplement): 10-12.

Hill, T.W. (1974). From Hell-Raiser to Family Man. In Spradley, J. and D. McCurdy (eds.) (1974). Conformity and Conflict: Readings in Cultural Anthropology. Boston: Little Brown and Company.

Hinde, J. (1993). Early Intervention for Alcohol-Affected Children. In Kleinfeld, J. and S. Wescott (eds.) (1993). Fantastic Antone Succeeds! Experiences in Educating Children with Fetal Alcohol Syndrome. Fairbanks: University of Alaska Press.

Hingson, R., J.J. Alpert, N. Day, E. Dooling, H. Kayne, S. Morelock, E. Oppenheimer and B. Zuckerman (1982). Effects of Maternal Drinking and Marijuana Use on Fetal Growth and Development. Pediatrics 70(4): 539-546.

Hoaken, P.N. and R.O. Pihl (2000). The Effects of Alcohol Intoxication on Aggressive Responses in Men and Women. Alcohol and Alcoholism 35(5): 471-477.

Hoffman, H.J., K. Damas, L. Hillman and E. Krongrad (1988). Risk Factors for SIDS: Results of the National Institute of Child Health and Human Development SIDS Cooperative Epidemiological Study. Annals New York Academy of Sciences 533: 13-30.

Hogue, C.J., J.W. Buehler, L.T. Strauss and J.C. Smith (1987). Overview of the National Infant Mortality Surveillance (NIMS) project-design, methods, results. Public Health Reports 102(2): 126-138.

Holmes, L.B. (1999). Need for Inclusion and Exclusion Criteria for the Structural Abnormalities Recorded in Children Born From Exposed Pregnancies. Teratology 59(1): 1-2.

Holmgren, C., B.J. Fitzgerald and R.S. Carmen (1983). Alienation and Alcohol Use by American Indian and Caucasian High School Students. The Journal of Social Psychology 120(1st half): 139-140.

Honigmann, J.J. (1979). Alcohol in its Cultural Context. In Marshall M. (ed.) (1979). Beliefs, Behaviors and Alcoholic Beverages: a Cross-Cultural Survey. Ann Arbor: University of Michigan Press.

Honigmann, J.J. (1980). Perspectives on Alcohol Behavior. In Hamer, J. and J. Steinbring (eds.) (1980). Alcohol and Native Peoples of the North. Lanham, MD: University Press of America: 267-324.

Hornby, R. (1993). Helping Families and Their Alcohol-Affected Children. In Kleinfeld, J. and S. Wescott (eds.) (1993). Fantastic Antone Succeeds! Experiences in Educating Children with Fetal Alcohol Syndrome. Fairbanks: University of Alaska Press.

References

Hornby, R. (2000). Community Involvement: Lessons from Native Americans. In Kleinfeld, J., B. Morse and S. Wescott (eds.) (2000). Fantastic Antone Grows Up: Adolescents and Adults with Fetal Alcohol Syndrome. Fairbanks, Alaska: University of Alaska Press.

Howell, E.M., N. Heiser and M.A. Harrington (1999). Review of Recent Findings on Substance Abuse Treatment for Pregnant Women. Journal of Substance Abuse Treatment 16(3): 195-219.

Howell, E.M. and I.J. Chasnoff (1999). Perinatal Substance Abuse Treatment: Findings from Focus Groups with Clients and Providers. Journal of Substance Abuse Treatment 17(1-2): 55-58.

Humphries, D., J. Dawson, V. Cronin, P. Keating, C. Wisniewski and J. Eichfeld (1992). Mothers and Children, Drugs and Crack: Reactions to Maternal Drug Dependency. In Feinman, C. (ed.) (1992). The criminalization of a woman's body. New York: Haworth Press.

Hunter, E. (1993). Aboriginal Health and History: Power and Prejudice in Remote Australia. Melbourne: Cambridge University Press.

Hurt, W.R. and R.M. Brown (1965). Social Drinking Patterns of the Yankton Sioux. Human Organization 24: 222-230.

Hussey, D.L. and M. Singer (1993). Psychological Distress, Problem Behaviours and Family Functioning of Sexually Abused Adolescent Inpatients. Journal of the American Academy of Child and Adolescent Psychiatry 32(5): 954-961.

Hutchings, D. E. (1985). Prenatal Opioid Exposure and the Problem of Causal Inference. In Pinkert, T.M. (ed.) (1985). Current Research on the Consequences of Maternal Drug Abuse. Rockville, MD, National Institute on Drug Abuse: 6-19.

Iber, F.L. (1980). Fetal Alcohol Syndrome. Nutrition Today. September/October: 4-11.

Ihlen, B.M., A. Amundsen and L. Tronnes (1993). Reduced alcohol use in pregnancy and changed attitudes in the population. Addiction 88: 389-394.

Ing, N.R. (1991). The Effects of Residential Schools on Native Child-Rearing Practices. Canadian Journal of Native Education 18(Supplement): 67-116.

Ingersoll, K.S., I.L. Lu and D.L. Haller (1995). Predictors of in-treatment relapse in perinatal substance abusers and impact on treatment retention: A perspective study. The Journal of Psychoactive Drugs 27: 375-387.

Jackson, R. J. (1997). Public Health Implications of FAS. In Streissguth, A.P. and J. Kanter (eds.) (1997). The Challenge of Fetal Alcohol Syndrome: Overcoming Secondary Disabilities. Seattle: University of Washington Press.

References

Jacobs, K. and K. Gill (2002). Substance Abuse in an Urban Aboriginal Population: Social, Legal and Psychological Consequences. Journal of Ethnicity in Substance Abuse 1(1): 7-25.

Jacobson, J.L., S.W. Jacobson and R.J. Sokol (1996). Increased Vulnerability to Alcohol-Related Birth Defects in the Offspring of Mothers Over 30. Alcoholism: Clinical and Experimental Research 20(2): 359-363.

Jacobson, J.L., S.W. Jacobson, R.J. Sokol and T.W. Ager (1998). Relation of Maternal Age and Pattern of Pregnancy Drinking to Functionally Significant Cognitive Deficits in Infancy. Alcoholism: Clinical and Experimental Research 22(2): 345-351.

Jacobson, S.W., J.L. Jacobson, R.J. Sokol, S.S. Martier, J.W. Ager and M.G. Kaplan (1991). Maternal Recall of Alcohol, Cocaine, and Marijuana Use During Pregnancy. Neurotoxicology and Teratology 13(5): 535-540.

Janzen, H.L., S. Skakum and W. Lightning (1994). Professional Services in a Cree Native Community. Canadian Journal of School Psychology 10(1): 88-102.

Jasinski, J.L., L.M. Williams and J. Siegel (2000). Childhood Physical and Sexual Abuse as Risk Factors for Heavy Drinking among African American Women: A Prospective for Study. Child Abuse and Neglect 24(8): 1061-1071.

Johansen, B. (2000). Education - The Nightmare and The Dream: A Shared National Tragedy, A Shared National Disgrace. Native American Hemispheric Journal of Indigenous Issues 17(4): 10-20.

Johnson, K.C. and J. Rouleau (1997). Temporal Trends in Canadian Birth Defects Birth Prevalences, 1979-1993. Canadian Journal of Public Health 88(3): 169-176.

Johnson, K.G. (1979). Fetal Alcohol Syndrome: Rhinorrhea, Persistent Otitis Media, Choanal Stenosis, Hypoplastic Sphenoids and Ethmoid. Rocky Mountain Medical Journal 76(2): 64-65.

Johnston, B. (1988). Indian School Days. Toronto: Key Porter Books Ltd.

Johnston, J.C. (2000). Aboriginal Federal Offenders Surveys: A Synopsis. Forum on Correctional Research 12(1): 25-27.

Jones, K.L., D.W. Smith, C.N. Ulleland and A.P. Streissguth (1973). Pattern of Malformation in Offspring of Chronic Alcoholic Mothers. Lancet 1: 1267-1271.

Jones, K.L. and D.W. Smith (1973). Recognition of the Fetal Alcohol Syndrome in Early Infancy. The Lancet 2(7836): 999-1001.

Jones, K.L., D.W. Smith, A.P. Streissguth and N.C. Myrianthopoulos (1974). Outcome in offspring of chronic alcoholic women. The Lancet 1: 1076-1078.

References

Jones, K.L., D.W. Smith, C.N. Ulleland and P. Streissguth (1973). Pattern of Malformation in Offspring of Chronic Alcoholic Mothers. The Lancet 1(7815): 1267-1271.

Jordan, E. (1998). Developing Collaboration Among Parents, Schools and Community to Provide Early Screening and Intervention for Children Prenatally Exposed to Alcohol. National Association of School Psychologists 30th Annual Convention. Orlando, Florida: Western New Mexico University.

Jurd, S. (1996). Addiction as Disease. Perspectives on Addiction: Making Sense of the Issues. W. B. Saunders. Perth: William Montgomery.

Kahn, M., E. Hunter, N. Heather and J. Tebbutt (1990). Australian Aborigines and Alcohol: A Review. Drug and Alcohol Review 10: 351-366.

Kamien, M. (1978). The Measurement of Alcohol Consumption in Australian Aborigines. Community Health Studies II(3): 149-151.

Kaminski, M., M. Franc, M. Lebouvier, D. Du Mazubrun and C. Rumeau-Rouquette (1981). Moderate Alcohol Use and Pregnancy Outcome. Neurobehavioral Toxicology and Teratology 3(2): 173-181.

Kaminski, M., C. Rumeau and D. Schwartz (1978). Alcohol Consumption in Pregnant Women and the Outcome of Pregnancy. Alcoholism: Clinical and Experimental Research 2(2): 155-163.

Kandall, S.R. and J. Gaines (1991). Maternal Substance Use and Subsequent Sudden Infant Death Syndrome (SIDS) in Offspring. Neurotoxicology and Teratology 13(2): 235-240.

Karp, R.W. (1992). D2 or not D2. Alcoholism: Clinical and Experimental Research 16(4): 786-787.

Kaskutas, L.A. and T.K. Greenfield (1992). First effects of warning labels on alcoholic beverage containers. Drug and Alcohol Dependence 31(1): 1-14.

Kattel, L.M., D.W. Branch and J.R. Scott (1988). Occult Placental Abruption After Maternal Trauma. Obstetrics Gynecology 71(3 Pt 2): 449-453.

Kearney, M.H., S. Murphy and M. Rosenbaum (1994). Mothering on Crack Cocaine: A Grounded Theory Analysis. Social Science & Medicine 38(2): 351-361.

Kellner, F., I. Webster and F. Chanteloup (1996). Describing and Predicting Alcohol-Use-Related Harm: An Analysis of the Yukon Alcohol and Drug Survey. Substance Use and Misuse 31(11 and 12): 1619-1638.

Kellner, F., I. Webster and F. Chanteloup (1998). High-Risk Alcohol Use in the Yukon: A synthesis of research results. Whitehorse, YT: Yukon Health and Social Services.

Kelm, M. (1996). 'A Scandalous Procession': Residential Schooling and the Reformation of Aboriginal Bodies, 1900-1950. Native Studies Review 11(2): 51-89.

References

Kelm, M. (1998). Colonizing Bodies: Aboriginal Health and Healing in British Columbia 1900-50. Vancouver: UBC Press.

Kemnitzer, L.S. (1972). The Structure of Country Drinking Parties on Pine Ridge Reservation, South Dakota. Plains Anthropology 17: 134.

Kempe, C.H., F.N. Silverman, B.F. Steele, W. Droegemuller and H.K. Silver (1962). The Battered Child Syndrome. The Journal of the American Medical Association (JAMA) 181(1): 17-24.

Kenkel, D.S. and W.G. Manning (1996). Perspectives on alcohol taxation. Alcohol Health and Research World 20: 230-238.

Kenner, C. and K. D'Apolito (1997). Outcomes for Children Exposed to Drugs In Utero. Journal of Obstetric, Gynecologic, and Neonatal Nursing 26(5): 595-603.

Kerson, T.S. (1990). Targeted Adolescent Pregnancy Substance Abuse Project. Health and Social Work 15(1): 73-74.

Kessler, R.C., R.M. Crum, L.A. Warner, C.B. Nelson, J. Schulenberg and J.C. Anthony (1997). Lifetime co-occurrence of DSM-III-R alcohol abuse and dependence with other psychiatric disorder in the national comorbidity survey. Archives of General Psychiatry 54(4): 313-321.

Kettle, P.A. (1993). Homicide in Alaska Natives. Alaska Medicine 35(2): 168-172.

Khera, K.S. (1987). Maternal Toxicity in Humans and Animals: Effects on Fetal Development and Criteria for Detection. Teratugenesis Carcinogenesis and Mutagenesis 7(3): 287-295.

King, C. (1993). Raising Alcohol-Affected Twins. In Kleinfeld, J. and S. Wescott (eds.) (1993). Fantastic Antone Succeeds! Experiences in Educating Children with Fetal Alcohol Syndrome. Fairbanks: University of Alaska Press.

Kirmayer, L.J., B. Hayton, M. Malus, V. Jimenez, R. Dufour, C. Quesney, Y. Ternar, T. Yu and N. Ferrara (1992). Suicide in Canadian Aboriginal Populations: Emerging Trends in Research and Intervention. Montreal: Culture and Mental Health Research Unit, Institute of Community and Family Psychiatry Sir Mortimer S. Davis-Jewish General Hospital.

Kirmayer, L.J., K. Gill, C. Fletcher, Y. Ternar, L. Boothroyd, C. Quesney, A. Smith, N. Ferrara and B. Hayton (1993). Emerging Trends in Research on Mental Health Among Canadian Aboriginal Peoples. Montreal: Culture and Mental Health Research Unit.

Kirmayer, L.J. (1994). Suicide in Canadian Aboriginal Populations: Emerging Trends in Research and Intervention. Montreal: Royal Commission on Aboriginal Peoples, Culture and Mental Health Research Unit: 1-97.

References

Kirmayer, L.J., Gregory M. Brass and Caroline L. Tait (2000). The Mental Health of Aboriginal Peoples: Transformations of Identity and Community. Canadian Journal of Psychiatry 45(7): 607-616.

Kleinfeld, J. (1993). Introduction. In Kleinfeld, J. and S. Wescott (eds.) (1993). Fantastic Antone Succeeds! Experiences in Educating Children with Fetal Alcohol Syndrome. Fairbanks: University of Alaska Press.

Kleinfeld, J., B.A. Morse and S. Wescott (eds.) (2000). Fantastic Antone Grows Up: Adolescents and Adults with Fetal Alcohol Syndrome. Fairbanks: University of Alaska Press.

Kleinfeld, J. and S. Wescott (eds.) (1993). Fantastic Anotone Succeeds! Experiences in Educating Children with Fetal Alcohol Syndrome. Fairbanks: University of Alaska Press.

Kleinman, A. (1995). Writing at the Margin: Discourse Between Anthropology and Medicine. Berkeley: University of California Press.

Kleinman, A., Veena Das and Margaret Lock (eds.) (1997). Social Suffering. Berkeley: University of California Press.

Kline, J.A. and A.C. Roberts (1973). A Residential Alcoholism Treatment Program for American Indians. Quarterly Journal of Studies on Alcoholism 34(3): 860-868.

Kline, J.A., P. Shrout, A. Stein, M. Susser and D. Warburton (1980). Drinking during pregnancy and spontaneous abortion. Lancet ii: 176-180.

Knisely, J.S., S.B. Barker, K.S. Ingersoll and K.S. Dawson (2000). Psychopathology in substance abusing women reporting childhood sexual abuse. Journal of Addictive Diseases 19(1): 31-44.

Knockwood, I. and G. Thomas (1992). Out of the Depths the Experience of Mi'Kmaw Children at the Indian Residential School at Shubenacadie, Nova Scotia. Nova Scotia: Roseway Publishing.

Knupfer, G. (1987). Drinking for Health: The Daily Light Drinker's Fiction. British Journal of Addiction 82(5): 547-555.

Kolata, G. (1989). A New Toll of Alcohol Abuse: The Indians' Next Generation. The New York Times 137(47): 936.

Koren, G., T. Koren and J. Gladstone (1996). Mild maternal drinking and pregnancy outcome: perceived versus true risks. Clinica Chimica Acta 246(1-2): 155-162.

Kovalesky, A. and S. Flagler (1997). Child Placement Issues of Women With Addictions. Journal of Obstetric, Gynecologic and Neonatal Nursing (JOGNN) 26(5): 585-591.

Kowalsky, L.O. and M. Verhoef (1999). Northern Community Members' Perceptions of FAS/FAE: A Qualitative Study. The Canadian Journal of Native Studies 19(1): 149-168.

References

Kumpfer, K.L. and J. Bays (1995). Child Abuse and Tobacco, Alcohol and Other Drug Abuse: Causality, Coincidence or Controversy? In Jaffe, J.H. (ed.) (1995). The Encyclopaedia of Drugs and Alcohol. New York: MacMillan: 217-222.

Kunitz, S.J. (1994). Disease and Social Diversity: The European Impact on the Health of Non-Europeans. New York: Oxford University Press.

Kuzma, J.W. and D.G. Kissinger (1981). Patterns of alcohol and cigarette use in pregnancy. Neurobehavioral Toxicology and Teratology 3(2): 211-221.

LaDue, R. and T. Dunne (1997). Legal Issues and FAS. In Streissguth, A.P. and J. Kanter (eds.) (1997). The Challenge of Fetal Alcohol Syndrome: Overcoming Secondary Disabilities. Seattle: University of Washington Press.

LaDue, R.A., A.P. Streissguth and S.M. Randels (1992). Clinical considerations pertaining to adolescents and adults with Fetal Alcohol Syndrome. In Sonderegger, T.B. (ed.) (1992). *Perinatal substance abuse: Research findings and clinical implications.* Baltimore, MD: The Johns Hopkins University Press: 104-131.

Lalinee-Michaud, M., M.E. Subak, A.M. Ghadirian and V. Kovess (1991). Substance Misuse Among Native and Rural High School Students in Quebec. International Journal of Addictions 26(9): 1003-1012.

Lam, M.K., J. Homewood, A.J. Taylor and E.J. Mazurski (2000). Second Generation Effects of Maternal Alcohol Consumption During Pregnancy in Rats. Progress in Neuro-Psychopharmacol & Biological Psychiatry 24(4): 619-631.

Landesman-Dwyer, S. and A.S. Ragozin (1981). Behavioral Correlates of Prenatal Alcohol Exposure: A Four-Year Follow-Up Study. Neurobehavioral Toxicology 3(2): 187-193.

Landry, M.J. (1997). Overview of Addiction Treatment Effectiveness. Rockville, MD: SAMHSA, Office of Applied Studies, US Department of Health and Human Services.

Langeland, W. and C. Hartgers (1998). Child Sexual and Physical Abuse and Alcoholism: A Review. Journal of Studies on Alcohol 59(3): 336-348.

LaPrairie, C. (1992). Dimensions of Aboriginal Over-representation in Correctional Institutions and Implications for Crime Prevention. Ottawa: Aboriginal People's Collection, Ministry of the Solicitor General.

LaRocque, E.D. (1993). Violence in Aboriginal Communities. The Path to Healing: Report of the National Round Table on Aboriginal Health and Social Issues. Royal Commission on Aboriginal Peoples. Ottawa: Minister of Supply and Services Canada.

Larroque, B. (1992). Alcohol and the Fetus. International Journal of Epidemiology 21(4-Supplement 1): S8-S16.

References

Larsson, G. (1983). Prevention of Fetal Alcohol Effects: An Antenatal Program for Early Detection of Pregnancies at Risk. Acta Obstetricia et Gynecologica Scandinavica 62(2): 171-178.

Larsson, G. and A.B. Bohlin (1987). Fetal alcohol syndrome and preventative strategies. Pediatrician 14(1-2): 51-56.

Larsson, G., A.B. Bohlin and R. Tunell (1985). Prospective study of children exposed to variable amounts of alcohol in utero. Archives of Disease in Childhood 60(4): 316-321.

Lasser, P. (1999). Challenges and Opportunities: A Handbook for Teachers of Students with Special Needs with a focus on Fetal Alcohol Syndrome (FAS) and partial Fetal Alcohol Syndrome (pFAS). Vancouver: District Learning Services, Vancouver School Board.

Laukaran, V.H. and B.J. Van den Berg (1980). The Relationship of Maternal Attitude Towards Pregnancy Outcomes and Obstetric Complications. American Journal of Obstetrics and Gynecology 136: 374-379.

Lauridsen-Hoegh, P. (1991). Caring for Chemically Dependent Babies. Nursing B.C. 23(1): 12-16.

Lauzon, R., T. Gregoire, L. Gliksman, I. McKay and R.R. Douglas (1991). "Too much sorry business." The report of the Aboriginal Issues Unit of Northern Territory. National Report of the Royal Commission into Aboriginal Deaths in Custody, Appendix D(1). E. Johnston. Canberra: Australian Government Publishing Service.

Lauzon, R., T. Gregoire, L. Gliksman, I. McKay and R.R. Douglas (1998). Mattagami First Nation's policy to reduce alcohol-related harm. Canadian Journal of Native Studies 18(1): 37-48.

Law Commission of Canada (2000). Institutional Child Abuse-Restoring Dignity: Responding to Child Abuse in Canadian Institutions. Ottawa: Minister of Public Works and Government Services.

Legge, C. (1999). Moving Forward: FAS Activities in B.C. Vancouver: British Columbia Ministry for Children and Families.

Legge, C., Gary Roberts and Mollie Butler (2000). Situational Analysis: Fetal Alcohol Syndrome/Fetal Alcohol Effects and the Effects of Other Substance Use During Pregnancy. Ottawa: Canada's Drug Strategy, Health Canada.

Leland, J. (1976). Firewater Myths: North American Indian Drinking and Alcohol Addiction. New Brunswick: Rutgers Centers of Alcohol Studies.

Lemaster, P.L. and Connell, C.M. (1994). Health Education Interventions Among Native Americans: A Review and Analysis. Health Education Quarterly 21(4): 521-538.

Lemoine, P., H. Harousseau, J.P. Borteyru and J.C. Menuet (1968). Les enfants de parents alcooliques. Anomalies observees. A propos de 127 cas. (Children of alcoholic parents: Abnormalities observed in 127 cases.) Paris, Ouest Medical 21: 476-482.

References

Lemoine, P. and H. Lemoine (1992). Avenir des enfants de mères alcooliques (étude de 105 cas retrouvés à l'âge adulte) et qelques constatations d'intéret prophylactique. Annales de Pédiatrie 39: 226-235.

Leslie, M. and G. Roberts (2001). Enhancing Fetal Alcohol Syndrome (FAS)-related Intervention at the Prenatal and Early Childhood Stages in Canada. Ottawa: Canadian Centre on Substance Abuse.

Lester, B.M., L. LaGasse, K. Freier and S. Brunner (1996). Studies of Cocaine-Exposed Human Infants. In Wetherington, C.L., V.L. Smeriglio and L.P. Finnegan (eds.) (1996). Behavioral Studies of Drug-Exposed Offspring: Methodological Issues in Human and Animal Research. Rockville, MD: National Institute on Drug Abuse: 175-210.

Leversha, A.M. and R.E. Marks (1995). The prevalence of fetal alcohol syndrome in New Zealand. The New Zealand Medical Journal 108(1013): 502-505.

Levy, J.E. and S. Kunitz (1971). Indian Reservations, Anomie, and Social Pathologies. Southwestern Journal of Anthropology 27: 97-128.

Levy, J.E. and S. Kunitz (1974). Indian Drinking: Navajo Practices and Anglo-American Theories. New York: Wiley and Sons.

Levy, J.E. and S.J. Kunitz (1973). Indian Drinking: Problems of Data Collection and Interpretation. Proceedings of the First Annual Conference of the National Institute of Alcohol Abuse and Alcoholism, Rockville, MD.

Lewontin, R.C. (1972). The Apportionment of Human Diversity. Evolutionary Biology 6: 381-396.

Lex, B.W. (1990). Prevention of Substance Abuse Problems in Women. In Watson, R.R. (ed.) (1990). Drug and Alcohol Abuse Prevention: Drug and Alcohol Abuse Reviews Series No. 1. Clifton, NJ: Humana Press: 167-221.

Liban, C.B. and R.G. Smart (1982). Drinking and Drug Use Among Ontario Indian Students. Drug Alcohol Dependence 9: 161-171.

Lieber, C.S. (1972). Metabolism of Ethanol and Alcoholism: Racial and Acquired Factors. Annals of Internal Medicine 76(2): 326-327.

Lieberman, L.D. (1998a). Overview of Substance Abuse Prevention and Treatment Approaches in Urban, Multi-Cultural Settings: The Center for Substance Abuse Prevention Programs for Pregnant and Postpartum Women and their Infants. Women's Health Issues 8(4): 218-229.

Lieberman, L.D. (1998b). Evaluating the Success of Substance Abuse Prevention and Treatment Programs for Pregnant and Postpartum Women and Their Infants. Women's Health Issues 8(4): 218-229.

References

Lipman, E.L., D.R. Offord, M.H. Boyle and Y.A. Racine (1993). Follow-up of Psychiatric and Educational Morbidity among Adopted Children. Journal of American Academy of Child & Adolescent Psychiatry 32(5): 1007-1012.

Little, B.B., L.M. Snell, C.R. Rosenfeld, L.C. Gilstrap 3rd and N.F. Grant (1990). Failure to Recognize Fetal Alcohol Syndrome in Newborn Infants. American Journal of Diseases in Childhood 144(10): 1142-1146.

Little, R.E., F.A. Schultz and W. Mandell (1976). Drinking During Pregnancy. Journal of Studies on Alcohol 37: 375-379.

Little, R.E. (1977). Moderate alcohol use during pregnancy and decreased infant birth weight. American Journal of Public Health 67(12): 1154-1156.

Little, R.E., A.P. Streissguth, and G.M. Guzinski (1980). Prevention of Fetal Alcohol Syndrome: A Model Program. Alcoholism: Clinical and Experimental Research 4(2): 185-189.

Little, R.E., R.L. Asker, P.D. Sampson and J.H. Renwick (1986). Fetal Growth and Moderate Drinking in Early Pregnancy. American Journal of Epidemiology 123(2): 270-278.

Little, R.E. and A.P. Streissguth (1978). Drinking During Pregnancy in Alcoholic Women. Alcoholism: Clinical and Experimental Research 2(2): 179-183.

Littlefield, A., Leonard Lieberman and Larry T. Reynolds (1982). Redefining Race: The Potential Demise of a Concept in Anthropology. Current Anthropology 23: 641-647.

Lock, M. and P.A. Kaufert (eds.) (1998). Pragmatic women and body politics. Cambridge Studies in Medical Anthropology. Cambridge: Cambridge University Press.

Loebstein, R. and G. Koren (1997). Pregnancy Outcome and Neurodevelopment of Children Exposed In Utero to Psychoactive Drugs: The Motherisk Experience. Journal of Psychiatry & Neuroscience 22(3): 192-196.

Loney, E.A., K.L. Green and J. Nanson (1994). A Health Promotion Perspective on the House of Commons' Report "Foetal Alcohol Syndrome: A Preventable Tragedy." Canadian Journal of Public Health 85(4): 248-251.

Loney, E.A., B.F. Habbick and J.L. Nanson (1998). Hospital Utilization of Saskatchewan People with Fetal Alcohol Syndrome. Canadian Journal of Public Health 89(5): 333-336.

Loock, C.A., C. Kinnis, G.C. Robinson, S. Segal, F.J. Blatherwick and R.W. Armstrong (1993). Targeting High Risk Families: Prenatal Alcohol/Drug Abuse and Infant Outcomes. Vancouver: Department of Pediatrics, Faculty of Medicine, University of British Columbia.

References

Loock, C.A. (1998). Poly Drug Use. Finding common ground: Working together for the future. Vancouver, B.C.: University of British Columbia Continuing Education in the Health Sciences.

Lurie, N. (1979). The World's Oldest On-Going Protest Demonstration: North American Indian Drinking Patterns. In Marshall, M. (ed.) (1979). Beliefs, Behaviors and Alcoholic Beverages: a Cross-Cultural Survey. Ann Arbor: University of Michigan Press.

Lutke, J. (1993). Parental Advocacy for Alcohol-Affected Children. In Kleinfeld, J. and S. Wescott (eds.) (1993). Fantastic Antone Succeeds! Experiences in Educating Children with Fetal Alcohol Syndrome. Fairbanks: University of Alaska Press.

Lutke, J. (1997). Spider Web Walking: Hope for Children with FAS Through Understanding. In Streissguth, A.P. and J. Kanter (eds.) (1997). The Challenge of Fetal Alcohol Syndrome: Overcoming Secondary Disabilities. Seattle: University of Washington Press.

Mable, A.L. and J. Marriott (2001). A Path to a Better Future: A Preliminary Framework for a Best Practices Program for Aboriginal Health and Health Care. Ottawa: National Aboriginal Health Organization.

MacAndrew, C. and R. Edgerton (1969). Drunken Comportment: A Social Explanation. Chicago: Aldine Publishing.

MacDonald, J.A. (1995). The Program of the Spallumcheen Indian Band in British Columbia as a Model of Indian Child Welfare. In Blake, R.B.. and J. Keshen (eds.) (1997). Social Welfare Policy in Canada: historical readings. Thornhill, ON: Copp Clark Professional: 380-391.

MacMillan, H.L., A.B. Macmillan, D.R. Orford and J.L. Dingle (1996). Aboriginal Health. Canadian Medical Association Journal 155(1): 1569-1578.

MacMillan, J. and S. Baldwin (1993). A Pilot Study of an Alcohol Education Course for Young Women Offenders: What's Good for the Goose? Alcohol and Alcoholism 28(4): 499-504.

Maher, L. (1992). Punishment and Welfare: Crack Cocaine and the Regulation of Mothering. In Feinman, C. (ed.) (1992). The criminalization of a women's body. New York: Haworth Press.

Maillard, T., D. Lamblin, J.F. Lesure and A. Fourmaintraux (1999). Incidence of Fetal Alcohol Syndrome on the Southern Part of Reunion Island (France). Teratology 60: 51-52.

Majewski, F., J.R. Bierich, H. Loser, R. Michaelis, B. Leiber and F. Bettecken (1976). Zur klinik und pathogenese der alkohol-embryopathie; berich uber 68 falle (Clinical aspects and pathogenesis of alcohol embryopathy: A report of 68 cases. Munchener Medizinische Wochenschrift 118: 1635-1642.

Majewski, F., H. Fischback, J. Pfeiffer, and J.R. Bierich (1978). Zur Frage der Interruptiones der alkohkrankken Frauen (A Question Concerning Interruption of Pregnancy in Alcoholic Women. Deutsche Medizinesche Wochenschrift 103: 895-898.

References

Majewski, F. (1981). Alcohol Embryopathy: Some Facts and Speculations About Pathogenesis. Neurobehavioral Toxicology and Teratology 3(2): 129-144.

Majewski, F. (1993). Alcohol Embryopathy: Experience in 200 Patients. Development Brain Dysfunction 6: 248-265.

Malbin, D.B. (1993). Stereotypes and Realities: Positive Outcomes With Intervention. In Kleinfeld, J. and S. Wescott (eds.) (1993). Fantastic Antone Succeeds! Experiences in Educating Children with Fetal Alcohol Syndrome. Fairbanks: University of Alaska Press.

Manning, W.G., L. Blumberg and L.H. Moulton (1995). The demand for alcohol: the differential response to price. Journal of Health Economics 14: 123-148.

Manuel, G. and M. Posluns (1974). The Fourth World: An Indian Reality. Don Mills: Collier-Macmillan Canada Ltd.

Maracle, B. (1994). Crazywater: Native Voices on Addiction Recovery. Toronto: Penguin Books.

Marinovich, N., O. Larsson and K. Barber (1976). Comparative Metabolism Rates of Ethanol in Adults of Aboriginal and European Descent. Medical Journal of Australia 1(Special Supplement): 44-46.

Marsh, J.C., T.A. D'Aunno and B.D. Smith (2000). Increasing access and providing social services to improve drug abuse treatment for women with children. Addiction 95(8): 1237-1247.

Marsh, J.C. and N. Miller (1985). Female clients in substance abuse treatment. International Journal of the Addictions 20: 995-1019.

Martens, T., B. Daily and M. Hodgson (1988). Characteristics and Dynamics of Incest and Child Sexual Abuse, with a Native Perspective. Edmonton: Nechi Institute.

Masis, K.B. and P.A. May (1991). A Comprehensive Local Program for the Prevention of Fetal Alcohol Syndrome. Public Health Reports 106(5): 484-489.

Mason, C. (2000). Cracked Babies and the Partial Birth of a Nation: Millennialism and Fetal Citizenship. Cultural Studies 14(1): 35-60.

Mattingly, S. (1992). The Maternal-Fetal Dyad: Exploring the Two-Patient Obstetric Model. Hastings Center Report 22: 13-18.

Mattson, S.N. and E.P. Riley (1997). Neurobehavioural and Neuroanatomical Effects of Heavy Prenatal Exposure to Alcohol. In Streissguth, A.P. and J. Kanter (ed.) (1997). The Challenge of Fetal Alcohol Syndrome: Overcoming Secondary Disabilities. Seattle: University of Washington Press.

May, P.A., K.J. Hymbaugh, M. Aase and J.J. Samet (1983). Epidemiology of Fetal Alcohol Syndrome Among American Indians of the Southwest. Social Biology 30: 374-387.

References

May, P.A. (1984). Explanation of Native American Drinking: A Literature Review. In Hornby, R. and R.H. Dana (eds.) (1984). Mni Wakan and the Sioux: Respite, Release and Recreation. Brandon: Justin Publishing: 13-27.

May, P.A. (1991). Fetal Alcohol Effects Among North American Indians: Evidence and Implications for Society. Alcohol Health and Research World 15(3): 239-248.

May, P.A. (1992). Alcohol Policy Considerations for Indian Reservations and Bordertown Communities. American Indian and Alaska Native Mental Health Research 4(3): 5-59.

May, P.A. (1995). A Multiple-Level, Comprehensive Approach to the Prevention of Fetal Alcohol Syndrome (FAS) and Other Alcohol-Related Birth Defects (ARBD). International Journal of the Addictions 30(12): 1549-1602.

May, P.A. (1998). The Challenges and Beauty of a Comprehensive Approach to the Prevention of FAS. Finding Common Ground: Working Together for the Future. Vancouver, BC: University of British Columbia.

May, P.A., L. Brooke, J.P. Gossage, J. Croxford, C. Adnams, K.L. Robinson and D. Viljoen (2000). Epidemiology of Fetal Alcohol Syndrome in a South African Community in the Western Cape Province. American Journal of Public Health 90(12): 1905-1912.

May, P.A. and K.J. Hymbaugh (1983). A Pilot Project on Fetal Alcohol Syndrome Among American Indians. Alcohol Health and Research World 7(2): 3-9.

May, P.A. and K.J. Hymbaugh (1989). A Macro-level Fetal Alcohol Syndrome Prevention Program for Native Americans and Alaska Natives: Description and Evaluation. Journal of Studies on Alcohol 30(6): 508-518.

May, P.A. and M.B. Smith (1988). Some Navajo Indian Opinions About Alcohol Abuse and Prohibition: A Survey and Recommendations for Policy. Journal of Studies on Alcohol 49(4): 324-334.

Maynard, E. (1969). Drinking as Part of an Adjustment Syndrome Among the Oglala Sioux. Pine Ridge Research Bulletin 9: 35-51.

McConnell, H. (1984). False Trails Hindering Discovery. The Journal, Addiction Research Foundation of Ontario 13.

McCormick, R. (1995). The Facilitating of Healing for the First Nations People of British Columbia. Canadian Journal of Native Education 21(2): 251-322.

McCubbin, H.I., E.A. Thompson, A.I. Thompson, M.A. McCubbin and A.J. Kaston (1993). Culture, Ethnicity, and the Family: Critical Factors in Childhood Chronic Illnesses and Disabilities. Pediatrics 91: 1063-1070.

References

McCuen, G.E. (1994). Born Hooked: Poisoned in the Womb. Hudson: Gary E. McCuen Publications, Inc.

McEvoy, M. and J. Daniluk (1995). Wounds to the Soul: The Experience of Aboriginal Women Survivors of Sexual Abuse. Canadian Psychology 36: 221-235.

McKee, P.H.D. (1997). FAS and the Social Security Disability Process: Navigating the System. In Streissguth, A.P. and J. Kanter (eds.) (1997). The Challenge of Fetal Alcohol Syndrome: Overcoming Secondary Disabilities. Seattle: University of Washington.

McKenzie, D. (1993). Aboriginal Substance Use: Research Issues. Joint Research Advisory Meeting, Canadian Centre on Substance Abuse and National Native Alcohol and Drug Abuse Program, Ottawa: Canadian Centre on Substance Abuse.

McKenzie, D. (1997). Fetal Alcohol Syndrome. Canadian Centre on Substance Abuse Canadian Profile. Ottawa: Canadian Centre on Substance Abuse: 193-205.

McLellan, A.T., G.R. Grissom, D. Zanis, M. Randall, P. Brill and C.P. O'Brien (1997). Problem-service "matching" in addiction treatment: a prospective study in 4 programs. Archives of General Psychiatry 54(8): 730-735.

Mcleod, N. (1998). Coming Home Through Stories. International Journal of Canadian Studies 18: 51-66.

Medicine, B. (1969). The Changing Dakota Family and the Stresses Therein. Pine Ridge Research Bulletin 9: 1-20.

Mehl, L.E. (1993). A Prenatal Psychosocial Prevention Program to Reduce Alcohol, Smoking and Stress and Improve Birth Outcome Among Minority Women. Annual Meeting of the Northeastern Region of the Society of Teachers of Family Medicine, Akron, Ohio.

Menees, M.M. and C. Segrin (2000). The Specificity of Disrupted Processes in Families of Adult Children of Alcoholics. Alcohol and Alcoholism 35(4): 361-367.

Mercer, P.W. and K.A. Khavari (1990). Are women drinking more like men? An empirical examination of the convergence hypothesis. Alcoholism: Clinical and Experimental Research 14: 461-466.

Messer, K., K.A. Clark and S.L. Martin (1996). Characteristics Associated With Pregnant Women's Utilization of Substance Abuse Treatment Services. American Journal of Drug and Alcohol Abuse 22(3): 403-421.

Miles, D.R., D.S. Svikis, J.L. Kulstad and N.A. Haug (2001). Psychopathology in Pregnant Drug-Dependent Women With and Without Comorbid Alcohol Dependence. Alcoholism: Clinical and Experimental Research 25(7): 1012-1017.

References

Miller, B.A., W.R. Downs and M. Testa (1993). Interrelationships between Victimization Experiences and Women's Alcohol Use. Journal of Studies on Alcohol Supplement No.11: 109-117.

Miller, J. and E. Danziger (2000). "In the Care of Strangers": Walpole Island First Nation's Experience With Residential Schools After The First World War. Ontario History 92(1): 71-88.

Miller, J.R. (1987). The Irony of Residential Schooling. Canadian Journal of Native Education 14(7): 3-14.

Miller, J.R. (1989). Skyscrapers Hide the Heavens: A History of Indian-White Relations in Canada. Toronto: University of Toronto Press.

Miller, J.R. (ed.) (1991). Sweet Promises: A Reader on Indian-White Relations in Canada. Toronto: University of Toronto Press.

Miller, J.R. (1992). Denominational Rivalry in Indian Residential Education. Western Oblate Studies 2: 139-155.

Miller, J.R. (1996). Shingwauk's Vision: A History of Native Residential Schools. Toronto: University of Toronto Press.

Miller, M., J. Israel and J. Cuttone (1981). Fetal Alcohol Syndrome. Journal of Pediatric Ophthalmology and Strabismus 18(4): 6-15.

Million, D. (2000). Telling Secrets Sex, Power and Narratives in Indian Residential School Histories. Canadian Woman Studies 20(2): 92-104.

Milloy, J.S. (1999). A National Crime: The Canadian Government and the Residential School System 1879-1986. Winnipeg: University of Manitoba Press.

Minor, M.B. and B. Van Dort (1982). Prevention research on the teratological effect of alcohol. Preventive Medicine 11: 346-359.

Moffatt, M.E.K., A.E. Chudley, D. Kowlessar and J. Evans (1996). Fetal Alcohol Syndrome, Fetal Alcohol Effects and the Impact of Alcohol Exposure during Pregnancy on School Performance and Behavior in School-Age Children in a First Nation Community. Winnipeg.

Mohatt, G. (1972). The Sacred Water: The Quest for Personal Power Through Drinking Among the Teton Sioux. In McClelland, D.C., W.N. Davis, R. Kalin and E. Wanner (eds.) (1972). The Drinking Man: Alcohol and Human Motivation. New York: The Free Press: 261-275.

Moore, D. (1992). Beyond the Bottle: Introducing Anthropological Debate to Research into Aboriginal Alcohol Use. Australian Journal of Social Issues 27(3): 173-193.

References

Morrow-Tlucak, M. and C.B. Ernhart (1987). Maternal Perinatal Substance Use and Behavior at Age 3 Years (Abs.). Alcoholism: Clinical and Experimental Research 11: 213.

Morse, B.A. (1991). Fetal Alcohol Syndrome in the Developing Child. Fetal Alcohol Syndrome and Other congenital Alcohol Disorders: A National Conference on Surveillance and Prevention, Center for Disease Control, Atlanta, Georgia.

Morse, B.A. (1993). Information Processing: Identifying the Behavioral Disorders of Fetal Alcohol Syndrome. In Kleinfeld, J. and S. Wescott (eds.) (1993). Fantastic Antone Succeeds! Experiences in Educating Children with Fetal Alcohol Syndrome. Fairbanks: University of Alaska Press.

Mosley, T.M. (1996). Prototypes: An Urban Model Program of Treatment and Recovery Services for Dually Diagnosed Perinatal Program Participants. Journal of Psychoactive Drugs 28(4): 381-388.

Motiuk, L. and M. Nafekh (2000). Aboriginal Offenders in Federal Corrections: A Profile. Forum on Correctional Research 12(1): 10-15.

Murphy, M. (1993). Shut Up and Talk to Me. In Kleinfeld, J. and S. Wescott (eds.) (1993). Fantastic Antone Succeeds! Experiences in Educating Children with Fetal Alcohol Syndrome. Fairbanks: University of Alaska Press.

Murphy, S. and M. Rosenbaum (1999). Pregnant Women on Drugs. New Brunswick: Rutgers University Press.

Murphy-Brennan, M.G. and T.P. Oei (1999). Is there evidence to show that Fetal Alcohol Syndrome can be prevented? Journal of Drug Education 29(1): 5-24.

Namyniuk, L., C. Brems and S. Clarson (1997). Southcentral Foundation-Dena A Coy: A Model Program for the Treatment of Pregnant Substance-Abusing Women. Journal of Substance Abuse Treatment 13(3): 285-295.

Nanson, J.L. (1997). Binge drinking during pregnancy: Who are the women at risk? Canadian Medical Association Journal 156(6): 807.

Nanson, J.L., R. Bolaria, R.E. Snyder, B.A. Morse and L. Weiner (1995). Physician Awareness of Fetal Alcohol Syndrome: A Survey of Pediatricians and General Practitioners. Canadian Medical Association Journal 152(7): 1071-1076.

Nanson, J.L. and M. Hiscock (1990). Attention Deficits in Children Exposed to Alcohol Prenatally. Alcoholism: Clinical and Experimental Research 14(5): 665-661.

National Institute on Drug Abuse (1991). National Household Survey on Drug Abuse: Population Estimates, 1990. Rockville, MD: U.S. Department of Health and Human Services.

References

Nechi Institute (1988). Healing Is Possible: A Joint Statement on the Healing of Sexual Abuse in Native Communities. Edmonton: Nechi Institute, the Four Worlds Development Project, the Native Training Institute and New Directions Training-Alkali Lake.

Nelson, C.H., M.L. Kelley and D.H. McPherson (1985). Rediscovering Support in Social Work Practice: Lessons from Indigenous Human Services Workers. Canadian Social Work Review 23(1): 231-248.

Nelson, L.J. and N. Milliken (1988). Compelled Medical Treatment of Pregnant Women: Life, Liberty, and Law in Conflict. The Journal of the American Medical Association (JAMA) 259(7): 1060-1066.

Niccols, G.A. (1994). Fetal Alcohol Syndrome: Implications for Psychologists. Clinical Psychology Review 14(2): 91-111.

Noble, A. (1997). Is Prenatal Drug Use Child Abuse?: Reporting Practices and Coerced Treatment in California. In Erickson, P.G., D.M. Riley, Y.W. Cheung and P.A. O'Hare (eds.) (1997). Harm Reduction: A new direction for drug policies and programs. Toronto: University of Toronto Press: 174-194.

Noble, E.P. (1992). The Association of the D2 Dopamine Receptor Gene with Alcoholism and Cocaine Dependence. Paper presented at the Drug Awareness Relief and Education Symposium. Perth: Western Australia.

Nöel, D. and L. Tassé (2001). The Four Insights From Mali Pili Kizos: Results of a research that is interested in the optimal quality of life attained by twelve native women former students of residential schools after a long process of devictimization. Montreal: Quebec Native Women Inc.

Nordstrom, M.L., S. Cnattingius and B. Haglund (1993). Social Difference in Swedish Infant Mortality By Cause of Death, 1983 to 1986. American Journal of Public Health 83(1): 26-30.

Normand, C. L. and D. Rutman (1996). Caring for Children with Fetal Alcohol Syndrome. Victoria: University of Victoria School of Social Work, Child, Family and Community Research Program.

Novick, N. (1997). FAS: Preventing and Treating Sexual Deviancy. In Streissguth, A.P. and J. Kanter (eds.) (1997). The Challenge of Fetal Alcohol Syndrome: Overcoming Secondary Disabilities. Seattle: University of Washington Press.

O'Connor, M.J., M. Sigman and C. Kasari (1993). Interactional Model for the Association Among Maternal Alcohol Use, Mother-Infant Interaction, and Infant Cognitive Development. Infant Behavior Development 16: 177-192.

O'Connor, R. (1984). Alcohol and Contingent Drunkenness in Central Australia. Journal of Social Issues 19(3): 173-183.

O'Neil, J.D. (1985). Community control over health problems: Alcohol prohibition in a Canadian Inuit village. In Fortuine, R. (ed.) (1985). Circumpolar Health 84: proceedings of the 6th International Symposium, 340-3. Seattle: University of Washington Press.

References

O'Neil, J.D. (1986). The Politics of Health in the Fourth World: A Northern Canadian Example. Human Organisation 45(2): 119-128.

O'Neil, J.D. (1988). Self-determination, Medical Ideology and Health Services in Inuit Communities. In Coates, K. and G. Dacks (eds.) (1988). Northern Communities: The Prospects for Empowerment. Edmonton: Boreal Institute for Northern Studies, University of Alberta.

O'Neil, J.D. (1991). Aboriginal Health Policy for the Next Century. The Path to Healing: Report of the National Roundtable on Aboriginal Health and Social Issues. Ottawa: Royal Commission on Aboriginal Peoples.

O'Neil, J.D. (1993). Aboriginal Health Policy for the Next Century. The Path to Healing. Royal Commission on Aboriginal Peoples. Ottawa: Minister of Supply and Services Canada.

O'Neil, J.D. and P.L. Kaufert (1990). The Politics of Obstetric Care: The Inuit Experience. In Handwerker, W. (ed.) (1990). Birth and Power: Social Change and the Politics of Reproduction. Boulder: Westview Press: 53- 68.

O'Nell, T.D. and C.M. Mitchell (1996). Alcohol Use Among American Indian Adolescents: The Role of Culture in Pathological Drinking. Social Science & Medicine 42(4): 565-578.

Oei, T.P.S., L. Anderson and J. Wilks (1986). Public Attitudes To and Awareness of Fetal Alcohol Syndrome in Young Adults. Journal of Drug Education 16(2): 135-147.

Oesterheld, J.R., L. Kofoed, R. Tervo, B. Fogas, A. Wilson and H. Fiechtner (1998). Effectiveness of Methylphenidate in Native American Children with Fetal Alcohol Syndrome and Attention Deficit/ Hyperactivity Disorder: A Controlled Pilot Study. Journal of Child and Adolescent Psychopharmacology 8(1): 39-48.

Oetting, E.R., R.C. Swaim, R.S. Edwards and F. Beauvais (1989). Indian and Anglo Adolescent Alcohol Use and Emotional Distress: Path Models. American Journal of Drug and Alcohol Abuse 15: 153-172.

Oetting, E.R. and F. Beavais (1984). Epidemiology and Correlates of Alcohol Use Among American Indian Adolescents Living on Reservations. A paper presented at NIAA Conference, Bethesda, MD.

Okwumbabua, O.J. and E.J. Duryea (1987). Age of Onset, Periods of Risk, and Patterns of Progression in Drug Use Among American Indian High School Students. International Journal of the Addictions 22(12): 1269-1276.

Olegard, R., K.G. Sabvel, J. Aronsson, B. Sadin, P.R. Johnsoon and C. Carlsson (1979). Effects on the Child of Alcohol Abuse During Pregnancy. Retrospective and Prospective Studies. Acta Paediatrica Scandinavica (Supplement) 275: 112-121.

Olegard, R. (1992). Alcohol and Narcotics: Epidemiology and Pregnancy Risks. International Journal of Technology Assessment in Health Care 8(Supplement 1): 101-105.

References

Olegard, R. and K. Sabel (1979). Effects on the Child of Alcohol Abuse During Pregnancy. Acta Paediatrica Scandinavia 275: 112-121.

Olson, H.C. and D.M. Burgess (1997). Early Intervention for Children Prenatally Exposed to Alcohol and Other Drugs. In Guralnick, M.J. (ed.) (1997). Effectiveness of Early Intervention. Baltimore, MD: Paul H. Brookes Publishing: 109-146.

Olson, H.C., D.M. Burgess and A.P. Streissguth (1992). Fetal alcohol syndrome (FAS) and fetal alcohol effects: A lifespan view, with implications for early intervention. Zero to Three 13(1): 24-99.

Olson, H.C., J.J. Feldman, A.P. Streissguth, P.D. Sampson and F.L. Bookstein (1998). Neuropsychological Deficits in Adolescents with Fetal Alcohol Syndrome: Clinical Findings. Alcoholism: Clinical and Experimental Research 22(9): 1998-2012.

Olson, H.C., A.P. Streissguth, P.D. Sampson, H.M. Barr, F.L. Bookstein and K. Thiede (1997). Association of Prenatal Alcohol Exposure With Behavioural and Learning Problems in Early Adolescence. Journal of the American Academy of Child & Adolescent Psychiatry 36(9): 1187-1194.

Osborn, J.A., S.R. Harris, S.R. Harris and J. Weinberg (1993). Fetal Alcohol Syndrome: Review of the Literature With Implications for Physical Therapists. Physical Therapy 73(9): 599-607.

Paine-Andrews, A., M.L. Vincent, S.B. Fawcett, M.K. Campuzano, K.J. Harris, E.L. Williams and J.L. Fisher (1996). Replicating a Community Initiative for Preventing Adolescent Pregnancy from South Carolina to Kansas. Community Health 19(1): 14-30.

Pallan, P. (2001). Fetal Alcohol Syndrome: A Call For Action in B.C. Vancouver: The Children's Commission.

Palmer, C. (1985). Fetal alcohol effects - incidence and understanding in the Cape. South African Medical Journal 68(11): 779-7800.

Paone, D., W. Chavkin, I Willets, P. Friedman and D. Des Jarlais (1992). The impact of sexual abuse: implications for drug treatment. Journal of Women's Health 1(2): 149-153.

Patterson, R. (1984). Trauma in Pregnancy. Clinical Obstetrics and Gynecology 27(1): 32-38.

Pauly, P.J. (1996). How Did the Effects of Alcohol on Reproduction Become Scientifically Uninteresting? Journal of the History of Biology 29(1): 1-28.

Pentz, M.A., J.H. Dwyer, D.P. MacKinnon, B.R. Flay, W.B. Hanson, E.Y. Wang and C.A. Johnson (1989). A Multi community Trial for Primary Prevention of Adolescent Drug Abuse. Journal of the American Medical Association 261(22): 3259-3266.

References

Perry, C.L., C.L. Williams, S. Veblen-Mortenson, T.L. Toomy, K.A. Komro, P.S. Anstein, P.G. McGovern, J.R. Finnegan, J.L. Forster, A.C. Wagenaar and M. Wolfson (1996). Project Northland: Outcomes of a Community-Wide Alcohol Use Prevention Program During Early Adolescence. American Journal of Public Health 86(7): 956-965.

Phelps, L. (1995). Psychoeducational Outcomes of Fetal Alcohol Syndrome. School Psychology Review 24(2): 200-212.

Phelps, L. and J.A. Grabowski (1992). Fetal Alcohol Syndrome: Diagnostic Features and Psychoeducational Risk Factors. School Psychology Quarterly 7(2): 112-128.

Phillpot, B. and N. Harrison (1993). A One-Room Schoolhouse for Children with FAS/FAE. In Kleinfeld, J. and S. Wescott (eds.) (1993). Fantastic Antone Succeeds! Experiences in Educating Children with Fetal Alcohol Syndrome. Fairbanks: University of Alaska Press.

Piasecki, J.M., S.M. Manson, M.P. Biernoff, A.B. Hiat, S.S. Taylor and D.W. Bechtold (1989). Abuse and Neglect of American Indian Children: Findings from a survey of federal providers. American Indian and Alaska native mental health research: journal of the National Center 3(2): 43-62.

Piatote, B.H. (2000). Boarding Schools and the Future: The Trend Toward Meeting Specialized Needs. Native American Hemispheric Journal of Indigenous Issues 17(4): 32-37.

Plant, M. and M. Plant (1997). Alcohol education and harm minimization. In Plant, M., E. Single and T. Stockwell (eds.) (1997). Alcohol: Minimizing the Harm. What Works? New York: Free Association Books.

Plant, M.L. (1985). Women, Drinking, and Pregnancy. New York: Tavistock Publications.

Polednak, A.P. (1991). Black-White Differences in Infant Mortality in 38 Standard Metropolitan Statistical Areas. American Journal of Public Health 81(11): 1480-1482.

Poole, N. (1997). Alcohol and Other Drug Problems and BC Women: A Report to the Minister of Health from the Minister's Advisory Council on Women's Health. Victoria: British Columbia Ministry of Health and Ministry Responsible for Seniors.

Poole, N. (2000). Evaluation Report of the Sheway Project for High-Risk Pregnant and Parenting Women. Vancouver: British Columbia Centre of Excellence for Women's Health.

Poole, N. and Issac, B. (1999). Mothering and substance use: An exploratory research study on barriers and supports for women who are pregnant and parenting when accessing services for alcohol and other drug problems. Vancouver, BC: BC Centre of Excellence for Women's Health.

Potter-Efron, R.T. (1989). Differential Diagnosis of Psychological, Psychiatric and Sociocultural Conditions Associated with Aggression and Substance Abuse. Journal of Chemical Dependency Treatment 3: 37-59.

References

Powless-Sage, G.E. (1987). Perceived Causal Attribution of Drinking Antecedents In American Indian and Caucasian 9th Graders, 11th Graders and College Freshmen, University of Montana.

Qazi, Q.H. and A. Masakawa (1976). Altered Sex Ratio in Fetal Alcohol Syndrome. The Lancet 2(7975): 42.

Rafter, N.H. (1992). Claims-Making and Socio-Cultural Context in the First U.S. Eugenics Campaign. Social Problems 39(1): 17-34.

Raibmon, P. (1996). "A New Understanding of Things Indian" George Raley's Negotiation of the Indian Residential School Experience. BC Studies 110: 69-96.

Rathbun, A. (1993). Overcoming the Cycle of Failure and Frustration: Art and Other Therapies. In Kleinfeld, J. and S. Wescott (eds.) (1993). Fantastic Antone Succeeds! Experiences in Educating Children with Fetal Alcohol Syndrome. Fairbanks: University of Alaska Press.

Ray, A.J. (1974). Indians in the Fur Trade: Their Role as Hunters, Trappers and Middlemen in the Lands Southwest of Hudson Bay, 1660-1870. Toronto: University of Toronto Press.

Red Horse, J., Y. Red Horse, E. Neubeck, J. Decker (1981). A Cultural Network Model: Perspectives from an Urban American Indian Youth Project. In Red Horse, Y., S. Beane and P.A. Tolson-Gonzales (eds.) (1981). Traditional and Non-traditional Community Mental Health Services with American Indians. Tempe, AZ: Arizona State University: 30-49.

Reed, T.E., H. Kalant, R.J. Griffins, B.M. Kapur and J.G. Rankin (1976). Alcohol and Acetaldehyde Metabolism in Caucasians, Chinese and Americans. Canadian Medical Association Journal 115: 851-855.

Reed, T.E. (1985). Ethnic Differences in Alcohol Use, Abuse and Sensitivity: A Review of Genetic Interpretations. Social Biology 32(3-4): 195-209.

Reich, W., F. Earls, D. Frankel and J.J. Shayka (1993). Psychopathology in Children of Alcoholics. Journal of the American Academy of Child & Adolescent Psychiatry. Adolescent Psychiatry 32(5): 995-1002.

Remkes, T. (1993). Saying No - Completely. The Canadian Nurse June: 25-28.

Rex, D.K., W.F. Bosron, J.E. Smialek and T. Li (1985). Alcohol and Aldehyde Dehydrogenase Isoenzymes in North American Indians. Alcoholism: Clinical and Experimental Research 9(2): 147-152.

Reynolds, H. (1981). The Other Side of the Frontier: Aboriginal Resistance to the European Invasion of Australia. Ringwood, Victoria: Penguin.

Rice, D.P., S. Kelman, L.S. Miller and S. Dussmeyer (1990). The Economic Costs of Alcohol and Drug Abuse and Mental Illness: 1985. Institute for Health and Aging. San Francisco, CA: University of California.

References

Riikonen, R.S. (1994). Difference in Susceptibility to Teratogenic Effects of Alcohol in Discordant Twins Exposed to Alcohol During the Second Half of Gestation. Pediatric Neurology 11(4): 332-336.

Riley, E.P. (1990). The Long-Term Effects of Prenatal Alcohol Exposure in Rats. Alcoholism: Clinical and Experimental Research 14(5): 670-673.

Riley, E.P. and S. Barron (1989). The Behavioral and Neuroanatomical Effects of Prenatal Alcohol Exposure in Animals. Annals New York Academy of Sciences 562: 173-177.

Rivadeneira, A., L. Hamilton, L. Pressley, K. Turner, P. Cress and P. Barner (1998). Project Link. Unpublished paper, phone: (804) 786-2615.

Roberts, G. and J. Nanson (2000). Best Practices: Fetal Alcohol Syndrome/Fetal Alcohol Effects and the Effects of Other Substances Use During Pregnancy. Ottawa: Canada's Drug Strategy Division, Health Canada.

Roberts, G. and A. Ogborne (1999a). Best Practices: Substance Abuse Treatment and Rehabilitation. Ottawa: Office of Alcohol, Drugs and Dependency Issues, Health Canada.

Roberts, G. and A. Ogborne (1999b). Profile: Substance Abuse Treatment and Rehabilitation in Canada. Ottawa: Office of Alcohol, Drugs and Dependency Issues, Health Canada.

Robertson, W.B. and P.J. Manning (1974). Elastic Tissue in Uterine Blood Vessels. Journal of Pathology 112: 237-243.

Robin, R.W., B. Chester, J.K. Rasmussen, J.M. Jaranson and D. Goldman (1997). Prevalence, Characteristics, and Impact of Childhood Sexual Abuse in a Southwestern American Indian Tribe. Child Abuse and Neglect 21(8): 769-787.

Robinson, G., J. Conry and R.F. Conry (1987). Clinical profile and prevalence of fetal alcohol syndrome in an isolated community in British Columbia. Canadian Medical Association Journal 137(3): 203-207.

Robinson, T.E. and K.C. Berridge (2000). The psychology and neurobiology of addiction: an incentive sensitization view. Addiction 95(Supplement 2): S91-S117.

Robles, N. and N.L. Day (1990). Recall of Alcohol Consumption during Pregnancy. Journal of Studies on Alcohol 51(5): 403-407.

Rodenhauser, P. (1988). Cultural Barriers to Mental Health Care Delivery in Alaska. The Journal of Mental Health Demonstration 21: 60-70.

Rosett, H.L., E.M. Ouellette, L. Wiener and E. Owens (1978). Therapy of heavy drinking during pregnancy. Obstetrics Gynecology 51: 41-46.

References

Rosett, H.L. and L. Weiner (1980). Clinical and Experimental Perspectives on Prevention of the Fetal Alcohol Syndrome. Neurobehavioral Toxicology 2: 267-270.

Rosett, H.L. and L. Weiner (1984). Alcohol and the Fetus. New York: Oxford.

Rosett, H.L., L. Weiner and K.C. Edelin (1983). Treatment experience with pregnant problem drinkers. Journal of the American Medical Association 249(15): 2029-2033.

Rostand, A., M. Kaminski, N. Lelong, P. Delaene, I. Delestret, C. Klein-Bertrand, D. Qerteu and G. Crepin (1990). Alcohol use in pregnancy, craniofacial features, and fetal growth. Journal of Epidemiology and Community Health 44(4): 302-306.

Rowley, C.D. (1974). The Destruction of Aboriginal Society. Harmondsworth: Penguin.

Royal Commission on Aboriginal Peoples (1993). The Path to Healing: Report of the National Round Table on Aboriginal Health and Social Issues. Ottawa: Minister of Supply and Services Canada.

Royal Commission on Aboriginal Peoples (1995). Choosing Life: Special Report on Suicide Among Aboriginal Peoples. Ottawa: Minister of Supply and Services Canada.

Royal Commission on Aboriginal Peoples (1996a). Gathering Strength. Report of the Royal Commission on Aboriginal Peoples. Ottawa, Minister of Supply and Services Canada.

Royal Commission on Aboriginal Peoples (1996b). Looking Forward Looking Back. Report of the Royal Commission on Aboriginal Peoples. Ottawa: Minister of Supply and Services Canada.

Royal Commission on New Reproductive Technologies (1993). Proceed With Care: Final Report of the Royal Commission on New Reproductive Technologies., vol. 2. Ottawa: Minister of Government Services.

Rubel, A.J. and H.J. Kupferer (1968). Perspective on the Atomistic-Type Society: Introduction. Human Organisation 27: 189-190.

Russell, D. (1983). The Incidence and Prevalence of Intrafamilial and Extrafamilial Sexual Abuse of Female Children. Child Abuse and Neglect 7(2): 133-146.

Russell, D. (1986). The Secret Trauma: Incest in the lives of girls and women. New York: Basic Books.

Russell, M., S.S. Martier, R.J. Sokol, P. Mudar, S. Jacobson and J. Jacobson (1996). Detecting Risk Drinking During Pregnancy: A Comparison of Four Screening Questionnaires. American Journal of Public Health 86(10): 1435-1439.

Rutman, D. and C.L. Normand (1996). Working with Families Affected by Fetal Alcohol Syndrome/ Effects. Victoria: University of Victoria School of Social Work, Child, Family and Community Research Program.

References

Ryland, S. and L. Lucas (1996). A Rural Collaborative Model of Treatment and Recovery Services for Pregnant and Parenting Women with Dual Disorders. Journal of Psychoactive Drugs 28(4): 389-395.

Sackett, L. (1988). Resisting Arrests: Drinking, Development and Discipline in a Desert Context. Social Analysis 24(December): 66-77.

Saggers, S. and D. Gray (1991). Aboriginal Health and Society. Sydney: Allen and Unwin.

Saggers, S. and D. Gray (1998). Dealing with Alcohol: Indigenous Usage in Australia, New Zealand and Canada. Cambridge: Cambridge University Press.

Saiz, M. (1993). Getting Jeffrey Ready for School: Kindergarten at Home. In Kleinfeld, J. and S. Wescott (eds.) (1993). Fantastic Antone Succeeds! Experiences in Educating Children with Fetal Alcohol Syndrome. Fairbanks: University of Alaska Press.

Salaspuro, M. (1993). Nutrient Intake and Nutritional Status in Alcoholics. Alcohol and Alcoholism 28(1): 85-88.

Sampson, P.D., A.P. Streissguth, F.L. Bookstein, R.E. Little, S.K. Clarren, P. Dehaene, J.W. Hanson and J.M. Graham Jr. (1997). Incidence of Fetal Alcohol Syndrome and Prevalence of Alcohol-Related Neurodevelopmental Disorder. Teratology 56(6): 317-326.

Sanchis, R., M. Sancho-Tello, M. Chirivella and C. Guerri (1987). The Role of Maternal Alcohol Damage on Ethanol Teratogenicity in the Rat. Teratology 36(2): 199-208.

Sancho-Tello, M., J. Renau-Piqueras, R. Baguena-Cerveller and C.A. Guerri (1987). A Biochemical and Stereological Study of Neonatal Rat Hepatocyte Subpopulations. Virchows Archive B, Cell pathology including molecular pathology 54(3): 170-181.

Sansom, B. (1980). The Camp at Wallaby Cross: Aboriginal Fringe-dwellers in Darwin. Canberra: Australian Institute of Aboriginal Studies.

Sarvela, P.D. and T.D. Ford (1993). An Evaluation of a Substance Abuse Education Program for Mississippi Delta Pregnant Adolescents. Journal of School Health 63(3): 147-152.

Satzewich, V. and L. Mahood (1995). Indian Agents and the Residential School System in Canada, 1946-1970. Historical Studies in Education 7(1): 45-69.

Saunders, B. and M. Phillips (1993). Is 'Alcoholism' Genetically Transmitted? And are there any implications for prevention? Drug and Alcohol Review 12: 291-298.

Savishinsky, J.S. (1991). The Ambiguities of Alcohol: Deviance, Drinking, and Meaning in a Canadian Native Community. Anthropologica 33(1-2): 81-98.

References

Savitz, D.A., P.J. Schwingl and M.A. Keels (1991). Influence of Paternal Age, Smoking, and Alcohol Consumption on Congenital Anomalies. Teratology 44: 429-440.

Scammon, D.L., R.N. Mayer and K. Smith (1991). Alcohol warnings: How do you know when you have had one too many? Journal of Public Policy and Marketing 10: 214-228.

Scarpellini, F., M. Sbracia and L. Scarpellini (1994). Psychological Stress and Lipoperoxidation in Miscarriage. Annals New York Academy of Sciences 709: 210-213.

Scarpetti, F.R. and M.L. Anderson (1989). Social Problems. New York: Harper and Row.

Schaefer, O. (1981). Firewater myths revisited. Journal of Studies on Alcohol 9: 99-117.

Schenker, S., H.C. Becker, C.L. Randall, D.K. Phillips, G.S. Baskin and G.I. Henderson (1990). Fetal Alcohol Syndrome: Current Status of Pathogenesis. Alcoholism: Clinical and Experimental Research 14(5): 635-647.

Scheper-Hughes, N. (1998). Institutionalized Sex Abuse and the Catholic Church. In Scheper-Hughes, N. and C. Sargent (eds.) (1998). Small Wars: The Cultural Politics of Childhood. Berkeley: University of California Press: 295-317.

Schmucker, C.A. (1997). Case Managers and Independent Living Instructors: Practical Hints and Suggestion for Adults with FAS. In Streissguth, A.P. and J. Kanter (eds.) (1997). The Challenge of Fetal Alcohol Syndrome: Overcoming Secondary Disabilities. Seattle: University of Washington Press.

Scholters, G. (1979). Liver Function and Liver Diseases During Pregnancy. Journal of Perinatal Medicine 7: 55-68.

Schorling, J.B. (1993). The Prevention of Prenatal Alcohol Use: A Critical Analysis of Intervention Studies. Journal of Studies on Alcohol 54: 261-267.

Schuckit, M.A., T.L. Smith, J. Kalmijn, J. Tsuang, V. Hesselbrock and K. Bucholz (2000). Response to Alcohol in Daughters of Alcoholics: A Pilot Study and a Comparison With the Sons of Alcoholics. Alcohol and Alcoholism 35(3): 242-248.

Schumacker, J.E., S.H. Siegal, J.C. Socol, S. Harkless and K. Freeman (1996). Making Evaluation Work in a Substance Abuse Treatment Program for Women with Children: Olivia's House. Journal of Psychoactive Drugs 28(1): 73-83.

Scott, K. (1986). Self-Evaluation: Its relationship to substance use in native adolescents. Unpublished Masters thesis. Health Studies Department, University of Waterloo.

Scott, K. (1997). Indigenous Canadians. Chapter 5. In McKenzie, D., R. Williams and E. Single (eds.) (1997). Canadian Profile: Alcohol, Tobacco and Other Drugs. Ottawa, ON: Canadian Centre on Substance Addiction: 133-164.

References

Seidenberg, J. and F. Majewski (1978). On the Frequency of Embryopathy in the Different Phases of Maternal Alcoholism. Suchtgefahren 24: 63-75.

Serdula, M., D.F. Williamson, J. Kendrick, R.F. Anda and T. Byers (1991). Trends in Alcohol Consumption by Pregnant Women: 1985 Through 1988. The Journal of the American Medical Association (JAMA) 265(7): 876-879.

Shepard, T.H., M. Barr Jr., R.L. Brent, A. Henderickx, D. Kochhar, G.Oakley and W.J. Scott Jr. (2000). A History of the Teratology Society. Teratology 62(5): 301-316.

Sher, K.J. (1991a). Psychological Characteristics of Children of Alcoholics: Overview of Research Methods and Findings. Recent Developments in Alcoholism 9: 301-326.

Sher, K.J. (1991b). Children of Alcoholics: A Critical Appraisal of Theory and Research. Chicago: University of Chicago Press.

Sher, K.J., B.S. Gershuny, L. Peterson and G.L. Raskin (1997). The Role of Childhood Stressors in the Intergenerational Transmission of Alcohol Use Disorders. Journal of Studies on Alcohol 58(4): 414-427.

Shiono, P.H., M.A. Klebanoff and G.G. Rhoads (1986). Smoking and Drinking During Pregnancy: Their effects on preterm birth. The Journal of the American Medical Association (JAMA) 255(1): 82-84.

Shkilnyk, A. (1985). A Poison Stronger Than Love: The Destruction of an Ojibwa Community. New Haven and London: Yale University Press.

Simmons, G. (1978). Explaining Social Policy: The English Mental Deficiency Act of 1913. Journal of Social History 2(3): 397-403.

Simpson, T.L., V.S. Westerberg, L.M. Little and J. Trujillo (1994). Screening for Childhood Physical Abuse and Sexual Abuse Among Outpatient Substance Abusers. Journal of Substance Abuse Treatment 11(4): 347-358.

Sinclair, E. (1998). Head Start Children At-Risk: Relationship of prenatal drug exposure to identification of special needs and subsequent special education kindergarten placement. Behavioural Disorders 23(2): 125-133.

Single, E. and S. Wortley (1993). Drinking in Various Settings As It Relates to Demographic Variables and Level of Consumption: Findings from a National Survey in Canada. Journal of Studies on Alcohol 54(5): 590-599.

Smart, R.G. and A.C. Ogborne (1986). Northern Spirits: Drinking in Canada Then and Now. Toronto: Addiction Research Foundation.

References

Smith, D.F., G.G. Sandor, P.M. MacLeod, S. Tredwell, B. Wood and D.E. Newman (1981). Intrinsic Defects in the Fetal Alcohol Syndrome: Studies on 76 Cases from British Columbia and the Yukon Territory. Neurobehavioral Toxicology and Teratology 3(2): 145-152.

Smith, I.E., C.D. Coles, J.S. Lancaster, P.M. Fernhoff and A. Falek (1986). The effect of volume and duration of prenatal ethanol exposure on neonatal physical and behavioural development. Neurobehavioral Toxicology and Teratology 8: 375-381.

Smith, I.E., J.S. Lancaster and S. Moss-Wells (1987). Identifying High-Risk Pregnant Drinkers: Biological and Behavioral Correlates of Continuous Heavy Drinking during Pregnancy. Journal of Studies on Alcohol 48(4): 304-309.

Smith, L.T. (1999). Decolonizing Methodologies: research and indigenous peoples. Dunedin, NZ: University of Otago Press.

Smylie, J. (2000). A Guide for Health Professionals Working with Aboriginal Peoples: The Sociocultural Context of Aboriginal Peoples in Canada. Journal of the Society of Obstetricians and Gynaecologists of Canada 100: 1070-1081.

Snyder, J., J.L. Nanson, R. Synder and G. Block (1997). A Study of Stimulant Medication in Children with FAS. In Streissguth, A.P. and J. Kanter (ed.) (1997). The Challenge of Fetal Alcohol Syndrome: Overcoming Secondary Disabilities. Seattle: University of Washington Press.

Society of Special Needs Adoptive Parents (1999). Parenting Children Affected by Fetal Alcohol Syndrome. Victoria: British Columbia Ministry for Children and Families Edition.

Sokol, R.J., J. Ager, S. Martier, S. Debanne, C. Ernhart, J. Kuzma and S.I. Miller (1986). Significant Determinants of Susceptibility to Alcohol Teratogenicity. Annals New York Academy of Sciences 477(1): 87-102.

Sokol, R.J. and S.K. Clarren (1989). Guidelines for Use of Terminology Describing the Impact of Prenatal Alcohol on the Offspring. Alcoholism: Clinical and Experimental Research 13(4): 597-598.

Sokol, R.J., S. Martier and J.W. Ager (1989). The T-ACE questions: Practical prenatal detection of risk-drinking. American Journal of Obstetrics and Gynecology 160(4): 863-870.

Sokol, R.J., S.I. Miller and G. Reed (1980). Alcohol Abuse During Pregnancy: An Epidemiologic Study. Alcoholism: Clinical and Experimental Research 4(2): 135-145.

Southall, D.P., J.R. Alexander, V.A. Stebbens, V.G. Taylor and N.E. Janczynski (1987). Cardiorespiratory Patterns in Siblings of Babies with Sudden Infant Death Syndrome. Archives of Disease in Childhood 62: 721-726.

Spak, L., F. Spak and P. Allebeck (1998). Sexual Abuse and Alcoholism in a Female Population. Addiction 93(9): 1365-1373.

References

Speck, D. C. (1987). An Error in Judgement: The Politics of Medical Care in an Indian/White Community. Vancouver: Talon.

Spicer, P. (1997). Toward a (Dys)functional Anthropology of Drinking: Ambivalence and the American Indian Experience with Alcohol. Medical Anthropology Quarterly 11(3): 306-323.

Spohr, H.L., J. Willms and H.C. Steinhausen (1983). Prenatal Alcohol Exposure and Long-Term Developmental Consequences. The Lancet 341(8850): 907-910.

Spohr, H.L., J. Willms and H.C. Steinhausen (1984). Discussion. In Pratt, O.E. and R. Doshik (eds.) (1984). Range of Alcohol-Induced Damage in the Developing Central Nervous System. London: Pitman: 153.

Spohr, H.L. and H.C. Steinhausen (1987). Follow-up Studies of Children with Fetal Alcohol Syndrome. Neuropediatrics 18: 13-17.

Spohr, H.L. and H.C. Steinhausen (1994). Fetal Alcohol Syndrome in Adolescence. Acta Paediatrica 404(Supplement): 19-26.

Square, D. (1997). Fetal alcohol syndrome epidemic on Manitoba reserve. Canadian Medical Association Journal 157(1): 59-60.

Square, D. (1999). Fetal alcohol syndrome diagnosed by telelink in Manitoba. Canadian Medical Association Journal 160(5): 627.

Standing Committee on Health and Welfare, Social Affairs, Seniors and the Status of Women: House of Commons (1992). Foetal Alcohol Syndrome: A Preventable Tragedy. Ottawa: House of Commons.

Statistics Canada (1993). Language, Tradition, Health, Lifestyle and Social Issues. 1991, Aboriginal Peoples Survey. Ottawa: Statistics Canada, Post Censal Surveys Program.

Steckley, J.L. and B. Cummins (2001). Full Circle. Canada's First Nations. Toronto: Prentice Hall.

Steinhausen, H.C., D. Gobel and V. Nestler (1984). Psychopathology in the Offspring of Alcoholic Parents. Journal of the American Academy of Child & Adolescent Psychiatry 23(4): 465-471.

Steinhausen, H.C., V. Nestler and H. Huth (1982). Psychopathology and Mental Functions in the Offspring of Alcoholic and Epileptic Mothers. Journal of the American Academy of Child & Adolescent Psychiatry 21(3): 268-273.

Steinhausen, H.C., J. Willms and H.L. Spohr (1993). Long-Term Psychopathological and Cognitive Outcome of Children with Fetal Alcohol Syndrome. Journal of the American Academy of Child & Adolescent Psychiatry 32(5): 990-994.

References

Steinhausen, H.C., V. Nestler and H.L. Spohr (1982). Development and Psychopathology of Children with the Fetal Alcohol Syndrome. Developmental and Behavioral Pediatrics 3(2): 49-54.

Stevens, R.G. and L. Hilakivi-Clarke (2001). Alcohol Exposure In Utero and Breast Cancer Risk Later In Life. Alcohol and Alcoholism 36(3): 276-277.

Stewart, D. (1993). Hey Monias! The Story of Raphael Ironstand. Vancouver: Arsenal Pulp Press.

Stout, M.D. and G.D. Kipling (1998). Aboriginal Women in Canada: Strategic Research Directions for Policy Development. Ottawa: Status of Women Canada.

Stratton, K., C. Howe and F. Battaglia (eds.) (1996). Fetal Alcohol Syndrome: Diagnosis, Epidemiology, Prevention, and Treatment. Washington, D.C.: National Academy Press.

Straus, P. (1981). A Study of the Recurrence of Father-Daughter Incest Across Generations. Berkeley, CA: School of Professional Psychology.

Streissguth, A.P., H.M. Barr, D.C. Martin and C.S. Harman (1980). Effects of Maternal Alcohol, Nicotine and Caffeine Use During Pregnancy on Infant and Motor Development at Eight Months. Alcoholism: Clinical and Experimental Research 4(2): 152-164.

Streissguth, A.P., D.C. Martin, H.M. Barr, B.M. Sandman, G.L. Kirchner and B.L. Darby (1984). Intrauterine Alcohol and Nicotine Exposure: Attention and Reaction Time in 4-year-old Children. Developmental Psychology 20: 533-541.

Streissguth, A.P., R.A. LaDue and S.P. Randels (1987). Indian Adolescents and Adults with Fetal Alcohol Syndrome: Findings and Recommendations. The Indian Health Service Primary Care Provider 12: 89-91.

Streissguth, A.P., R.A. LaDue and S.P. Randels (1988). A Manual on Adolescent and Adults with Fetal Alcohol Syndrome with Special Reference to American Indians. Rockville, MD: The Indian Health Services.

Streissguth, A.P. (1990). Prenatal Alcohol-Induced Brain Damage and Long-Term Postnatal Consequences: Introduction to the Symposium. Alcoholism: Clinical and Experimental Research 14(5): 648-649.

Streissguth, A.P., F.L. Bookstein, P.C. Sampson, H.M. Barr (1993). The Enduring Effects of Prenatal Alcohol Exposure on Child Development: Birth Through Seven Years, a Partial Least Square Solution. Ann Arbor, MI: University of Michigan Press.

Streissguth, A.P., H.M. Barr, J. Kogan and F.L. Bookstein (1996). Understanding the Occurrence of Secondary Disabilities in Clients with Fetal Alcohol Syndrome (FAS) and Fetal Alcohol Effects (FAE). Seattle, WA: University of Washington School of Medicine.

References

Streissguth, A.P. (1997). Fetal Alcohol Syndrome: A Guide for Families and Communities. Toronto: Paul H. Brooks Publishing Co.

Streissguth, A.P., J.M. Aase, S.K. Clarren, S.P. Randels, R.A. La Due and D.F. Smith (1991). Fetal Alcohol Syndrome in Adolescents and Adults. The Journal of the American Medical Association (JAMA) 265(15): 1961-1967.

Streissguth, A.P., H.M. Barr, J. Kogan and F. Bookstien (1997). Primary and Secondary Disabilities in Fetal Alcohol Syndrome. In Streissguth, A.P. and J. Kanter (eds.) (1997). The Challenge of Fetal Alcohol Syndrome: Overcoming Secondary Disabilities. Seattle: University of Washington Press.

Streissguth, A.P., H.M. Barr and P.D. Sampson (1990). Moderate Prenatal Alcohol Exposure: Effects on Child IQ and Learning Problems at Age 7 1/2 Years. Alcoholism: Clinical and Experimental Research 14(5): 662-669.

Streissguth, A.P., S.K. Clarren and K.L. Jones (1985). Natural History of the Fetal Alcohol Syndrome: A 10-Year Follow-up of Eleven Patients. The Lancet 2(8446): 85-91.

Streissguth, A.P., B.L. Darby, H.M. Barr, J.R. Smith and D.C. Martin (1983). Comparison of drinking and smoking patterns during pregnancy over a six-year interval. American Journal of Obstetrics and Gynecology 145(6): 716-724.

Streissguth, A.P. and P. Dehaene (1993). Fetal Alcohol Syndrome in Twins of Alcoholic Mothers: Concordance of Diagnosis and IQ. American Journal of Medical Genetics 47(6): 857-861.

Streissguth, A.P. and C.T. Giunta (1988). Mental Health and Health Needs of Infants and Preschool Children with Fetal Alcohol Syndrome: Symposium on Addiction and the Family. International Journal of Family Psychiatry 9(1): 29-47.

Streissguth, A.P. and J. Kanter (eds.) (1997). The Challenges of Fetal Alcohol Syndrome: Overcoming Secondary Disabilities. Seattle: University of Washington Press.

Streissguth, A.P. and R.A. La Due (1985). Psychological and Behavioral Effects in Children Prenatally Exposed to Alcohol. Alcohol Health and Research World Fall: 6-12.

Streissguth, A.P. and J.C. Martin (1983). Prenatal Effects of Alcohol Abuse in Humans and Laboratory Animals. In Kissin, B. and H. Begleiter (eds.) (1983). The Pathogenesis of Alcoholism: Biological Factors: the Biology of Alcoholism Volume 7. New York: Plenum Publishing: 539-589.

Streissguth, A.P. and K. O'Malley (2000). Neuropsychiatric Implications and Long-term Consequences of Fetal Alcohol Spectrum Disorders. Seminars in Clinical Neuropsychiatry 5(3): 177-190.

Streissguth, A.P. and S.P. Randels (1989). Long Term Effects of Fetal Alcohol Syndrome. In Robinson, G. (ed.) (1989). Child/Family Health. Vancouver: University of British Columbia Press.

References

Streissguth, A.P., P.D. Sampson and H.M. Barr (1989). Neurobehavioural Dose-Response Effects in Humans from Infancy to Adulthood. Annals New York Academy of Sciences 562: 145-158.

Streissguth, A.P., P.D. Sampson, H.C. Olson, R.L. Bookstein, H.M. Barr, J. Scott-Feldman and A.F. Mirksy (1994). Maternal Drinking During Pregnancy: Attention and Short-Term Memory in 14-Year-Old Offspring - A Longitudinal Prospective Study. Alcoholism: Clinica and Experimental Research 18(1): 202-217.

Strick, B.R., G.M. Shaw and J.A. Harris (1999). Anthropological Approach to Inform Epidemiologic Research on Birth Defects. Teratology 60(3): 109-111.

Stromland, K. (1985). Ocular Abnormalities in the Fetal Alcohol Syndrome. Acta Ophthalmologica 171(Supplement): 1-50.

Stromland, K. (1996). Present state of the fetal alcohol syndrome. Acta Ophthalmologica Scandinavica 219(Supplement): 10-12.

Suchman, N.E. and S.S. Luthar (2000). Maternal addiction, child maladjustment and sociodemographic risks: implications for parenting behaviors. Addiction 95(9): 1417-1428.

Sumner, G.S., M.W. Mandoki and K. Matthews-Ferrari (1993). A Psychiatric Population of Prenatally Cocaine-Exposed Children. Journal of the American Academy of Child & Adolescent Psychiatry 32(5): 1003-1006.

Sutton, M. and C. Godfrey (1995). A grouped data regression approach to estimating economic and social influences on individual drinking behaviour. Health Economics 4(3): 237-247.

Svikis, D.S., S. Gorenstein, P. Paluzzi and M. Fingerhood (1998). Personality characteristics of treatment-seeking HIV+ and pregnant drug dependent women. Journal of Addictive Diseases 17(3): 91-111.

Swanson, D.W., A.P. Bratrude and E.M. Brown (1971). Alcohol Abuse in a Population of Indian Children. Disease of the Nervous System 32(12): 835-842.

Swift, K.J. (1991). Contradictions in Child Welfare: Neglect and Responsibility. In Baines, C.T., P.M. Evans and S. Neysmith (eds.) (1991). Women's Caring: Feminist Perspectives on Social Welfare. Toronto: McClelland and Stewart: 234-271.

Swift, K.J. (1995). Manufacturing 'Bad Mothers': A Critical Perspective on Child Neglect. Toronto: University of Toronto.

Szabo, P., Member of Parliament (2000). Fetal Alcohol Syndrome: The Real Brain Drain. Ottawa : P. Szabo.

Tait, C.L. (2000a). A Study of the Service Needs of Pregnant Addicted Women in Manitoba. Winnipeg: Prairie Women's Health Centre of Excellence.

References

Tait, C.L. (2000b). Aboriginal Identity and the Construction of Fetal Alcohol Syndrome. In Kirmayer, L.J., M.E. Macdonald and G.M. Brass (eds.) (2000). The Mental Health of Indigenous Peoples: Proceedings of the Advanced Study Institute. Montreal: Culture and Mental Health Research Unit. Report No. 10: 95-111.

Tait, C.L. (2003). "The Tip of the Iceberg:" The 'Making' of fetal alcohol syndrome in Canada. Unpublished doctoral thesis. Montreal: McGill University.

Tanner-Halverson, P. (1993). Snagging the Kite String: The Elementary Years. In Kleinfeld, J. and S. Wescott (eds.) (1993). Fantastic Antone Succeeds! Experiences in Educating Children with Fetal Alcohol Syndrome. Fairbanks: University of Alaska Press.

Tanner-Halverson, P. (1997). A Demonstration Classroom for Young Children with FAS. In Streissguth, A.P. and J. Kanter (eds.) (1997). The Challenge of Fetal Alcohol Syndrome: Overcoming Secondary Disabilities. Seattle: University of Washington Press.

Tapert, S.F. and S.A. Brown (2000). Substance dependence, family history of alcohol dependence and neuropsychological functioning in adolescence. Addiction 95(7): 1043-1053.

Taussig, M. (1987). Shamanism, Colonialism, and the Wild Man. Chicago: University of Chicago Press.

Taylor, A. (1997). Female Drug Injectors and Parenting. In Erickson, P.G., D.M. Riley, Y.W. Cheung and P.A. O'Hare (eds.) (1997). Harm Reduction: A new direction for drug policies and programs. Toronto: University of Toronto Press: 383-392.

Theidon, K. (1995). Taking a hit: pregnant drug users and violence. Contemporary Drug Problems 22: 663-686.

Thomas, R.K. (1981). The History of North American Indian Alcohol Use as a Community- Based Phenomenon. Journal of Studies in Alcohol Supplement 9: 29-39.

Timpson, J.B., S. McKay, S. Kakegamic, D. Roundhead, C. Cohen and G. Matewapit (1988). Depression in a Native Canadian in Northwestern Ontario: Sadness, Grief or Spiritual Illness. Canada's Mental Health June/September: 5-8.

Tishler, P.V., C.E. Henschel, T.A. Ngo, E. Walters and T.G. Worobec. (1998). Fetal Alcohol Effects in Alcoholic Veteran Patients. Alcoholism: Clinical and Experimental Research 22(8): 1825-1831.

Tookenay, V.F. (1996). Improving the health status of aboriginal people in Canada: new directions, new responsibilities. Canadian Medical Association Journal 155(11): 1581-1583.

Topper, M.D. (1974). Drinking Patterns, Culture Change, Sociability and Navajo "Adolescents." Addictive Disorders 1(10): 97.

References

Topper, M.D. (1980). Drinking as an Expression of Status: Navajo Male Adolescents. In Waddell, J.O. and M.W. Everett (eds.) (1980). Indian Drinking in the Southwest. Tucson: University of Arizona Press: 103-147.

Trasler, J.M. and T. Doerksen (1999). Teratogen Update: Paternal Exposures - Reproductive Risks. Teratology 60(3): 161-172.

Trevithick, S. (1998). Native Residential Schooling in Canada: A Review of the Literature. The Canadian Journal of Native Studies 28(1): 49-86.

Tsai, M., S. Feldman-Summers and M. Edgar (1979). Childhood Molestations: Variables Related to Differential Impacts on Psychosocial Functioning in Adult Women. The Journal of Abnormal Psychology 88(4): 407-417.

U.S. Department of Health and Human Services, Public Health Services Centre for Disease Control and Prevention (1993). Advance Report of Final Mortality Statistics, 1990. Monthly Vital Statistics Report 41(7-supplement): 1-51.

U.S. Preventive Services Task Force (1996). Guide to Clinical Preventive Services: Report of the US Preventive Services Task Force. Rockville, MD: US Department of Health and Human Services.

United Nations (1998). Guidelines for Transferring Effective Practices-A Practical Manual for South-South Cooperation, City Net, Regional Network of Local Authorities for the Management of Human Settlements, UNDP Special Unit for Technical Cooperation among Developing Countries; and UNCHS (Habitat) Best Practices and Local Leadership Programme. Bangkok, Thailand: Mitmara Printing.

Vaillant, G.E. (1983). The Natural History of Alcoholism. Cambridge, MA: Harvard University Press.

Van Bibber, M. (1997). It Takes A Community: A Resource Manual for Community-based Prevention of Fetal Alcohol Syndrome and Fetal Alcohol Effects. Ottawa: Aboriginal Nurses Association of Canada.

Van Kirk, S. (1980). 'Many Tender Ties': Women in Fur-Trade Society, 1670-1870. Winnipeg: Watson and Dwyer.

Van Kirk, S. (1991). The Impact of White Women on Fur Trade Society. In Miller, J.R. (ed.) (1991). Sweet Promises: A Reader on Indian-White Relations in Canada. Toronto: University of Toronto Press: 180-204.

Vernon, I.S. and R. Bubar (2001). Child Sexual Abuse and HIV/AIDS in Indian Country. Wicazo Sa Review: A Journal of Native American Studies 16(1): 47-64.

Virji, S.K. (1991). The Relationship Between Alcohol Consumption During Pregnancy and Infant Birthweight. An Epidemiologic Study. Acta Obstetricia et Gynecologica Scandinavica 70(4-5): 303-308.

References

Vitez, M., G. Koranyi, E. Gonczy, T. Rudas and A. Czeizel (1984). A Semiquantitative Score System For Epidemiologic Studies of Fetal Alcohol Syndrome. American Journal of Epidemiology 119(3): 301-308.

Vizenor, G. (1990). Crossbloods: Bone Courts, Bingo and Other Reports. Minneapolis: University of Minnesota Press.

Vohees, C.V., S. Rauch and R. Hitzermaun (1988). Effects of Short-Term Prenatal Alcohol Exposure on Neuronal Membrane Order in Rats. Brain Research 466(2): 161-166.

Voyageur, C.J. (1996). Contemporary Indian Women. In Long, D.A. and O.P. Dickason (eds.) (1996). Visions of the Heart: Canadian Aboriginal Issues. Toronto: Harcourt Brace: 93-115.

Wagmen, B. (1995a). The Effects of Tobacco Smoke and Second-Hand Smoke in the Prenatal and Postpartum Periods: A Summary of the Literature. Ottawa: Health Canada.

Wagmen, B. (1995b). Smoking and Pregnancy: A Woman's Dilemma. Ottawa: Health Canada.

Waldman, H.B. (1989). Fetal alcohol syndrome and the realities of our time. Journal of Dentistry for Children 56(6): 435-437.

Waldram, J.B., D. Ann Herring and T. Kue Young (1995). Aboriginal Health in Canada: Historical, Cultural, and Epidemiological Perspectives. Toronto: University of Toronto Press.

Waldram, J. B. (1997). The Way of the Pipe: Aboriginal Spirituality and Symbolic Healing in Canadian Prisons. Peterborough, Ontario: Broadview Press.

Walpole, I., S. Zubrick and J. Pontré (1990). Is there a fetal effect with low to moderate alcohol use before or during pregnancy? Journal of Epidemiology and Community Health 44(4): 297-301.

Walpole, I.R. and A. Hoclig (1980). Fetal Alcohol Syndrome: Implications to Family and Society in Australia. Australian Paediatric Journal 16(2): 101-105.

Warner, R.H. and H.L. Rosett (1973). The Effects of Drinking on Offspring: An Historical Survey of the American and British Literature. Journal of Studies on Alcohol 36(11): 1395-1420.

Warren, K.R. and R.J. Bast (1988). Alcohol-Related Birth Defects: an Update. Public Health Reports 103(6): 638-642.

Warren, K.R., F.J. Calhoun, P.A. May, D.L. Viljoen, T.K. Li, H. Tanaka, G.S. Marinicheva, L.K. Robinson and G. Mundle (2001). Fetal Alcohol Syndrome: An International Perspective. Alcoholism: Clinical and Experimental Research 25(5): 202S-206S.

Warren, M. A. (1989). The Moral Significance of Birth. Hypatia 4(3): 46-65.

References

Warry, W. (1998). Unfinished Dreams: Community Healing and the Reality of Aboriginal Self-Government. Toronto: University of Toronto Press.

Waterson, E.J. and I.M. Murray-Lyon (1990). Preventing Alcohol Related Birth Damage: A Review. Social Science & Medicine 30(3): 349-364.

Watson, C., J. Fleming and K. Alexander (1988). A Survey of Drug Use Patterns in Northern Territory Aboriginal Communities: 1986-1987. Darwin: Northern Territory Department of Health and Community Services.

Wattie, B. (1988). Native Mental Health: Problems and Proposals. Ottawa: Medical Services Branch, Health Canada.

Wente, M. (2000). Our Poor ruined babies: the hidden epidemic. The Globe and Mail, Saturday, October 7, 2000.

Weibel-Orlando, J. (1990). American Indians and Prohibition: Effect or Affect? Views from the Reservation and the City. Contemporary Drug Problems 17(2): 293-322.

Weinberg, N.Z. (1997). Cognitive and Behavioral Deficits Associated With Parental Alcohol Use. Journal or the American Academy of Child & Adolescent Psychiatry 36(9): 1177-1186.

Weiner, L. and G. Larsson (1987). Clinical Prevention of Fetal Alcohol Effects - A Reality: Evidence for the Effectiveness of Intervention. Alcohol Health and Research World 11(4): 60-63, 92-93.

Weiner, L., H.L. Rosett, K.C. Edelin, J.J. Alpert and B. Zuckerman (1983). Alcohol Consumption by Pregnant Women. Obstetrics and Gynecology 61(1): 6-12.

Weiner, L., H.L. Rosett and E.A. Mason (1985). Training Professionals to Identify and Treat Pregnant Women Who Drink Heavily. Alcohol Health and Research World 10(1): 32-35.

Weiner, L. and B.A. Morse (1994). Intervention and the Child With FAS. Alcohol Health and Research World 18(1): 67-73.

Weisner, C. and L. Schmidt (1993). Alcohol and Drug Problems among Diverse Health and Social Service Populations. American Journal of Public Health 83(6): 824-829.

Wentz, T. (1997). A National Survey of State Directors of Special Education Concerning Students with FAS. In Streissguth, A.P. and J. Kanter (eds.) (1997). The Challenge of Fetal Alcohol Syndrome: Overcoming Secondary Disabilities. Seattle: University of Washington Press.

West, J.R. and C.R. Goodlett (1990). Teratogenic Effects of Alcohol on Brain Development. Annals of Medicine 22(5): 319-325.

References

West, J.R., C.R. Goodlett and J.P. Brandt (1990). New Approaches to Research on the Long-Term Consequences of Prenatal Exposure to Alcohol. Alcoholism: Clinical and Experimental Research 14(5): 684-689.

West, J.R. and D.R. Pierce (1986). Perinatal Alcohol Exposure and Neuronal Damage. In West, J.R. (ed.) (1986). Alcohol and Brain Development. New York: Oxford University Press.

West, M.O. and R.J. Prinz (1987). Parental Alcoholism and Childhood Psychopathology. Psychological Bulletin 102(2): 204-218.

Wheeler, S.F. (1993). Substance Abuse During Pregnancy. Primary Care 20(1): 191-207.

Whiteford, L.M. and J. Vitucci (1997). Pregnancy and Addiction: Translating Research into Practice. Social Science & Medicine 44(9): 1371-1380.

Whitehead, P.C. and M.J. Hayes (1998). The Insanity of Alcohol: Social Problems in Canadian First Nations Communities. Toronto: Canadian Scholar's Press Inc.

Wiebe, J. (1997). Addiction: Its Position among Health Determinants. Winnipeg: Addiction Foundation of Manitoba and Alberta Alcohol and Drug Abuse Commission.

Williams, A.M. (1997). Canadian Urban Aboriginals: A Focus on Aboriginal Women in Toronto. The Canadian Journal of Native Studies 17(1): 75-101.

Williams, D.R., R. Lavizzo-Mourey and R.C. Warren (1994). The Concept of Race and Health Status in America. Public Health Reports 109(1): 26-41.

Williams, R.J. and S.P. Gloster (1999). Knowledge of Fetal Alcohol Syndrome (FAS) among Natives in Northern Manitoba. Journal of Studies on Alcohol 60(6): 833-836.

Williams, R.J., F.S. Odaibo and J. McGee (1999). Incidence of Fetal Alcohol Syndrome in Northeastern Manitoba. Canadian Journal of Public Health 90(3): 192-194.

Wilsnack, S.C., A.D. Klassen, B.E. Schur and R.W. Wilsnack (1991). Predicting the Onset and Chronicity of Women's Problem Drinking: A Five-Year Longitudinal Analysis. American Journal of Public Health 81(3): 305-317.

Winick, P. (1993). Mainstreaming Children with FAS in a Small Rural School. In Kleinfeld, J. and S. Wescott (eds.) (1993). Fantastic Antone Succeeds! Experiences in Educating Children with Fetal Alcohol Syndrome. Fairbanks: University of Alaska Press.

Woessner, J.F. (1963). Age-Related Changes in the Human Uterus and Its Connective Tissue Framework. Journal of Gerontology 18: 220-226.

References

Women's Health Bureau (2001). Aboriginal Women with Substance Use Issues: Improving Access and Quality of Care. Vancouver: Women's Health Bureau.

Women's Legal Education and Action Fund (1997). Factum of the Intervenor, Supreme Court of Canada. Court File No. 25508.

Wong, N. (1983). Fetal Alcohol Syndrome in British Columbia. Vancouver, British Columbia Surveillance Registry, Ministry of Health.

World Health Organization (1995). Women's Health Initiative Conference: Position Paper on Mental Health. New York: WHO.

Wortley, M. and D. Wortley (1993). On Raising Lisa. In Kleinfeld, J. and S. Wescott (eds.) (1993). Fantastic Antone Succeeds! Experiences in Educating Children with Fetal Alcohol Syndrome. Fairbanks: University of Alaska Press.

Wyatt, G.E., M. Newcomb and C.M. Notgrass (1991). Internal and External Mediations of Women's Rape Experiences. In Burgess, A.W. (ed.) (1991). Rape and Sexual Assault III: A research handbook. New York: Garland Publishing, Inc.: 167-179.

Wyatt, G.E. and G.J. Powell (1988). Lasting Effects of Child Sexual Abuse. Newbury Park, CA: Sage Publications, Inc.

Yahne, C.E. and W.R. Miller (1999). Enhancing Motivation for Treatment and Change. In Mccrady, B.S. and E.E. Epstein (eds.) (1999). Addictions: A Comprehensive Guidebook. New York: Oxford: 235-249.

Yellowknife Association for Community Living (n.d.). Helping Families-Helping Children. Yellowknife: Yellowknife Association of Community Living.

Young, I.M. (1994). Punishment, Treatment, Empowerment: Three Approaches to Policy for Pregnant Addicts. Feminist Studies 20(1): 33-57.

Young, L. (1992). Sexual Abuse and the Problem of Embodiment. Child Abuse and Neglect 16(1): 89-100.

Young, N. and S. Gardner (1998). Children at the Crossroads. Public Welfare 56(1): 3-10.

Young, T.K. (1984). Indian Health Services in Canada: A Socio-historical Perspective. Social Science and Medicine 18(3): 257-264.

Young, T.K. and G. Sevenhuysen (1989). Obesity in Northern Canadian Indians: Patterns, Determinants, and Consequences. American Journal of Clinical Nutrition 49(5): 786-793.

References

Zapata, C., A. Rebolledo, E. Atalah, B. Newman and M. King (1992). The Influence of Social and Political Violence on the Risk of Pregnancy Complications. American Journal of Public Health 82(5): 685-690.

Zeiner, A.R., A. Paredes and L. Cowden (1976). Physiologic Responses to Ethanol Among the Tarahumara Indians. Annals of the New York Academy of Science 273: 151-158.

Zelson, C. (1975). Acute management of neonatal addiction. Addiction Disease 2(1-2): 159-168.